Collins

EDEXCEL 360

SCIENCE

FOR EDEXCEL
GCSE SCIENCE

KT-487-750

WITHDRAWN

S083563

Brian Arnold SERIES EDITOR
Gareth Price
Phil Routledge
Rob King
Mike Tingle
Jane Cartright
Gurinder Chadha
Edmund Walsh

William Collins' dream of knowledge for all began with the publication of his first book in 1819. A self-educated mill worker, he not only enriched millions of lives, but also founded a flourishing publishing house. Today, staying true to this spirit, Collins books are packed with inspiration, innovation and a practical expertise. They place you at the centre of a world of possibility and give you exactly what you need to explore it.

Collins. Freedom to teach.

Published by Collins
An imprint of HarperCollinsPublishers
77–85 Fulham Palace Road
Hammersmith
London
W6 8JB

Browse the complete Collins catalogue at
www.collinseducation.com

© HarperCollinsPublishers Limited 2005

10 9 8 7 6 5 4

ISBN-13 978 0 00 721448 8
ISBN-10 0 00 721448 0

The authors assert their moral right to be identified as the authors of this work.

All rights reserved. No part of this publication may be reproduced, stored in a retrieval system or transmitted in any form or by any means – electronic, mechanical, photocopying, recording or otherwise – without the prior written consent of the Publisher or a licence permitting restricted copying in the United Kingdom issued by the Copyright Licensing Agency Ltd, 90 Tottenham Court Road, London W1T 4LP.

British Library Cataloguing in Publication Data. A Catalogue record for this publication is available from the British Library.

Commissioned by Kate Haywood and Cassandra Birmingham

Publishing Manager: Michael Cotter

Project Editor: Penny Fowler

Project management, editing, page make-up and picture research by Hart McLeod, Cambridge

Page make-up by eMC Design

Additional editor: Anita Clark

Internal design by JPD

Cover design by John Fordham

Cover artwork by Bob Lea

Exam questions written by Dr Martin Barker, Lesley Owen and Karen Nicola Thomas

Glossary written by Gareth Price

Illustrations by Peters and Zabransky, Rory Walker, Bob Lea, Pete Smith and Peter Richardson (Beehive Illustration), Angela Knowles (Specs Art)

Production by Natasha Buckland

Printed and bound in Hong Kong by Printing Express Ltd

Acknowledgements

The authors and publishers are grateful to the following for permission to reproduce photographs. Whilst every effort has been made to trace the copyright holders, in cases where this has been unsuccessful or if any have been inadvertently overlooked, the Publishers will be pleased to make the necessary arrangements at the first opportunity.

GORE-TEX®, GORE® and designs are registered trade marks of W L Gore & Associates.
Thinsulate is a trademark of the 3M Company.

SOUTHALL AND WEST
LONDON COLLEGE
LEARNING CENTRE

S083563
500 HA

Weird and wonderful animals

More chromosomes than us?

Contents

Why is this angel rusty?

Chemistry gets smart.

A week in Spain or a week in orbit?

Welcome to Collins GCSE Science!

This book aims to give you a fascinating insight into contemporary science that is relevant and useful to you, right now today. We have written it to convey the excitement of Biology, Chemistry and Physics, and hope it will help you to carry a knowledge and understanding of science and scientific thinking with you throughout life.

USING THIS BOOK

What you should know

It is amazing how much knowledge you gain each year in your studies. Hopefully you can then build on this in the following years. In science there are many key ideas that are continually revisited and developed. To remind you of these, there are summaries for each of the main sections: biology, chemistry and physics.

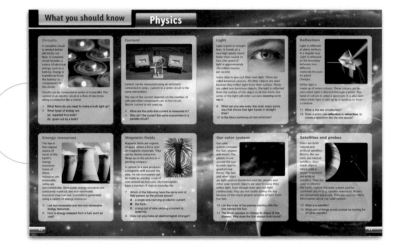

Unit opener

Altogether there are six units: two biology, two chemistry and two physics. At the start of each unit there is an introductory spread, consisting of a large image showing just some of the exciting science you will learn about. Also listed on this page are the spreads you will work through in the unit.

Main content

Each of the six units contains two topics and each topic has approximately 10 double page spreads. An introductory paragraph at the start of each spread puts the material in an everyday context. Separate sections then look at progressively more demanding ideas and applications. Titles marked with an (H) mean the following paragraphs are Higher Tier.

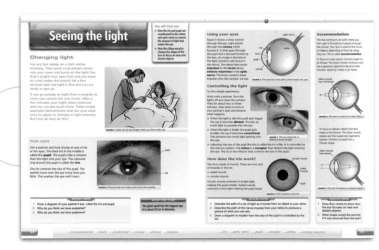

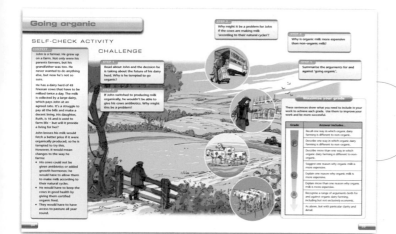

The mid-unit assessment questions enable you to recap on several weeks' work and assess your own level of understanding. Achieving good marks in these will confirm your progress and highlight any areas of weakness that need to be addressed.

Unit summary

Unit summaries offer the opportunity to visualise links between key ideas through the use of spider diagrams. Constructing your own versions of these would be a useful way to begin your revision. The unit finishes with a number of questions designed to sharpen up your skills in these areas.

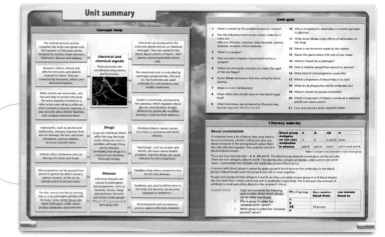

Exam practice

Developing a good exam technique will ensure that you take full advantage of the skills and knowledge you have gained. You need to give clear answers with working out and reasoning shown, in order to earn top marks. To help you achieve this we have included some practice questions. Try your best with these and don't rush them. Tackle one or two, see where you went wrong and then try some more, ensuring that you don't make the same mistakes. Remember: practice makes perfect – so use the questions well!

Internal assessment

While you are studying GCSE Science, your teacher will assess your practical skills, and give you assessment activities to complete. These pages should give you some helpful guidance and practice.

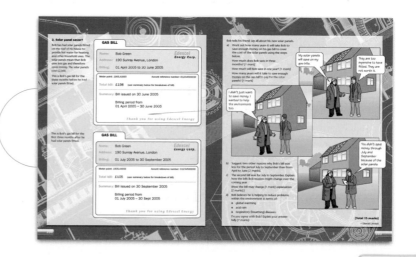

Classification

Biologists sort living things into groups so that they can identify different living organisms. This is called classification. Every living thing has a common name and a Latin scientific name. So humans are called Homo  sapiens and your pet dog is Canis canis. The largest groups are called kingdoms (for example, animals or plants) and the smallest are called species (for example, humans or dogs). Organisms that belong to the same species can breed together to produce living offspring.

1   What does the word classification mean?
2   Why do biologists sort organisms into groups?

Variation

Classification is made difficult by natural variation between organisms. The people at this concert are all human beings – but they are all slightly different! Sometimes  it is difficult to decide if two organisms are the same type or from completely different species.

Variation can be caused by the environment. Some variation is inherited from parents. Farmers have used these inherited variations for thousands of years to breed cows that give more milk. This is called selective breeding.

3   What are the two sources of variation?
4   Why are animals on farms now different to their ancestors of 5000 years ago?

Habitats and adaptation

The environment includes living organisms, the soil and oceans, the air and even the sunlight. All living things are adapted to cope with their  environment. So, a yak has a warm fur coat to protect against Tibetan winters. A UK cow would die in such an environment. The area where an organism lives is called its habitat. All the habitats in an area are linked into an ecosystem. Damage to one part of an ecosystem can lead to trouble elsewhere.

5   Suggest two adaptations of a polar bear to life in the Arctic.
6   Global warming may melt the ice in the Arctic. Why would this be a problem for polar bears?

Food webs

Plants capture energy from the Sun and use it to build food. Animals, like this panda, eat the plants. Some animals, called  predators, eat other animals. Food chains and webs show these connections.

The numbers of organisms in an area is affected by the food supply and whether they are eaten by other organisms. So, every winter the number of insects living in the UK drops because plants cannot grow to produce food for them.

7   What is the energy source for the living world?
8   How would a sudden decline in the number of plants growing in an area affect the number of animals living there?

Electrical signals

Animal cells are made up of a cytoplasm surrounded by a cell membrane. The cytoplasm contains a nucleus which contains genetic information. Nerve cells have a complex structure which helps them to perform their function of coordinating information detected by our senses, and our responses to it.

We have five senses. Our sense organs detect external stimuli. Nerves connect these sense organs to the central nervous system and then to effectors such as muscles. The time taken between sensing a stimulus and responding to it is called reaction time.

9 Draw a simple diagram of an animal cell showing the cell membrane, cytoplasm and nucleus.

Chemical signals

Blood comprises plasma and cells. It transports substances through the body. One substance which is transported is glucose. This is absorbed into the bloodstream from digested food and is used by the body as a source of energy. Oxygen is also transported in blood from the lungs to the cells of the body. Carbon dioxide is transported to the lungs, where it is breathed out.

Secondary sexual characteristics develop at puberty due to changes in hormone concentration. Hormones are substances which are made in endocrine glands and are transported in the blood system.

10 Draw a table showing secondary sexual characteristics of men and women.
11 Name three substances that are transported in the blood.
12 Write down the word equation for respiration.

Diseases

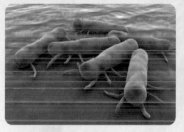

There are different types of micro-organism some of which are useful and some of which cause disease. Micro-organisms can enter the body in a number of different ways. The body has natural defences to keep micro-organisms out. If micro-organisms manage to enter the body, white blood cells will try to destroy them.

We can become immune to some diseases, either by being infected with the microbe or by vaccination. Antibiotics are drugs that help to prevent the reproduction of micro-organisms in the body.

13 Suggest three examples of foods that are made using micro-organisms.
14 Write down three ways in which microbes can get into your body.
15 Name an example of an antibiotic.

Use, misuse and abuse – drugs

Alcohol and smoking can affect our health. Smoking increases our chances of getting diseases such as lung cancer, emphysema, bronchitis and heart disease. Alcohol damages the liver and increases our chances of getting cancer. Nicotine in tobacco smoke is a drug, as is alcohol. Drugs are substances that affect the way our body works physically or mentally. People can become dependent on drugs. This is called addiction.

16 Name three harmful substances that are found in cigarette smoke.
17 List three diseases that can be caused by smoking cigarettes.

Chemical elements

Elements are substances that cannot be broken down to form simpler substances. There are about 100 different chemical elements and all have a chemical symbol. For

example, the chemical symbol for sodium is Na and for chlorine, it is Cl. Elements are pure substances and react with each other to make compounds. Elements react with each other in a chemical reaction to make new substances that have different properties from the elements that make them.

1   What is meant by a chemical element?
2   What is the chemical formula for water?

A closer look at the chemical elements

Elements fit into two classes called metals and non-metals. Metals conduct electricity very well
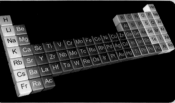
whereas non-metals are poor electrical conductors. Some metals react with acids to form a flammable gas called hydrogen. Hydrogen gas can be tested by placing a lighted splint over the end of a test tube and listening for a squeaky 'pop'. During a chemical reaction, elements react together to make new substances called compounds. The number of atoms and the total mass of the chemicals reacting are the same at the end of the reaction as at the start.

3   What happens to the total number of atoms before and after a chemical reaction has taken place?
4   Suggest a simple test to show the presence of hydrogen gas in a test tube.

Chemical reactions

All substances and living things are made of chemicals. Some are elements or compounds, but most are mixtures. All are produced by chemical reactions. Some are formed by natural reactions,

but most are man-made. Chemical reactions keep us alive, and produce the materials we use.

No atoms are created or destroyed in a chemical reaction. The starting materials (reactants) are just rearranged to make different substances (products). We describe these changes using word equations. They show what chemicals react, and what they produce.

5   Can you name a substance that is not made up of chemicals?
6   Write the word equation for the reaction that produces water from hydrogen and oxygen.

Patterns in reactions

Chemical reactions follow certain patterns. Metals react with air, water and acids in a predictable way. Metals high up the reactivity series react more vigorously with

oxygen in the air and water. They displace hydrogen from water and acids and also displace a less reactive metal from its oxide or from solutions of its salts.

Acids and bases also react predictably. They neutralise each other to form salts. Everyday uses of neutralisation include curing indigestion and making fertilisers. Acids dissolved in rain corrode metals and rocks, such as limestone. The pH scale measures how acidic or alkaline a solution is.

7   Which three metals have traditionally been used to make coins and jewellery as they are unreactive?
8   A solution has pH 5. What does this tell you?

Fuels

Crude oil is a mixture of compounds called hydrocarbons. These are compounds made up of  hydrogen and carbon only. Crude oil can be separated into fractions using a process called fractional distillation. In this process, hydrocarbons which have different boiling points are separated.

The fractions that are produced from crude oil are all extremely useful. Petrol, diesel and liquid petroleum gas are all particularly important fractions that are obtained from crude oil.

9   Name the process in which crude oil is separated to make useful substances.

10 What is the name given to the compounds found in crude oil?

Chemicals from the air and the sea

The atmosphere is a layer of gases that surrounds the Earth. It contains many different gases. Some, like oxygen, are really important for life. Others, like nitrogen and argon, are a lot less reactive than oxygen. Air is therefore a mixture of gases. Plants photosynthesise to make oxygen gas and they take in carbon dioxide gas. Photosynthesis is a very important chemical reaction as it allows life to be found on our planet.

The Sea also has many important chemicals dissolved in it. For example, sodium chloride, sometimes known as 'salt', can be removed from sea water. Sodium chloride is a chemical compound with the formula NaCl.

11 Is the air a mixture, a compound or an element?

12 What is the chemical name and formula of the main substance that is dissolved to make sea water?

Very long molecules

Molecules are small 'clusters' of atoms chemically bonded together. A chemical bond is a strong bond that holds atoms together. Crude oil is made up of many different molecules; some are very small while others are very long. Sometimes it is possible for small molecules to join together to make very long chain molecules called polymers. An example of a polymer is polythene. Another word for polymer is 'plastic' and these materials are extremely important in our lives. Polymers have largely replaced other materials like wood and metals in most everyday objects. Polymers are light and do not corrode.

13 Provide an example of a polymer.

14 State two properties of polymers.

Modern materials

Materials are the substances that we use to make everyday objects. For example, wood, metal, polymers and glass are all materials that we use for  making lots of different things. Materials have different properties that make them good for certain jobs. For example, steel is a good material for making the body of a car because it is strong. Glass is an important material for making windows as it is transparent – an essential property for this purpose!

15 Suggest three examples of modern materials.

16 Why is steel a good material for making a car body?

Circuits

A complete circuit is needed before electricity can flow. A complete circuit includes a source of electrical energy, such as a battery. Energy is transferred from the battery to components in the circuit.

Circuits can be connected in series or in parallel. The current in an electric circuit is a flow of electrons along a conductor like a metal.

1   What items do you need to make a bulb light up?
2   What types of energy are:
    (a) supplied to a bulb?
    (b) given out by a bulb?

Current

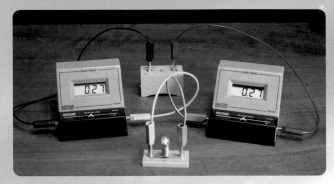

Current can be measured using an ammeter connected in series. Current in a series circuit is the same everywhere.

The size of the current depends on the number of cells and what components are in the circuit. Electric current is not used up.

3   What are the units that current is measured in?
4   Why isn't the current the same everywhere in a parallel circuit?

Energy resources

The Sun is the original source of most of the Earth's energy resources. Some of these resources are renewable, some are non-renewable. Renewable energy resources are constantly replaced, but non-renewable resources may run out. Electricity is generated using a variety of energy resources.

5   List two renewable and two non-renewable energy resources.
6   How is energy released from a fuel, such as coal?

Magnetic fields

Magnetic fields are regions of space where a force acts on magnetic materials. They can be shown using iron filings (as in the photo) or a plotting compass.

A current in a wire produces a magnetic field around the wire. An electromagnet can be made by winding a coil of wire around an iron core. Electromagnets have a number of uses in everyday life.

7   Which of the following have the same sort of field pattern as the picture above?
    A   a single wire carrying an electric current
    B   the Earth
    C   a long coil of wire carrying a current (a solenoid)
8   How can you make an electromagnet stronger?

Light

Light travels in straight lines. It travels at a very high speed, much faster than sound. In fact, the speed of light is approximately 300 million metres per second.

Some objects give out their own light. These are called luminous sources. All other objects are seen because they reflect light from their surface. These are called non-luminous objects. The light is reflected from the surface of the object in all directions, but some of the light will enter our eyes enabling us to see it.

9   What can you see every day (well, every sunny day) that shows that light travels in straight lines?

10 Is the Moon luminous or non-luminous?

Reflection

Light is reflected at plane surfaces in a regular way. Light is refracted at the boundary between two different materials because its speed changes.

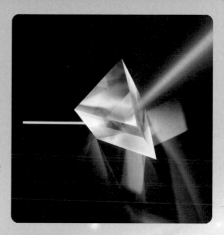

White light is made up of seven colours. These colours can be seen when light is directed through a prism. This band of colours is called a spectrum. It is also seen when white light is split up by a raindrop to form a rainbow.

11 What is the law of reflection?

12 Does a prism use reflection or refraction, to create a spectrum like the one above?

Our solar system

Our solar system contains the Sun, planets and moon. The planets move around the Sun in orbits due to gravitational forces. The Sun and other stars

are light sources (luminous) and the planets and other solar system objects are seen because they reflect light. Even though stars give out light continuously, they are not visible during the day because of the much greater amount of light from the Sun.

13 List the order of the planets starting with the one nearest the Sun.

14 The Moon appears to change its shape (it has phases). Why does the Sun always look round?

Satellites and probes

There are both natural and artificial satellites. Moons, like our own, are natural satellites. Man-made objects which orbit a planet or a moon are artificial satellites. They are used to observe

the Earth, explore the solar system and for communications (e.g. satellite television). Probes are unmanned spacecraft. They are used to collect information about our solar system.

15 What is a satellite?

16 What sort of things would probes be looking for on other planets?

DISCOVER GENETIC ENGINEERING!

No, it's not a Christmas decoration – it's a real mouse that glows in the dark! A gene called GFP from a jellyfish has been inserted into its DNA and it is this gene that makes it glow. The technique that makes this possible is very clever – but is it right? Should we be using animals in this way?

Some people might argue that research like this could end up with glowing humans, and that we should ban this research now before we end up creating monsters. What do you think?

Researchers are hoping that cancer cells labelled with the same gene will become visible so that medics can watch them moving through a patient's body. This could lead to new treatments.

The egg from which this mouse developed was infected with a virus carrying the jellyfish gene, causing the gene to be incorporated into the mouse's DNA.

CONTENTS

Sorted!

You will find out:
- Why classification is useful to biologists
- How we name and define a species
- About the main groups of organisms
- About hybrids

Monkey business

A chimpanzee has 99.5% of the same **genes** as a human being. So how different are we to monkeys? Biologists sort organisms into groups. These groups help us to understand how different living things are related and how they may have evolved.

FIGURE 1: This manis is from the Borneo rainforest. How human do those eyes look?

Classification

Sorting things into groups is called **classification**. You could sort organisms by:

- what they eat (for example, herbivores for plant-eaters, carnivores for meat-eaters)
- when they are active (for example, nocturnal animals only come out by night)
- where they live (for example, marine animals in the seas, alpine plants which only grow high in the mountains).

Biologists also classify living things depending on physical features. The dogs in figure 2 both have features like eyes, ears and fur. These features come in different shapes and sizes though! Short hair is a characteristic of Alsations. The longer hair is a characteristic of the Yorkshire Terrier. The smallest groups are called **species**. All human beings belong to one species called *Homo sapiens*. Only organisms of the same species can breed together to produce living offspring. All members of the same species have the same number of chromosomes.

It is not always easy to put something in a group. Some organisms change a lot during their lifetimes, for example, tadpoles and frogs. Many types seem to fall between groups – maybe you know some people who look like chimpanzees!

FIGURE 2: So, are these two animals from the same species? In fact, they could breed together to produce offspring – called a mongrel.

QUESTIONS

1. What does the word 'classification' mean?
2. List **three** different ways to classify living organisms.
3. What is a species?
4. List **two** problems that biologists face when they classify organisms.

...classification ...genes ...hybrid

Friends and family

Large groups like 'plants' or 'animals' can be very varied. Smaller groups like shellfish or grasses contain organisms that are much more similar.

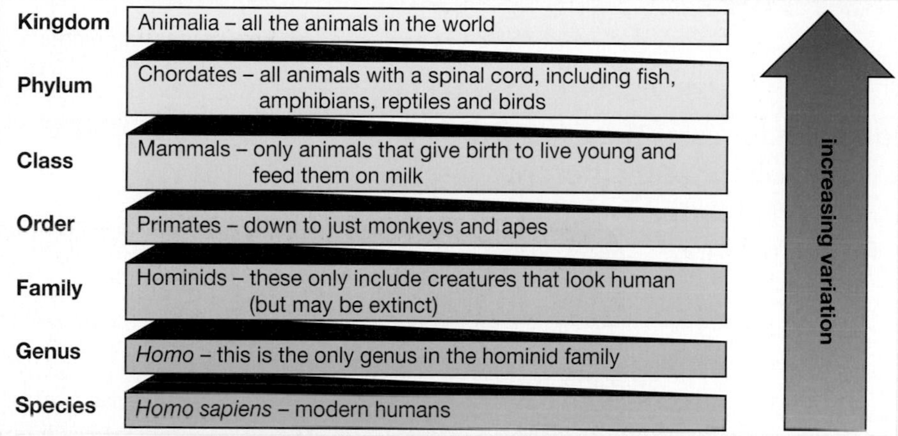

Kingdom	Animalia – all the animals in the world
Phylum	Chordates – all animals with a spinal cord, including fish, amphibians, reptiles and birds
Class	Mammals – only animals that give birth to live young and feed them on milk
Order	Primates – down to just monkeys and apes
Family	Hominids – these only include creatures that look human (but may be extinct)
Genus	*Homo* – this is the only genus in the hominid family
Species	*Homo sapiens* – modern humans

increasing variation

FIGURE 3: Groupings from species to kingdom.

It is easy to tell a daffodil from an elephant – but can you tell two elephants apart? Every species includes some **variation**. These are the normal differences between individuals of the same type. Biologists have to decide if any of these differences show the individuals belong to different species.

You could have a coconut tree on your windowsill in London but the same species growing in southern India could be 10 m tall! This difference is due to the environment and is a problem for biologists trying to classify plants. Which one is the 'typical' coconut – the potted plant or the tree?

The best features to use to classify organisms are usually to do with the sexual organs. These change much less than other features. If you could get your coconut to flower on your windowsill the flowers would look just like the ones in India.

FIGURE 4: Yes, this is exactly the same species of coconut that you could have on your kitchen windowsill!

░░░ QUESTIONS ░░░

5   Rank these groups in order starting with the most varied and finishing with the least varied: kingdom, genus, order, species, family.

6   What does the word 'variation' mean?

7   Why is size often a bad way to classify organisms?

8   Which features are useful to decide on whether two organisms belong to the same species?

Strange mixtures

Different species usually cannot interbreed – but sometimes they do to produce a **hybrid**. A zedonk is a hybrid that is the result of breeding a zebra with a donkey. Look at the picture below – his head and body look like a donkey's but his legs are stripey like a zebra's.

Zedonks are bred in captivity – and it's not easy. Other hybrids appear in nature and some are very important. The wheat used to make the flour in your bread is a hybrid of three different plant species. These plants interbred thousands of years ago by accident but over half of the people on the planet now depend on this plant for food.

FIGURE 5: A zedonk called Adam – a hybrid between a zebra and a donkey.

░░░ QUESTIONS ░░░

9   What is a hybrid?

10 Why are hybrids between species quite rare?

11 Lions and tigers can produce hybrids. A lion cannot breed with a puma. What does this tell you about the similarities between lions, tigers and pumas?

...species ...variation

Biomass

You will find out:
- How living things get their energy
- How energy transfers through the natural world
- How to draw food chains and webs
- How to measure biomass

Orang-utans

Orang-utans live in the jungles of Borneo and Indonesia. They weigh up to 120 kg and eat ants, termites, leaves and about 300 different types of fruit. They tend to live alone and the males and females only meet to mate. This may be because orang-utans produce the worst-smelling faeces in the rainforest!

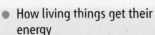

FIGURE 1: This orang-utang mother is called Uce.

Food chains and webs

The plants in the jungle use **energy** in light to produce sugars by **photosynthesis**. These sugars can be used to build other chemicals so the plant gets bigger. Only plants can do this. They are known as **producers** because they produce their own food. The orang-utan is an example of a **consumer** because it consumes food produced by the plants.

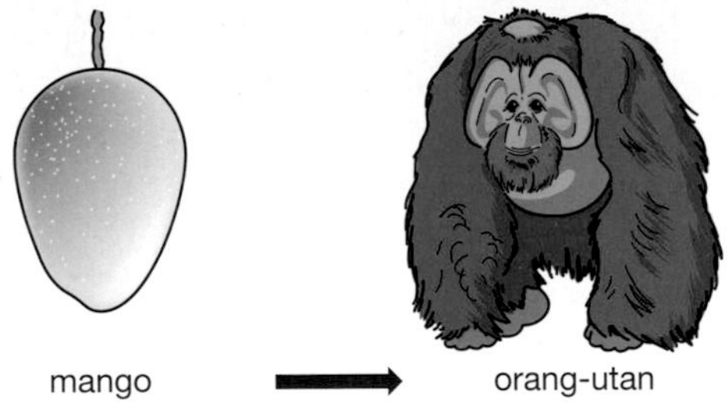

mango → orang-utan

FIGURE 2: In this food chain the mango is a producer and the orang-utang is a consumer.

Biologists use **food chains** to show the way food or energy moves in the natural world. An arrow shows the direction of the energy transfer. A food chain usually contains up to five links. Many chains linked together produce a much more complex **food web**.

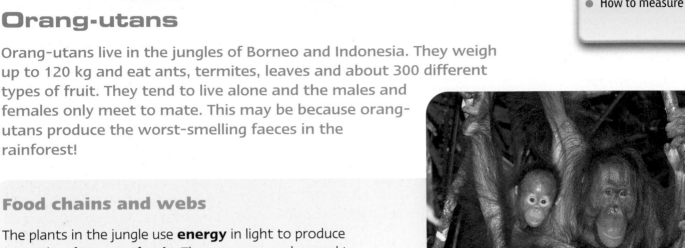

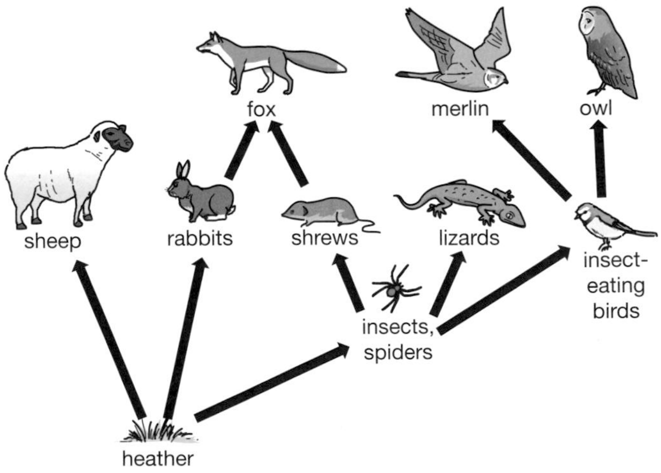

FIGURE 3: A simple food web for a heather moorland.

QUESTIONS

1. What does the word 'consumer' mean?
2. Why are all producers plants?
3. Why is it an advantage for the orang-utan to be able to eat many different types of food?

EXAM HINTS AND TIPS

Make sure you get the arrow in the food web pointing the correct way. It shows the direction of the energy flow – towards the eater!

Energy and biomass

The weight of all of the plants in an area is called the plant **biomass**. When animals eat plants the energy is transferred into animal biomass. **Primary consumers** are animals that eat plants. **Secondary consumers** are animals that eat animals that have eaten plants. The most dangerous **predator** in the jungle is the leopard. It often acts as a **third consumer** – it eats animals that are two steps away from the original plants.

Pyramids of biomass

An **ecosystem** is the collection of living things in an area along with all the important non-living components, such as the climate and mineral salts in the soil. A rainforest, a large pond and woodland are all good examples of ecosystems. A pyramid of biomass is a chart that shows the total biomass at different **feeding levels** in an ecosystem. In every ecosystem, the higher up the pyramid you go, the smaller the biomass.

FIGURE 4: Here's a bit of jungle biomass you may have put onto your rice pudding. The brown nut in the middle is called nutmeg. The orange covering is powdered to make a spice called mace.

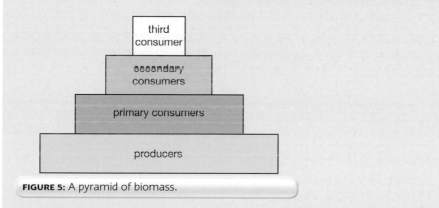

FIGURE 5: A pyramid of biomass.

Energy is wasted as it passes from one level to the next one up. Only about 25% of the energy in the plant biomass is converted into biomass in the primary consumers. There is a similar loss at every step up the pyramid. This explains why food chains never have more than five links – the biomass at the top of level five is too small to support another level.

QUESTIONS

4   What does the word 'biomass' mean?

5   What is a pyramid of biomass?

6   Why do food chains never have more than about five links?

Orang today, gone tomorrow?

Orang-utans are under threat; one report claims they will be extinct by 2025. The main threat to these creatures is **deforestation**. Loggers harvest trees to make furniture, buildings and firewood.

FIGURE 6: The forest patrol in the Balikpappan rainforest, Borneo. The guns are to protect the workers from illegal loggers – not from animals!

The trees shade the soil from bright sunlight and when they are gone the soil and leaf litter dries out. A fire almost always follows, killing plants and animals and leaving a charred desert behind. The jungle does not grow back quickly – if at all. In the last 20, years about 80% of the orang-utan's habitat has been lost.

QUESTIONS

7   Orang-utans do not climb the tall trees the loggers take. Why does logging pose such a threat to orang-utan survival?

8   Tree spikers are environmentalists that knock metal spikes into trees. When the tree is processed in a saw mill the spikes fly out and destroy the milling machines. This can put a company out of business. Flying metal fragments may also harm workers. Do you think this is a good way to protect the forests? Give reasons on both sides of the argument.

Feed the world

You will find out:
- How energy travels through the natural world
- Where the lost energy ends up
- How we can maximise the amount of food we produce

Energy snacks

Athletes, mountaineers and explorers often have little 'energy snacks' or 'energy drinks' before they start work. What's in these energy snacks and do they work?

FIGURE 1: Do energy drinks do what their makers claim?

Energy input

We get our energy from our food. A typical energy snack will be full of **sugar** and other **carbohydrates**. We absorb this sugar quickly into the bloodstream. Our muscles use this extra boost to work better.

- Soluble sugars are absorbed quickly and give an instant 'boost'.
- Starches and other carbohydrates need to be digested first. These can give you a slower, but longer, boost.

Where do animals get their energy? A rabbit eats grass and this is quite difficult to digest. No problem – rabbits just eat their food twice! That's right. They eat grass and a lot of it passes through the gut undigested to make the first **faeces**. Most of the energy remains in this rather wet, sloppy waste. So ... the rabbit eats it and the food passes through the gut again. The second faeces contain much less energy and are drier – they look like small balls of mud.

FIGURE 2: Yes, he looks terribly cute but this is an animal that passes food through its gut twice. Yes, twice. Think about it!

WOW FACTOR!

Pandas eat every second that they are awake! Their diet is so difficult to digest and has so little energy that they have to keep cramming food in all day!

▪▪ QUESTIONS ▪▪

1. Which sorts of chemicals do food companies put into energy snacks?
2. Why do they use these sorts of foods?
3. Why do rabbits eat their own faeces?

...carbohydrate   ...faeces   ...mammal

A waste of energy!

Some of the energy animals eat in food is wasted in faeces. Even the energy that gets into the animal is not all used for growth. Some is used to:

- move around (think how much energy a **predator** like a leopard needs to find and catch its **prey**)
- repair broken cells or body parts (you do need more energy when you are ill or recovering from injury)
- keep warm (this is very important for **mammals**)
- respiration – this keeps the animal alive
- excretion – some of the food an animal eats cannot be digested and is passed out in the faeces.

Making lunch

Every step along a food chain, some energy is wasted as heat which radiates into space. To feed the world we should reduce this waste. The easiest way to do this is to eat lower down the food chain. A field can produce about ten times as much food if we grow vegetables or rice rather than grass to feed cattle.

Unfortunately, plants are more difficult to digest than animals. Plants also tend to contain less energy and protein than animal foods.

Also, some areas in the world have the wrong climate for growing crops. The wet hills of North Wales are good to walk on, great to look at and perfect for sheep – but dreadful for growing vegetables! If we raise sheep there we can get wool and meat from an area that would otherwise produce nothing.

In Chinese villages, waste from toilets is washed into large lagoons. The waste encourages the growth of plants. These plants clean the water and provide food for fish and ducks. These are caught and eaten to provide valuable protein. Sometimes the plants are harvested to feed the pigs. Even though China's **population** is very large, everyone has enough to eat because of methods like this.

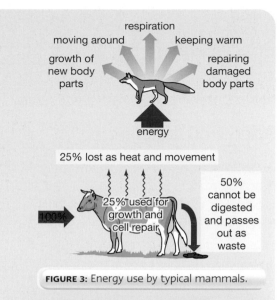

FIGURE 3: Energy use by typical mammals.

FIGURE 4: Careful use of resources makes sure no-one starves. These lagoons are purifying water and growing plants for fish food.

FIGURE 5: This tiny hillside garden in China can produces enough food to feed a family. If they insisted on keeping a cow they would need a space ten times the size!

QUESTIONS

4 List **three** things, other than growth, that an animal needs energy to do.

5 What percentage of the energy supplied to a cow in grass is made into meat or milk?

6 Look at table 1. Why do birds store so little of their energy intake compared with fish?

7 Give **three** reasons why animals are better as food than plants.

8 Give **three** reasons why plants are better as food than animals.

9 Give **two** advantages of using fish as a food in Chinese villages.

10 It is more efficient to produce a field of wheat than raising beef cattle to feed human beings. Use the idea of energy flow through ecosystems to explain why.

Animal	Percentage of energy input made available in meat
mammals	3.14
birds	1.29
fish	9.7

TABLE 1: Conversion rates for energy input in different herbivores.

Organic veg?

You will find out:
- How organic farming and conventional farming differ
- How human activity affects the environment
- How levels of poisons in the environment change
- How bioaccumulation can be used to clean waste sites

Manic organic?

Organic food seems like the latest craze. People are more and more worried about chemicals in their food. They are prepared to pay extra for food that they say is 'organic'. This means no artificial **pesticides** or **fertilisers** were used to produce the food. Is this sensible or just a fad?

Organic farming

Modern agriculture, sometimes called conventional agriculture, uses a huge amount of artificial **chemicals** to:

- increase the amount of food produced per hectare of ground
- protect against pests which damage the crops.

Food produced without these chemicals is called organic. Organic food and farming methods are supposed to be healthier for the consumer and safer for the **environment**. Organic farmers tend to use 'natural' fertilisers such as **manure**. They also change the crop growing in a field every year to prevent build-up of pests and to keep the soil fertile. But can we produce enough food this way?

Conventional farming uses a large amount of energy to produce fertilisers, drive large machines, and transport food and chemicals long distances. This energy often comes from fossil fuels and produces a range of **pollutants** that damage more than just the local farms.

Conventional farming can also damage soil. This occurred in the USA in the 1930s where a combination of poor farming techniques and bad weather led to dust bowls. The soil literally blew away leaving infertile deserts behind. This process is called **desertification** and is very difficult to undo.

Crop	Organic yield (%)	Conventional yield (%)
wheat	25.3	35.2
barley	45.7	60.9
oats	45.9	64.8
peas	18.7	34.5

TABLE 1: Organic and conventional yields.

Crop	Organic price	Conventional price
wheat	6.08	4.60
peas	9.10	5.50
oats	3.81	1.90

TABLE 2: Prices for organic and conventional crops (C$ per bushel).

FIGURE 1: This volunteer is planting trees to try to prevent the erosion of soil in the 1930s in the southern USA.

QUESTIONS

1. List **three** differences between organic and conventional farming methods.
2. Does organic farming increase or decrease the productivity of the land?
3. A farmer plants a hectare with wheat. Would they make more money from a hectare of organic wheat or conventional farming?
4. What is the percentage increase in yield for a hectare of conventional peas compared with organic peas?

VANISHING FARMLAND

Every year over 6 million hectares of farmland becomes desert.

Pesticides and poisons

Conventional farming uses lots of pesticide. Pesticides are poisons but chemists have tried to make sure they only poison pests – not the crop plants or the consumers of the food. But can we be sure?

Pesticides are used in very low concentrations – sometimes so low that they cannot be detected on the original plants. An organism that eats the plant will absorb the pesticide and can store it in its body. If it eats 20 plants, will it collect 20 times the pesticide? If another animal eats this one will it take in 20 times the dose of pesticide it would get from a plant? If it eats 20 animals will it absorb 20 times 20?

Research done in the 1950s and 1960s showed how the levels of a pesticide called **DDT** changed in the environment. Low levels of DDT were sprayed onto a lake in the USA to kill mosquitos. It was a success – but green plants absorbed some of the DDT. These plants were eaten by small animals which in turn were eaten by small fish and so on up to the large **predatory** birds such as ospreys. At every step in the chain the levels of DDT detected in the organism rose. This increase in concentration is called **bioaccumulation**.

FIGURE 2: Birds of prey like this hawk almost became extinct because of a pesticide designed to kill mosquitos.

By the 1970s, the levels of DDT in large birds were so high that populations were beginning to crash. A tiny amount of DDT in the water threatened to make some birds extinct and DDT was banned. Even after 30 years the number of predatory birds is still quite low – the recovery will take many more years. Some birds many miles away from the original sprayed sites showed surprisingly high levels of DDT.

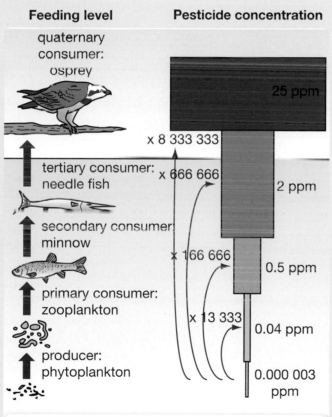

FIGURE 3: Bioaccumulation of DDT in the osprey food chain.

QUESTIONS

5 What does the word 'bioaccumulation' mean?

6 How can bioaccumulation raise the concentration of pesticides in animals that are not pests?

7 Do human beings bioaccumulate? How could you find out?

8 Is bioaccumulation a strong argument for organic farming?

Biotic and abiotic

The natural world contains two groups of factors: **biotic** and **abiotic**.

- Abiotic factors are to do with non-living parts of the environment like temperature, light levels and oxygen levels.
- Biotic factors are to do with the living parts of the environment and include prey, predators and other organisms competing for food and shelter.

Pesticides are good examples of abiotic factors – but they can be changed by biotic factors such as bioaccumulation. For this reason we need to be careful when we regard the natural world as simply a machine with set rules – sometimes the 'machine' seems to be able to change its programming and do unexpected things!

Biotic and abiotic factors work together to change the environment.

QUESTIONS

9 Explain the difference between biotic and abiotic factors.

10 Why are things that depend on biotic factors often more difficult to predict than things that depend on abiotic factors?

Winner takes all

You will find out:
- Why organisms compete
- How competition affects population size
- How predators and prey depend on each other

First past the post

It's a rough old world! Animals and plants are constantly competing amongst themselves for food and water, energy and space to breed and grow. Only the best competitors survive – it is a case of winner takes all. Or is it?

FIGURE 1: In the racing world, winning is everything – is it the same in the natural world? Well … in a way.

It's a tough old life!

Rabbits are great breeders! A female is ready to **breed** at about six months and produces four babies in about 31 days. Within six months some of these babies may be breeding as well. You can see how the population of rabbits could easily get out of hand!

But rabbits need to eat and if there are too many rabbits, the food runs out. The rabbits have to compete with each other for food. **Competition** is always fiercest when the organisms are looking for the same things. So competition between rabbits is much stronger than competition between rabbits and woodpeckers.

Competition is fiercest when:

- **resources** are in short supply
- organisms are trying to get the same resources.

Animals compete for food, water, shelter, oxygen and mates. Plants compete for water, space to grow, light and mineral salts.

Competition between members of the same species is called **intraspecific** competition. Competition between members of different species is called **interspecific** competition.

FIGURE 2: Why is the saying 'to breed like rabbits' used so frequently?

☰ QUESTIONS ☰

1 What does the word competition mean?
2 Competition between members of the same species is usually much fiercer than competition between different species. Explain why.
3 Give an example of an animal that competes with other members of its own species for a mate.
4 Why does a sudden rise in the local rabbit population often lead to a sudden drop in the next season?

WOW FACTOR!

Starting with two enthusiastic rabbits you could produce a colony of over 100 in three years!

…breed …competition …interspecific

Mouseville!

The people of Kern County, California, did not like skunks, or weasels, or foxes, or snakes, or owls, or coyotes or any of the other small predators on their farms. So they started a campaign to remove them. By 1924 the job was almost done and when 1926 produced a bumper harvest, the people thought their problems were over. The harvest was gathered leaving 25 000 acres (about 10 000 ha) of stubble and scattered seed in the low-lying fields near the lake.

October came and people began to notice a minor annoyance. There were mice everywhere. These mice were breeding in the fields, unrestrained by predators. But a few mice were not a problem. Better mice than coyotes or weasels!

The real problem began on 6 January 1927. Millions of mice that had over-wintered in the fields suddenly realised that they were hungry. Driven by starvation they left the fields in their millions. Farmers looking to protect their grain stores waded ankle deep through mice all looking for a meal. A teacher at a local school opened her desk one morning to find twelve mice nesting there. But there was not one skunk, or weasel, or snake, or owl or coyote to eat this plague of furry rodents!

FIGURE 3: Imagine all the seeds scattered during the processing and harvesting of the corn in 1926. Plenty to keep the mice fed, and breeding, during the early winter.

There were mice everywhere!

Something had to be done. On 22 January, Stanley E. Piper (yes Piper as in Pied Piper!) arrived from the US Biological Survey, Washington, with 25 men. They set up camp in the middle of the fields where 100 000 000 mice were living in 1000 separate burrows! It took 40 tonnes of chopped alfalfa poisoned with strychnine but by the end of February the war was over. Kern County was back to normal levels of mouse population.

FIGURE 4: This coyote could have helped to keep the mouse population in check – but the people of Kern County had killed them all.

FIGURE 5: They look very sweet but imagine if there were a hundred million of them!

▦ QUESTIONS ▦

5   List **three** predators of mice in Kern County.

6   The competition between the mice was low in the autumn in the freshly-harvested fields but very fierce in January. Explain why.

7   Give **two** reasons why 1926 was such a good year for mice in Kern County.

8   Why did the removal of the predators increase competition between the mice?

9   Write a letter to the town council of Kern County explaining how they can prevent another plague of mice.

Virtually real

You will find out:
- How living populations can be modelled by computer
- Why computer models can be useful to predict future events
- That computer predictions are not always accurate
- About a real-world model that reduces pesticide use

Behaving like lemmings?

Lemmings are small rodents which live in the cold grassland of the Arctic. Most of the time their habitat is covered with snow and ice, but during a good summer, there is plenty of food and the lemming population rises dramatically. There are even stories of crazed herds of millions of lemmings rushing over cliffs!

FIGURE 1: Lemmings – look like hamsters and breed like rabbits.

Modelling

Many different things affect the lemming population. To work out how all of them work you really need a computer. In fact, computers are used to simulate populations and their changes. These computer **models** use rules to work out what will happen to the population over time.

An increase in the lemming population leads to an increase in the predator population. The predators hunt and eat the lemmings. This means that there is less food for the predators and so their numbers go down. This means that the number of lemmings goes up again because there are fewer predators.

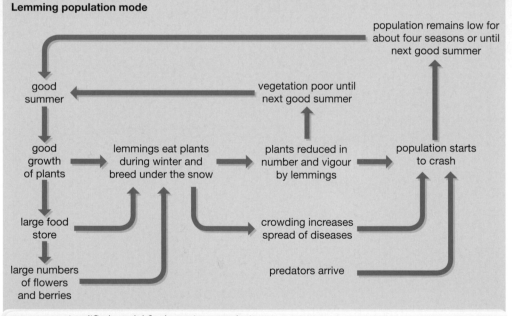

Lemming population mode

- good summer
- good growth of plants
- large food store
- large numbers of flowers and berries
- lemmings eat plants during winter and breed under the snow
- plants reduced in number and vigour by lemmings
- vegetation poor until next good summer
- crowding increases spread of diseases
- predators arrive
- population starts to crash
- population remains low for about four seasons or until next good summer

FIGURE 2: A simplified model for lemming population.

⁞⁞ QUESTIONS ⁞⁞

1. List the factors that will increase the lemming population.
2. List the factors that would decrease the lemming population.
3. What would happen to the lemming population if extra food was supplied during the summer?

...factors   ...global warming   ...interdependence

Bigger models

The lemming population model (figure 2) shows how different organisms are interdependent. A change in the food plants or an increase in the predators will change the lemming numbers. Of course, these organisms are also interdependent with the lemmings. The plants rely on the lemmings to distribute their seeds. The predators need lemmings for food.

Humans are not immune to **interdependence**. Our population is affected by many **factors** including birth rate, death rate, food supply, wars and conflicts, pollution and so on. Can we predict how it will change over the next 50 years?

The Limits to Growth (H)

In 1976, a study called 'The Limits to Growth' predicted that by 2076 the Earth would have run out of many resources, pollution would have peaked and the human population would crash due to lack of food. Hardly a cheerful **prediction**! The prediction was based on a computer model running on what was one of the world's biggest computers of the day. Their predictions are shown as a graph in figure 3.

Global temperature (H)

There are a number of computers running models of our atmosphere to look at **global warming**. Scientists load in data about change over the past twenty years and the computer predicts future changes. As with modelling of population changes, a model can only provide a guide – and sudden, unexpected changes could make our prediction completely wrong.

A model can also predict possibilities based on a range of possible future events. Some of these events could fail to occur while some hit the target. The computer follows rules set up by the researchers. If we do not understand the factors affecting the outcomes, our set of 'rules' will be wrong and the prediction will be wrong.

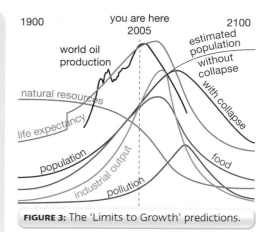

FIGURE 3: The 'Limits to Growth' predictions.

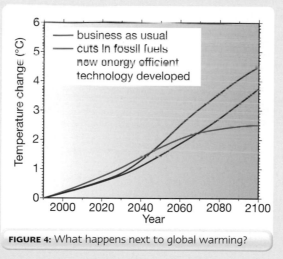

FIGURE 4: What happens next to global warming?

Planning pesticides (H)

In the USA, a university department has created a population model for insects that damage plant crops. Their model uses factors such as night-time temperature, humidity, number of adult insects in a field and number of predators of these insects to predict the population of the insects up to two weeks in advance.

When the model predicts a massive rise in insect population, the farmers are told to spray pesticides onto their plants. Using the computer model means that plants are only sprayed when there is a real threat of an insect plague. The alternative would be to spray every few weeks and this would cost more money and be environmentally more damaging.

QUESTIONS

8   Give **two** advantages of the pest-predicting model used here.

9   The model depends on farmers collecting data about the number of pests in their fields. This data is used in the model to predict future pest populations. What would happen if the farmers did not count the pests accurately?

10 Give **one** disadvantage of the model compared with spraying every fortnight to keep the pests controlled.

QUESTIONS

4   List **three** factors included in the Limits to Growth model.

5   Give **one** advantage of using a computer to model populations and other systems.

6   How can you tell if a model is a good one?

7   A number of the Limits to Growth predictions have not taken place yet. Does this mean the other predictions are wrong? (Think carefully about this question – there may not be a definite answer!)

SOUTHALL & WEST LONDON COLLEGE
LEARNING CENTRE

...model ...prediction

Global Bigfoot?

You will find out:
- How human activities are damaging the Earth
- About your global footprint
- How industrialisation affects the Earth
- Why we need to build for sustainability

Myths and monsters

Bigfoot – a strange creature that is half animal, half human. It has been reported in the forests of North America. It is a shy, giant creature in tune with the woods. But there is another Bigfoot – entirely human, leaving destruction everywhere it goes and far too easy to find! Maybe you are a Bigfoot?

FIGURE 1: Bigfoot could be a monster of our own creation!

Bigfoot – monster of the malls! (H)

The USA has some of the biggest shopping malls in the world. Citizens are encouraged to buy more and more stuff to keep the shop owners in profits. But putting a T-shirt on a shelf in Boston, USA, costs more than you might imagine.

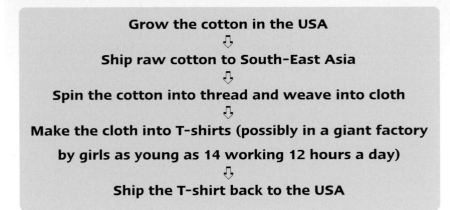

Grow the cotton in the USA
⇩
Ship raw cotton to South-East Asia
⇩
Spin the cotton into thread and weave into cloth
⇩
Make the cloth into T-shirts (possibly in a giant factory by girls as young as 14 working 12 hours a day)
⇩
Ship the T-shirt back to the USA

So cotton travels right round the world on its journey from raw cotton to a T-shirt! This costs a huge amount of energy and produces a lot of **waste**. A **global footprint** tells us how much we are costing the Earth in terms of resources used and waste produced by our normal lifestyles. Different countries and different types of people have different sizes of global footprint.

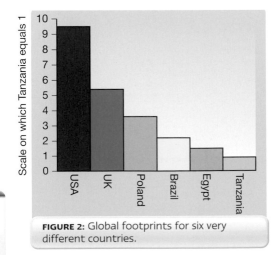

FIGURE 2: Global footprints for six very different countries.

QUESTIONS

1. What is a global footprint?
2. Can you see any pattern in the size of the global footprints shown?
3. The US government gives money to its cotton farmers to produce more cotton. This means that it is cheaper than cotton in South-East Asia growing near to the T-shirt factories. Why is this a bad idea?

How many Earths? (H)

Global footprints are a useful way to compare the impact of different countries and lifestyles on the planet. Your footprint can be measured by the amount of land needed to support your lifestyle. Since we know how much land there is on the Earth we can work out if the planet can cope if everyone lived like you.

If we all lived like...	We would need this many Earths...
people from Leicester, UK	3.3
New Yorkers	5.7
city folk from Guilin, China	1.2
farmers from Tanzania	0.4

It is clear that we cannot all live like New Yorkers, or even people from Leicester! The Earth is just not big enough. The threats to our survival include:

- running out of energy and other raw materials
- running out of food and water
- producing too much toxic waste.

As countries develop they become richer and their global footprint increases. China and India are developing very rapidly. Will the impact of this on the planet be too great? Should countries be forced to slow down their development to protect the planet? Or should richer countries like the USA and those in Europe use less to balance the increase?

FIGURE 3: You can buy anything in Hong Kong. But can China develop in the same way as the USA?

Population (H)

World population is increasing. The population in the USA and western Europe is increasing very slowly but our impact on the planet is much higher than countries like Tanzania in Africa with rapidly growing populations. The population growth in China is relatively low, yet its increase in industrialisation has resulted in a massive increase in its global footprint. Since many of the goods produced in China are shipped to the West, the total cost of that new mobile phone, T-shirt or plastic toy is even higher.

QUESTIONS

4 How many Tanzanian farmers does it take to produce a global footprint as large as a single man living in New York?

5 The global footprint for someone living in Guilin is rising rapidly. Why?

6 Why is total population less important in looking at the Earth than the global footprint?

So where next? (H)

Modern environmental planning promotes **sustainability**. Sustainable technologies do not damage the Earth for future generations. If we do not develop sustainable energy sources and recycle more of the materials we use, our children and our children's children will inherit a poorer and more dangerous planet.

Sustainable technologies:

- create no waste that cannot be used in some other process
- use natural cycles to prevent the build-up of poisons in the environment
- can carry on forever without damaging the planet.

One crucial area of sustainable development is the use of **renewable energy** sources, like wind and wave power, rather than **fossil fuels** which we know will become much rarer in the future and will eventually run out.

QUESTIONS

7 What is 'sustainable development'?

8 List **three** technologies that contribute to sustainable development.

9 List **three** technologies that are not sustainable.

10 'Sustainability is about doing more – but doing it with less.' Write a short paragraph to explain what this slogan means.

Dino death!

You will find out:
- The meaning of the word extinct
- How scientists use fossils to investigate past ages
- How species can disappear
- Why Darwin's idea of evolution was not accepted immediately

Mesosaurs and movie stars!

Dinosaurs are probably the most amazing animals that have ever walked the Earth. A bit like giant lizards, and the stars of many modern computer-generated films, these beasts dominated the planet for millions of years. Yet now, not one of them is left. What happened? And could it happen to us?

Fossil formation

When a living organism dies, it breaks down into simple chemicals. Organisms called **decomposers** actually cause this **decay**.

But decomposers do not always get the chance to do their job. If the dead body is covered with mud and no **oxygen** can get through, the decomposers die. The body is preserved, although it is usually only the hard parts like bones and teeth that are well preserved. Over millions of years the chemicals in the body are swapped with minerals in the surrounding mud and stone until the body becomes more like rock than living tissue. It has become a **fossil**.

Interpreting fossils

Fossils are not easy to interpret. They can be crushed flat so scientists have to reconstruct the three-dimensional shape from a flattened sheet. Imagine recreating an egg from a crushed eggshell! Sometimes the fossils are damaged by heat or broken into small pieces by earth movements or careless fossil hunters. Also fossils are rare. Some of our ideas about dinosaurs depend on only a few fossilised teeth and claws. But fossils do give us important clues.

- A fossilised tooth that looks like the tooth of a modern predator like a tiger suggests the dinosaur was a meat-eater.
- Bones from fossilised limbs can tell us whether the dinosaur walked on four legs or two.
- Looking through fossilised dinosaur faeces can show us what the animal had to eat before it died.

FIGURE 1: Dinosaurs once ruled the planet.

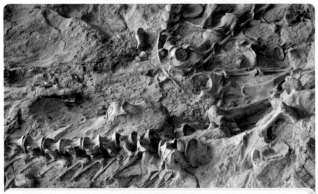

FIGURE 2: Slowly this mess of dinosaur bones will be excavated and then reconstructed into models of what we think the original dinosaurs looked like.

□ QUESTIONS □

1. What is a fossil?
2. Give **two** reasons why it is sometimes difficult to interpret a fossil.
3. List **two** things we can determine from a fossil.
4. Suggest **one** thing about a dinosaur that a fossil could never tell us.

WOW FACTOR!

The largest dinosaurs lived 120 million years ago and each weighed 50 tonnes! The beast could be 35 m from nose to tail!

...cold-blooded ...decay ...decomposer ...element ...evolution

Dino death

Why did dinosaurs die out? There are a number of theories and they all depend on a change in the environment. A drop in temperature meant that the dinosaurs were not as well-adapted to their environment and their numbers began to decline. Eventually not one was left and the dinosaurs became **extinct**. A species that is extinct has no living members.

Dinosaurs were **cold-blooded** like **reptiles**. This meant that, when the temperature dropped, the reactions in their cells slowed down and they became sluggish. A slow-moving predator is not good!

But why did the herbivorous dinosaurs die out? A change in temperature will lower the productivity of plants. Lower growth means less food for herbivores and, therefore, less food for the carnivores that eat them.

Sudden change

But what could cause this change? Two theories are:

- asteroid impact
- a giant volcanic eruption.

A thin layer of soot in 65 million-year old clay exists in many places across the world. The same clay also contains surprisingly large amounts of the **element** iridium. Iridium is very rare. It comes from falling **meteorites** or from eruptions of material from deep inside the Earth. Scientists believe that the soot and iridium may indicate a catastrophic meteorite impact or a series of giant volcanic eruptions. One group even claim to have found the site of the impact in northern Mexico.

A meteorite measuring 10 km across would have exploded with the same force as millions of tonnes of high explosive. Everything within 500 km of the impact would be instantly destroyed. Trillions of tonnes of dust, gases and water vapour would have been shot into the atmosphere and led to an immediate 25% reduction in light levels and a large fall in temperature. A shock wave would pass round the world setting fire to forests up to 1000 km away.

Doubting Darwin? (H)

Most people recognise nowadays that **evolution** explains the development of life on our planet and the **extinction** of the dinosaurs. However, when Charles Darwin published his book, *The Origin of Species*, in 1859, it created a huge controversy. Some said it contradicted the Bible's account of creation. The power of the established church was so great at the time that some scientists were frightened to support Darwin. The theory of evolution also drew on a number of different areas of study (biology, chemistry, geology, geography) and scientists did not tend to cooperate across disciplines in those days.

Nowadays the vast majority of serious scientists, and many Christians, accept the theory of evolution as the best explanation we currently have. The original antagonism to the idea may have been because it was so shocking. Even today in some parts of the USA, science teachers have to be very careful to explain that evolution is just a theory (which is true for almost everything in science lessons!) to avoid criticism from fundamentalist believers.

FIGURE 3: This crater is in Arizona, USA. The meteorite that created it was small compared with the one that would have been needed to kill off the dinosaurs!

QUESTIONS

5 What does the word 'extinct' mean?

6 Give **two** pieces of evidence to suggest a catastrophe occurred 65 million years ago.

7 Why were large slow-moving animals like dinosaurs damaged by a sudden change in the environment?

8 Smaller mammals seemed to be able to fill the ecological spaces left by the dinosaurs. Suggest **two** reasons why this happened.

9 Why do you think some people with particular types of religious faith find the idea of evolution difficult while others do not?

Faster, stronger, fitter

You will find out:
- How natural selection works
- How new species arise
- How humans can interfere with natural selection

SuperRat and MRSA

SuperRat thrives on poison that kills other rats! MRSA is a bacterium that is resistant to many of our modern **antibiotics**. Like the SuperRat, it seems to have evolved recently. Can we prevent these super pests from developing? And where do they come from in the first place?

FIGURE 1: SuperRat actually likes poison!

SuperRat and the poison picnic

Warfarin is a poison that affects rat's blood so that the animal bleeds to death. In 1958, the first warfarin-resistant rats were reported near Welshpool in mid-Wales. They seemed to thrive on warfarin and were rapidly replacing the other rats in the area.

A **mutation** is a sudden, unpredictable change to a **gene**. Most mutations are dangerous, but some are useful. The warfarin-**resistance** mutation appeared in an unknown rat before 1958. This 'SuperRat' was able to eat the warfarin-laced seed that was put down to kill the other rats. This food, provided by human beings, kept the rat alive and it bred to produce offspring. Some of these would have the warfarin-resistance gene. The gene spread rapidly and within ten years it had appeared in west Wales. Nowadays you can find warfarin-resistant rats all over the UK.

The spread of SuperRat is an example of **natural selection**. The strongest, fittest rats survived and went on to reproduce, while the others died out. Natural selection always allows the best-adapted organisms to survive and grow.

FIGURE 2: Yes, it's a poison – and SuperRat loves it.

QUESTIONS

1 What is a mutation?
2 When and where was the first warfarin-resistant rat discovered?
3 Why did the percentage of warfarin-resistant rats in the population around Welshpool increase?
4 If people did not put down warfarin to kill rats how would that affect the warfarin-resistant rat's advantage?

WOW FACTOR!

Rats produce about ten babies in a litter and can have five litters in a year. The young rats also breed before they are a year old.

...adaptation   ...antibiotic   ...gene   ...mutation

MRSA

MRSA stands for *Methicillin Resistant Staphylococcus Aureus*. It's known as a 'superbug' because it is resistant to so many antibiotics. *Staphylococcus aureus* is a very common bacterium and lives harmlessly on the skin and in the throats of up to half of the people in the UK. It normally causes few problems but can become dangerous when it gets inside the body.

MRSA is particularly dangerous in hospitals and other areas where there are lots of sick people. If people who are already weak catch the bug it can cause serious, even life-threatening, illnesses. Since MRSA is resistant to many antibiotics it can be difficult to treat.

Where did MRSA come from?

Whilst lack of hygiene encourages the spread of MRSA in hospitals, its true cause is natural selection at the microbial level.

When you have a bacterial infection you might take some antibiotics to kill the bacteria. The bacteria causing your illness are not all the same. Some will need more antibiotic to kill them (these are the resistant forms) and some will die with the first dose (the susceptible forms). If you do not finish the bottle of antibiotics some of the resistant ones will be left. They will have a **selective advantage** and will multiply like the SuperRats of Welshpool.

MRSA seems to have developed after years of prescribing antibiotics for illnesses like sore throats. The bugs have become resistant to antibiotics and can cause major problems when they get into the body. Bacteria can reproduce two or three times every hour so evolution can be very rapid.

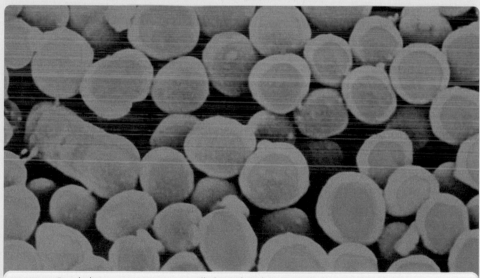

FIGURE 3: *Staphylococcus aureus* – usually harmless but potentially very dangerous.

New species

The Galapagos Islands are a group of islands 500 km west of Ecuador, South America. Each island has an isolated population of finches which have developed particular **adaptations** to help with their diet. The finches on different islands are related, but separate, species. The separation between the islands prevented the mutated genes from mixing in with the original population.

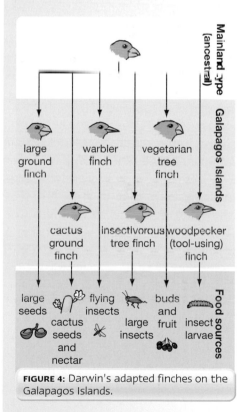

FIGURE 4: Darwin's adapted finches on the Galapagos Islands.

QUESTIONS

5   What does the phrase 'natural selection' mean?

6   What is an antibiotic?

7   You should always complete a course of antibiotics – even if you feel better before all of the tablets are gone. Why?

QUESTIONS

8   Do you think the finches would have developed into different species if they all lived on the same island? Give reasons for your answer.

Golden rice

You will find out:
- Why crop plants are genetically modified
- About the advantages and disadvantages of genetically modified (GM) crops

Rice – food for billions

In many countries over 25% of the energy in food comes from rice. It produces a heavy crop and in some countries it is possible to grow two crops every year. Rice – the perfect plant? Not quite – it does not contain enough of some vitamins and this can lead to blindness.

Golden rice

'White rice' is actually the **endosperm** of the seed with the outer seed layers removed. Endosperm is the food-storage part of the seed. It is almost pure starch with some protein. Good for energy supplies but bad for vitamin intake. 'Brown rice' is rice that has been cooked in the outer seed layer. It contains more vitamins but does not taste as nice and does not last as well as white rice.

Many people in poor countries cannot afford a varied diet. The rice is cheap and keeps them alive but may lead to vitamin deficiencies. The most significant is **vitamin A** deficiency (VAD) which causes a type of blindness. Scientists in Switzerland wondered if they could genetically modify rice to produce vitamin A in the endosperm.

Beta-carotene is the chemical that makes carrots orange. It is converted in the human body into vitamin A. Rice can produce beta-carotene but the gene that makes it in the endosperm is normally switched off. The scientists moved a gene from daffodils into the rice and the level of beta-carotene went up so much that the rice seed looked yellow. This gave it its new name 'golden rice'.

FIGURE 1: This woman is separating rice grains from the outer seed coats in the same way that it has been done for hundreds of years.

▒ QUESTIONS ▒

1 What is the endosperm?
2 What illness does a lack of vitamin A cause?
3 Why is beta-carotene useful in the diet?
4 Where did the gene come from to turn rice yellow?

ESSENTIAL VITAMIN A

17 children in the Philippines go blind every day because of lack of Vitamin A in their diet.

...beta-carotene   ...endosperm

Not so golden? (H)

Golden rice was sent for trials in 2000. The scientists behind the development announced that the new rice could 'save the sight of a million kids a year'. A bit of good news for the **genetic modification** (**GM**) industry?

In fact, there are problems:

- the level of beta-carotene in the original golden rice was so low that three golden rice meals a day will only provide about 10% of the daily vitamin A requirement
- cooking the rice damages the beta-carotene
- some people don't use yellow rice because of the colour
- golden rice is unpopular with environmental organisations.

In 2005, the scientists introduced a new variety using a gene from maize plants. This has ten times the level of beta-carotene.

FIGURE 2: Rice cooked in bamboo. Will golden rice taste as good as these traditional recipes?

However, people are suspicious of yellow rice and stick with the familiar white rice. A frustrated Dr Potrtykus, one of the developers of golden rice, has said "If some people decide that they want blind children and white rice, it's their choice. I'm offering the possibility of yellow rice and no blind children." Hardly fair – no-one would choose to blind their own children but it shows that the real world is sometimes more complicated than scientists' plans.

Environmental organisations oppose all GM crops. They point out that GM technologies seem to benefit the big companies more than the consumers or farmers.

In fact, child blindness due to VAD has been reduced in Bangladesh by promoting a more varied diet and supplying vitamin A pills and the golden rice will be given away free to poor farmers. However, this still means that poor farmers will depend on large multinational companies for their seed rather than producing it themselves.

The new rice could 'save the sight of a million kids a year'

Natural selection	Selective breeding	Genetic modification
Random – there is nothing controlling the direction of the change except for the changing requirements of the environment.	Humans control the direction of change by selecting the best new plants and animals. Only related organisms can be bred together and breeding programmes can take many years to produce the required organisms.	Humans control the direction of the change. We can transfer genes between unrelated organisms. GM requires expensive technical equipment and knowledge of the genes available in a species.

TABLE 1: A comparison of natural selection, selective breeding and genetic modification.

〰 QUESTIONS 〰

5 Where did the gene for beta-carotene come from in the second variety of yellow rice?

6 What was the advantage of this new gene?

7 List the arguments against using yellow rice. Which is the strongest one?

8 List the arguments for using yellow rice. Which is the strongest one?

9 Pick one side of the argument about yellow rice. Write an article for a magazine arguing for your view. The article must be fewer than 250 words and include **one** chart and a suggestion for **two** diagrams or photographs.

Going organic

SELF-CHECK ACTIVITY

John is a farmer. He grew up on a farm. Not only were his parents farmers, but his grandfather was too. He never wanted to do anything else, but now he's not so sure.

He has a dairy herd of 48 Friesian cows that have to be milked twice a day. The milk is collected by a large dairy, which pays John at an agreed rate. It's a struggle to pay all the bills and make a decent living. His daughter, Ruth, is 16 and is used to farm life – but will it provide a living for her?

John knows his milk would fetch a better price if it were organically produced, so he is tempted to try this. However, it would mean changes to the way he farms:

- His cows could not be given antibiotics or added growth hormones; he would have to allow them to make milk according to their natural cycles.
- He would have to keep the cows in good health by giving them certified organic feed.
- They would have to have access to pasture all year round.

CHALLENGE

STEP 1

Read about John and the decision he is taking about the future of his dairy herd. Why is he tempted to go organic?

STEP 2

If John switched to producing milk organically, he wouldn't be able to give his cows antibiotics. Why might this be a problem?

STEP 3

Why might it be a problem for John if the cows are making milk 'according to their natural cycles'?

STEP 4

Why is organic milk more expensive than non-organic milk?

STEP 5

Summarise the arguments for and against 'going organic'.

Maximise your grade

These sentences show what you need to include in your work to achieve each grade. Use them to improve your work and be more successful.

Grade	Answer includes...
F	Recall one way in which organic dairy farming is different to non-organic.
	Describe one way in which organic dairy farming is different to non-organic.
	Describe more than one way in which organic dairy farming is different to non-organic.
	Suggest one reason why organic milk is more expensive.
C	Explain one reason why organic milk is more expensive.
	Explain more than one reason why organic milk is more expensive.
A	Recognise a range of arguments both for and against organic dairy farming, including but not exclusively economic.
	As above, but with particular clarity and detail.

Clone alone

You will find out:
- How organisms pass information from parent to offspring
- How to clone a sheep
- Why clones are useful – but rare
- About the dangers of cloning

Copy cat

There is a company in the USA which will **clone** your cat for $32 000 (about £18 000). If you're not ready for the full clone you could always just save a few cells (only £750 a year) and produce a clone in a year or 20 years' time. At the same time, the Raëlian Movement claims that it has cloned humans. A brave new world or a technological nightmare?

FIGURE 1: This man will clone your cat!

Reproduction

To understand about clones you need to know about reproduction and genes. There are two types of reproduction.

- **Asexual reproduction** is quite common in plants and microbes. It produces clones of the parents. In asexual reproduction, only one parent is needed.

- **Sexual reproduction** needs two parents and involves specialised cells called **gametes**. Each parent produces a gamete and one from each parent join to make the first cell of the new individual. This individual is genetically different from the parents.

What are clones?

- You have almost certainly already eaten clones – sprinkled with salt and doused in vinegar! Many potatoes are clones. A single plant produces many **tubers** and each of these can grow into a new plant. The tubers are genetically identical to the parent so all the new plants are the same.

- Spider plants, or **Chlorophytum**, are also clones. All of the little plants growing at the ends of the stalks are clones with exactly the same genes.

- **Genes** are coded instructions needed to produce a new organism. One of the reasons why we are all different is that we all have different genes. Clones have the same genes – so are they all identical?

FIGURE 2: Probably the tastiest clones you'll meet today – chips!

QUESTIONS

1. What is a gene?
2. Draw up a table of differences between sexual and asexual reproduction.
3. What does the word 'clone' mean?
4. 'All clones are very dangerous!' Give one piece of evidence to show this statement is nonsense.

You have almost certainly already eaten clones

...asexual reproduction   ...chlorophytum   ...clone   ...DNA   ...gamete

Well clone me!

Animals tend to reproduce sexually and clones are rare. This means that there is much more variation in a litter of six piglets than in all of the potato plants in a giant field. Genes are shuffled during sexual reproduction to produce new combinations that lead to new, slightly different organisms.

The first cloned mammal was Dolly the Sheep. Dolly was created at the Roslin Institute in Scotland in 1997 from a single udder cell from her 'mother'. She was genetically identical to that sheep. Figure 3 shows the sequence but does not point out that it took 277 attempts to produce the first living lamb. This is not easy or cheap!

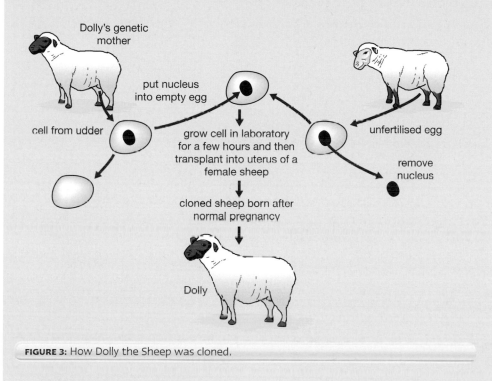

FIGURE 3: How Dolly the Sheep was cloned.

Possible but not easy

Cloning is possible because every cell in the body contains a complete set of genes. Most of these are switched off most of the time. Sexual reproduction uses special cells called gametes. Normally a gamete from a male joins with a gamete from a female to form a **zygote**. Genes in zygotes seem to be 'switched on' and start the development of a new organism. The scientists trying to clone Dolly replaced the nucleus in a gamete with the nucleus from a normal body cell. The nucleus was 'kick started' by a small electric shock. This meant it behaved like a normal zygote and started to grow. The cell was then implanted into another sheep for it to develop in her uterus.

QUESTIONS

5 How many attempts did it take to produce Dolly?
6 How did the Roslin scientists 'switch on' the nucleus from the udder cell to make it grow into Dolly?
7 What normally 'switches on' the genes in the nucleus to start producing a new individual?

WOW FACTOR!

Dolly was cloned from the udder of a sheep and got her name from Dolly Parton, the country singer.

Is cloning safe?

Genes are coded into **DNA** molecules in cells. The ends of these DNA molecules have structures called telomeres. Telomeres are long in young cells but get shorter as they age. Dolly's cells had surprisingly short telomeres for her age. Perhaps she was 'born old' because she had come from an 'old' cell?

But Dolly was a healthy sheep who gave birth to some perfectly normal lambs. She had arthritis when she died (a characteristic of older animals) but it was a lung infection that killed her in the end – not old age. This could affect any sheep – cloned or not.

QUESTIONS

8 Give **one** piece of evidence that Dolly was 'older' than she looked.
9 Give **one** piece of evidence that suggests Dolly's death had nothing to do with the fact that she had been cloned.
10 Do you think people are right to worry about clones? Give reasons to support your answer.

...gene   ...sexual reproduction   ...tuber   ...zygote

Gene genie!

You will find out:
- How genes work
- How DNA copies itself
- About the history of genetic research

Nice pair of genes

Modern microscopes can show individual genes. We can even take individual genes from one cell and transfer them into another cell. Yet it is only about 50 years since the first scientific description of DNA. At this rate of progress you might soon be able to buy a do-it-yourself gene kit when you get your mobile phone topped up in 2010! Or maybe not!

Genes

A gene is a set of instructions that tells a cell how to make something. So, you have a gene for eye colour, hair colour, your blood group and even whether you are likely to suffer from a particular disease. Most of the characteristics of an organism are controlled by many genes working together. The effects of genes are also often changed by the environment.

- A gene is a length of a chemical called deoxyribonucleic acid or **DNA**. DNA is shaped like two spirals wound around each other. The DNA carries the genetic information as a code based on the sequence of four chemicals in the molecule.

- The code uses three-letter 'words' made from just four letters (A, T, C and G). So, a gene might read as ATT/CCG/TGC and so on. There may be as many as 20 000 words in one gene.

- Each word represents a particular **amino acid**. The order of these words controls the order of amino acids in giant molecules called **enzymes**.

- The enzymes build other chemicals and body parts. So, there is a link between the order of the three-letter words in a DNA molecule and the brown chemical in your eye that gives you brown eyes.

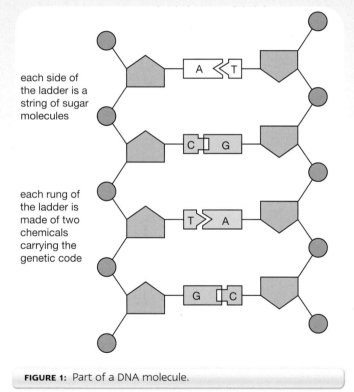

each side of the ladder is a string of sugar molecules

each rung of the ladder is made of two chemicals carrying the genetic code

FIGURE 1: Part of a DNA molecule.

QUESTIONS

1 What is a gene?
2 What are the **four** letters in the DNA 'alphabet'?
3 Genes build enzymes. How do these affect the way the body develops?

WOW FACTOR!

Human beings have about 20 000 working genes. The DNA also contains a lot of nonsense words that don't seem to do anything.

...adenine   ...amino acid   ...cytosine   ...diffraction pattern

Keeping the code safe

DNA is a large and complex molecule made of repeating units rather like a ladder is made of repeating rungs. The side pieces of the DNA ladder are sugar and phosphate groups joined together by strong chemical bonds. DNA gets its name from the sugar – deoxyribose. The rungs are made of pairs of bases joined by weaker bonds. The whole ladder is twisted into a double spiral.

The bases connecting the two sugar–phosphate chains can only link up in particular patterns. There are four bases: **adenine**, **thymine**, **cytosine** and **guanine**. Adenine can only link with thymine and cytosine can only join with guanine. If you know the sequence of one sugar–phosphate chain you can create the opposite chain by adding in the relevant matching bases and then joining them together with the sugar–phosphate chain. This means DNA can copy itself and even repair itself if one of the chains is damaged.

The first gene genies?

The structure of DNA was described by Francis Crick and James Watson in an article in the scientific journal *Nature* in 1953. In 1962, Crick, Watson and another scientist called Wilkins received the Nobel Prize for their work on DNA.

But this is not the whole story. A number of researchers had been working on the structure of DNA for many years before this. One, a woman called Rosalind Franklin, had a crucial role. She shone X-rays through samples of DNA to produce an image called a **diffraction pattern**. This gave clues about how the atoms were arranged. Only Franklin seemed to be able to carry out this fiddly procedure with any degree of success. Watson and Crick almost certainly used her results. But Franklin was a perfectionist, and while she was checking and rechecking her data Watson and Crick made a leap of faith and published.

FIGURE 2: A large-scale model of DNA demonstrated by its discoverers.

> **DNA can copy itself and even repair itself**

Who owns your genes?

In 1988 a Harvard researcher was granted a patent on a genetically-engineered mouse. This means that anyone who wants to use that mouse in research has to pay a royalty. The gene in the mouse has become a valuable property rather like a computer program or a top-selling album. Do you think this is ethical?

- Gene research is expensive – if there are no patents, companies will not make any money and so the research will stop.
- A gene has no value until a research company isolates and uses it. They should be paid for this.
- How can you patent life? It is morally wrong!
- Who owned the gene in the first place – the organism who had it or the company who extracted it?

QUESTIONS

4　What are the names of the **four** bases in DNA?

5　This is the sequence of one side of a DNA molecule: AACGGATTC. Write down the sequence of the bases in the other half starting at the A end.

6　What is the name of the sugar in a DNA molecule?

7　Does it matter who gets the credit for a scientific breakthrough? Would you have been more like Watson and Crick and taken a chance or like Franklin and checked your results?

QUESTIONS

8　What do you think? List the arguments for and against patenting genes.

9　Imagine you have a gene which protects against a disease like AIDS. Would you allow it to be used by a research company? And would you expect to be paid?

Chromosomes

You will find out:
- How genes are organised into chromosomes
- The meaning of the terms haploid and diploid
- How the diploid number is maintained in sexual reproduction

Packets of genes

You have about 20 000 genes in every cell in your body. If any of these go missing, you could end up with severe problems. Every time a cell divides it needs to get a copy of every gene safely delivered to the daughter cells. How is this organised?

Chromosomes

Every cell in your body contains packages of genes called **chromosomes**. A chromosome consists of a giant molecule of DNA that contains hundreds of genes.

Human beings have 46 chromosomes in total arranged in 23 pairs. This means that you have two versions of every gene in your body – one on each chromosome in a pair.

Chromosomes are only visible during cell division. If you treat a dividing cell with a special poison and then stain the chromosomes you can see 46 small, worm-like bundles.

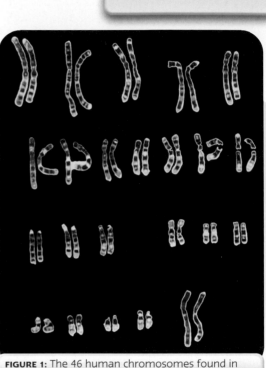

FIGURE 1: The 46 human chromosomes found in all normal body cells.

If you take a photograph you can sort these chromosomes into their pairs and produce a diagram called a **karyotype**. This shows all of the chromosomes arranged neatly in pairs.

Diploid number

The number of chromosomes in body cells is called the **diploid number**. In humans it is 46. One special set of cells has only got one chromosome from each pair to make 23 in total. These cells are the **gametes** – sperms in males and eggs in females. 23 is the **haploid number**.

During sexual reproduction, a sperm joins with an egg and the two sets of 23 chromosomes are mixed together to reach 46 again.

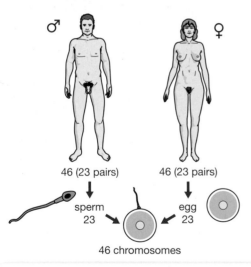

46 (23 pairs)   46 (23 pairs)

sperm 23   egg 23

46 chromosomes

FIGURE 2: Your father and mother gave you an equal number of chromosomes.

❚❚ QUESTIONS ❚❚

1   How many chromosomes are present in a normal human liver cell?
2   How many chromosomes are present in a human sperm?
3   What is a karyotype?
4   What is a gamete?

...chromosome ...diploid number ...gamete ...haploid number

Sex and fertilisation

All normal human body cells have 46 chromosomes. When they divide all daughter cells also have 46. This sort of cell division is called **mitosis** and produces two cells that are genetically identical to the parent. When cells in the sex organs divide to produce a gamete they use a special sort of cell division called **meiosis**. Meiosis produces cells with only one chromosome from each pair – so the total number of chromosomes is halved. Why does this happen?

During sexual reproduction, sperms from the male pass into the body of the female. The sperms eventually reach an egg and a single sperm passes its nucleus into the egg. The two nuclei fuse or join together to produce a new nucleus containing 23 chromosomes from the father and 23 from the mother. This fertilised egg with its new nucleus is the first cell of the new individual. It is genetically different from the mother and the father. It contains 46 chromosomes (the diploid number) and divides repeatedly by mitosis over the next nine months until the baby is born.

Imagine what would happen if gametes were produced by normal cell division. They would contain 46 chromosomes and the fertilised egg would have 46 + 46 = 92 chromosomes. After another generation the number would double again! This would lead to an impossible situation in a very short time.

FIGURE 3: How many chromosomes does the African elephant have?

You have two versions of every gene in your body

Sexual or asexual?

Sexual reproduction involves a lot of hard work – finding a mate, courting, mating – and it also often requires extensive support of the offspring after they are born. Why bother to do this when asexual reproduction is so much easier?

Sexual reproduction builds in variation between the offspring and parents, and between the offspring. The production of gametes and their fusion to produce a **zygote** shuffles the chromosomes and the genes they carry. Some of the differences produced in the offspring may lead to better survival or the ability to cope with changes in the environment.

FIGURE 4: Worms are both male and female – all can produce offspring.

QUESTIONS

5 Give **two** differences between mitosis and meiosis.

6 The diploid number of African elephants is 56. How many chromosomes are present in an unfertilised egg from an African elephant?

7 The haploid number in a species is 16. How many chromosomes would a fertilised egg contain?

QUESTIONS

8 Potatoes can reproduce sexually by seed or asexually by tuber. Give **one** advantage to the plant of each type of reproduction.

9 What is a zygote and how is it different from a gamete?

Nature or nurture?

You will find out:
- How genes are affected by the environment
- How genes can be limited by the action of the environment
- Why the eventual form of an organism depends on a combination of genetics and the environment

Food for everyone

The Green Revolution planned to feed the world by using science to increase food production everywhere. It used fertilisers and new types of crops that could grow faster than traditional versions. These new crops, called **high-yielding varieties** (**HYVs**), were made in plant-breeding centres. The first results were very impressive.

The 'miracle rices'   (H)

- A HYV of rice produced twice as much grain as the old variety. New breeding programmes produced even better varieties. Rice plants from around the world were crossed in breeding experiments to produce the so-called '**miracle rices**'.

- Cross-breeding plants involved taking pollen from one plant and adding it to the seed-producing parts of other plants. In this way, useful characteristics could be built up in the new seeds. Scientists began to control the normal sexual reproduction of crop plants, and even animals, to produce the best new breeds.

- But the plants required extra fertiliser and plenty of water to produce the high yields. The modern seeds were also very expensive.

- If the conditions were not perfect, the new HYVs could sometimes do worse than the traditional varieties. Scientists began to appreciate how important the **environment** was to the success of the crops. The old-fashioned varieties had evolved over thousands of years to cope with bad conditions.

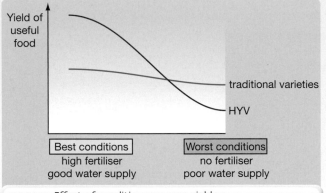

FIGURE 1: Effect of conditions on crop yields.

FIGURE 2: The narrow fields in LongJi, China, increase the surface available for planting enormously but make it difficult to use some of the modern machinery and techniques that the HYV rice needs to succeed.

QUESTIONS

1. What is an HYV?
2. How were HYVs created?
3. What is the main advantage of an HYV?
4. Give **two** disadvantages of HYV rice.

...environment ...high-yielding varieties (HYVs)

Genes and environment (H)

What an organism looks like depends on its genes and its environment. The size of a plant depends on the amount of mineral resources available to it, as well as on its genes. Similarly, your parents may be very thin but if you eat too much and do too little exercise you will get fat – your genes can't help!

Large parents tend to produce large babies – probably due to genes that control body size that pass from parents to children. However, environmental factors also have an effect. One research project looked at the effect of cigarette smoking on the weight of babies. Any baby born below 3500 g was classified as a low birth weight baby in this study. The researchers then looked at the number of cigarettes smoked during pregnancy by the mother. Figure 3 shows the data.

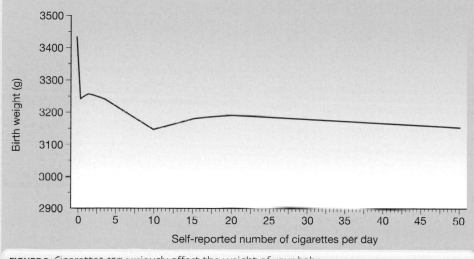

FIGURE 3: Cigarettes can seriously affect the weight of your baby.

Nature or nurture? (H)

Scientists are undecided about whether genes or environment have a greater effect on the development of living organisms. The 'nature' idea says that genes have by far the larger effect. 'Nurture' argues that environment has a stronger effect. The correct answer may be that both are equally important.

These Tibetan women can breathe easily in the thin air in Lhasa. Western tourists can be breathless for a few days until their body adjusts. The locals probably have different genes, but also benefit because they have always lived at this altitude. Both genes and the environment have an effect.

FIGURE 4: Pilgrims and tourists in Lhasa, Tibet.

▥▥ QUESTIONS ▥▥

5 Your genes decide exactly what you will be like as an adult. Is this true or false? Give reasons for your answers.

6 List **three** ways in which your environment can affect your development.

7 Does the data here show that smoking during pregnancy reduces birth weight?

Smoking during pregnancy can reduce the weight of babies

Smoking and genes (H)

A research project in the USA looked at why some women who smoke during pregnancy produce low weight babies but others do not. Was something protecting some of the foetuses from the mothers' smoke? The body has a number of enzymes that break down the products of smoking. Two of these are coded for by genes called CVP1A1 and GSTT1. Women with **mutations** of these genes produced less of these enzymes and tended to produce low weight babies. The study showed:

- smoking during pregnancy reduces the weight of babies
- women with CVP1A1 and GSTT1 mutations produced less 'smoke-clearing' enzymes
- women with these genotypes were more likely to produce low weight babies if they smoked.

▥▥▥ QUESTIONS ▥▥▥

8 Smoking is an environmental factor. Do the studies here show it is the only factor involved in birth weights?

9 Doctors can detect normal and abnormal versions of the CVP1A1 and GSTT1 genes. What advice should they give about smoking during pregnancy to **a)** women with normal genes and **b)** women with the abnormal forms?

Blue or brown?

You will find out:
- How genes control the colour of our eyes
- The meaning of the words dominant and recessive
- How to predict the results of simple genetic crosses

The eyes have it!

Our eyes are some of the most noticeable things about us. Even Clark Kent seemed to be able to keep his identity as Superman secret by putting on glasses! Eye colour is controlled by a very simple genetic system. Whether you have blue or brown eyes depends on just one pair of genes!

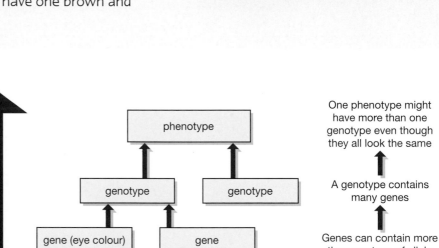

FIGURE 1: The colour of your eyes is determined by alleles.

Genes, alleles and eye colour   **(H)**

The genes for eye colour exist in a number of different forms called **alleles**. Your eye colour is controlled by a pair of genes with one on each chromosome.

A man with two blue alleles has blue eyes. A woman with two brown alleles has brown eyes. But what happens if you have one brown and one blue allele in the pair?

In fact, one of the alleles takes control. If you have one brown allele and one blue allele, your eyes will be brown. The brown allele that takes control is called **dominant**. The hidden blue allele is called **recessive**.

The alleles you have are called your **genotype**. What you actually look like is called your **phenotype**. So a phenotype of brown eyes might have two genotypes: two brown alleles or one brown and one blue.

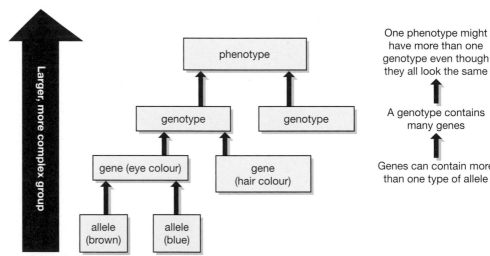

FIGURE 2: How alleles are linked to what you look like.

QUESTIONS

1. What does the word 'allele' mean?
2. What is the difference between a 'gene' and an 'allele'?
3. What does the word 'recessive' mean?
4. Write down the only possible genotype for blue eyes.

Watch Out People often confuse the words gene and allele. A gene is something that controls a characteristic (e.g. eye colour). An allele is a particular form of a gene (e.g. brown eyes or blue eyes).

...allele ...dominant ...first generation (F1) ...genetic cross ...genotype

Inheriting eye colour

Figure 3 shows a **genetic cross**. The children produced by this cross are known as the **F1** or **first generation**. The alleles are shown by letters. A capital letter is used for the dominant allele. Br is the allele for brown eyes and bl is the allele for blue eyes.

Figure 4 shows what happens if the mother has one brown gene and one blue one.

If both of the alleles of a gene are the same, for example blbl, the combination is **homozygous**. Someone who is **heterozygous** has two different alleles for a gene, for example Brbl. In figure 4 the father is homozygous and the mother is heterozygous.

Genes and disease

Damaged genes can cause diseases. These are often recessive. Cystic fibrosis is a genetic disease. A gene codes for a protein that controls movement of water in and out of cells. If this gene is damaged, the sufferer has very sticky mucus in the lungs. This mucus cannot be cleared easily and the sufferer easily picks up lung infections.

About one in 25 people carry the damaged (cystic) gene. However, since it is recessive, they will not suffer from any symptoms. If both parents carry the gene, what are the chances of producing a child with cystic fibrosis?

Parents	Cc	Cc
Gametes	C or c	C or c
F1	CC or cC or cC or cc	

Three out of the four possible combinations have a normal gene. There is only one chance in four that a child born to these parents will have cystic fibrosis.

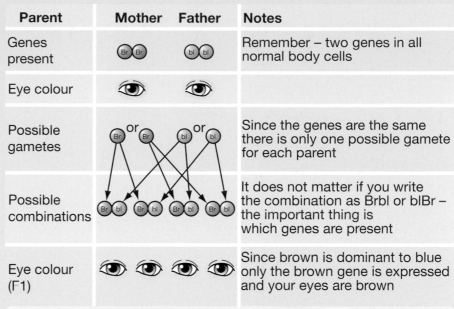

Parent	Mother	Father	Notes
Genes present	Br Br	bl bl	Remember – two genes in all normal body cells
Eye colour	👁	👁	
Possible gametes	Br or Br	bl or bl	Since the genes are the same there is only one possible gamete for each parent
Possible combinations	Br bl Br bl Br bl Br bl		It does not matter if you write the combination as Brbl or blBr – the important thing is which genes are present
Eye colour (F1)	👁 👁 👁 👁		Since brown is dominant to blue only the brown gene is expressed and your eyes are brown

FIGURE 3: The children in this genetic cross can only ever have brown eyes.

Parent	Mother	Father	Notes
Genes present	Br bl	bl bl	Remember – two genes in all normal body cells
Eye colour	👁	👁	Even though the mother has a blue allele it is covered up by the dominant brown
Possible gametes	Br or bl	bl or bl	The mother will produce two types of gametes – one containing Br and one containing bl genes
Possible combinations	Br bl Br bl bl bl bl bl		The easiest way to work out what is possible is to use the diagram shown – called Punnet's square
Eye colour (F1)	👁 👁 👁 👁		Since the gametes join up randomly there is a 2:2 or 1:1 chance of brown eyes or blue eyes

FIGURE 4: The children in this genetic cross can have brown or blue eyes.

▦▦▦ QUESTIONS ▦▦▦

5 What does the word 'homozygous' mean?

6 Why does the cystic gene often go unnoticed in a population?

7 A father with cystic fibrosis has children with a mother who has no cystic genes. What is the chance that their children will have the disease?

8 Two healthy parents have a child. The boy suffers from cystic fibrosis. Draw a genetic cross to show how this could happen.

9 What is the chance that the next child born to the parents in question 8 will have cystic fibrosis?

10 What is the chance that the next child will carry the hidden cystic gene?

11 What is the chance that the next child will be free of any cystic genes?

…heterozygous …homozygous …phenotype …recessive

All change!

You will find out:
- About mutations and their importance
- How mutations occur
- How the environment affects the way our genes work

The Fantastic Four?

In lots of comics our heroes and heroines are zapped by radiation and are changed... the Fantastic Four gained special powers and the X-men were born with special powers. The word '**mutation**' is often used to explain these miraculous changes. But what is a mutation? And are we ever likely to become superheroes?

FIGURE 1: Superheroes are usually mutations!

Mutations

Our genes are made of a very tough chemical called DNA. DNA has been preserved in thousand-year-old Egyptian mummies. But DNA can be damaged. A sudden change in a DNA molecule is called a mutation.

Mutations can be caused by:

- radiation such as ultraviolet light from the sun, X-rays in hospitals and gamma rays from radioactive materials
- radioactive chemicals
- some chemicals in tobacco smoke, and some pesticides.

So you want to be a superhero?

So, if you want to be a superhero you should smoke a lot and hope for a mutation? No, mutations are **random** and are almost always harmful. The impact of a mutation depends on where it happens. A mutation in:

- a body cell could make that cell divide out of control and become a cancer
- a cell that divides to make a sperm or an egg could be passed on to the offspring.

Mutations in body cells only affect that cell and cells that grow from it. However, a genetic mutation could be passed on for many generations and will affect the whole body.

FIGURE 2: This radioactive waste will remain radioactive for hundreds of thousands of years. Radiation given off can produce mutations in living things.

⊓ QUESTIONS ⊓

1. What does the word 'mutation' mean?
2. List **three** things that could cause a mutation.
3. Give **one** difference between a body cell mutation and a mutation that affects sperms or eggs.

WOW FACTOR!

Mutations are happening all of the time. You almost certainly have some mutated genes in your DNA. Most are recessive and so do not show in the phenotype.

Gene mutation

Almost all mutations are neutral or a disadvantage. Many can have a devastating effect on the growth of offspring. Damage to genes that code for essential enzymes in a cell will mean that the cell cannot develop at all and the offspring dies. Many mutations simply die out before they develop. But some mutations can be helpful. The SuperRat of Welshpool (see page 30) was created by a random mutation.

Inheriting haemophilia

Haemophilia is a good example of a genetic disease caused by mutation. It is caused by a damaged gene on the X chromosome that codes for a chemical called **Factor VIII**. If the levels of Factor VIII are low the blood clots very slowly or not at all. This can cause major problems if a person is cut. Even a knock could produce massive, painful bruises as the body bleeds internally. Women have two X chromosomes but males only have one. This explains why females can carry the disease but do not suffer from it.

Haemophilia is not affected at all by the environment. A good diet, plenty of exercise and avoiding smoking will do nothing to help. It is treated by injecting the missing chemical, Factor VIII, when a haemophiliac has been hit or cut.

Factor VIII used to be produced from blood. The chemical was isolated by a long and complex process. It took many litres of blood to produce even enough Factor VIII for a single injection. There were also problems with purifying blood. HIV, the virus that produces AIDS, slipped through and many haemophiliacs were infected by the medicine that was supposed to cure them.

In 1984 the gene for producing Factor VIII was isolated and added to a bacterium which could produce large amounts of the protein relatively quickly and cheaply.

Since then even more sophisticated methods have been used to produce purer Factor VIII. The tale of Factor VIII is a good example of how **genetic technology** has helped to cure diseases that only a few years ago were difficult and expensive to treat.

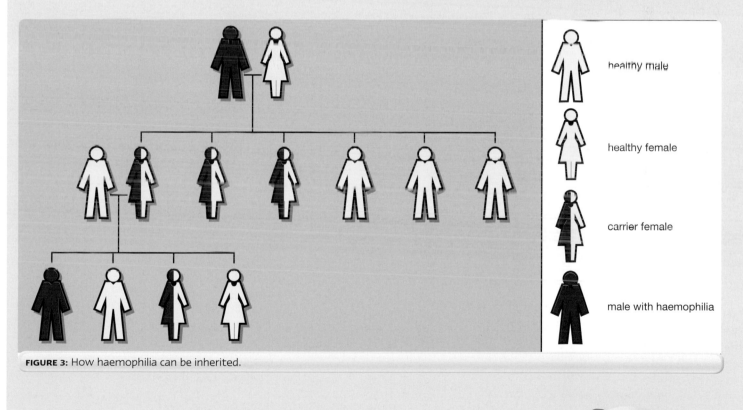

FIGURE 3: How haemophilia can be inherited.

healthy male

healthy female

carrier female

male with haemophilia

QUESTIONS

4   Are most mutations helpful or harmful?

5   Give **one** example of a disease caused by a mutation.

6   Explain why a haemophiliac man can pass the 'haemophilia gene' onto his daughter but not his son.

7   Why was genetic engineering so useful in treating haemophilia?

Genetic technology has helped to cure diseases

Medical genetics

You will find out:
- Why doctors are interested in our genes
- How gene therapy is used to treat cystic fibrosis
- What gene therapy cannot do

Doctor Gene

Staying alive is not easy! There are so many ways to die or become ill. An infection from bacteria or viruses, poor diet, accidents, wars, natural disasters ... the list goes on! One cause of possible problems is a fault in our genes.

Cystic fibrosis

Cystic fibrosis is an illness caused by a problem with a single gene which codes for a protein called CFTR. This chemical controls the movement of fluid across a cell membrane. Cystic fibrosis sufferers have very sticky mucus in their lungs which is difficult to clear. This thick sticky mucus can:

- block narrow airways in the lungs so that the sufferer can become breathless
- trap bacteria which lead to infections.

The only way to treat cystic fibrosis is to cough up the sticky mucus and spit it out. A special sort of massage on the back can help to loosen the mucus and make this easier – but it has to be done two or three times a day. Doctors also treat the first sign of infection quickly with antibiotics.

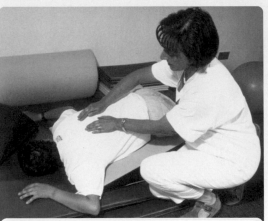

FIGURE 1: Tapping this patient on the back loosens the mucus so it can be coughed up. People with cystic fibrosis may need this treatment up to three times a day.

Gene therapy

Genetic engineers can isolate a healthy CFTR gene and copy it. It is then sprayed into the lungs of someone with cystic fibrosis.

Doctors have been able to show that:

- CFTR genes pass into cells
- cells start to produce working CFTR molecules.

Unfortunately, at the moment, the amounts produced are very low and patients still need other treatments to keep them healthy.

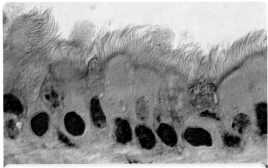

FIGURE 2: Cells from the lungs that produce and move mucus.

QUESTIONS

1. What does the protein CFTR do in normal cells?
2. How is the CFTR gene given to cystic fibrosis sufferers?
3. Why is it better to give cystic sufferers the gene rather than just the CFTR molecule?
4. Why don't doctors stop all other treatments for patients to see if the CFTR gene therapy works?

WANT TO KNOW MORE?

In a class of 30 students one person will probably have a damaged cystic fibrosis gene. You can find out more from: www.cftrust.org.uk.

Treating genetic diseases

Cystic fibrosis was one of the first genetic illnesses treated with **gene therapy**. The early results are very encouraging but there are still many problems.

- Genes are large molecules and do not pass easily through cell membranes.
- Even after they get through they may not be used to produce new chemicals because the cell may not recognise them as genes. The cell normally looks for genes in the chromosomes rather than floating around loose inside the cell.

Getting the gene in

There are two approaches to getting the gene into lung cells.

Adenoviruses are special types of virus that can insert DNA into other cells. Researchers have created genetically-engineered adenoviruses that contain the CFTR gene. These are sprayed into the lungs and they pass the CFTR gene into the lung cells.

Liposomes are protein and lipid packages that can pass through cell membranes. By putting a CFTR gene in a liposome the gene can pass into the lung cells. Inside the cells the liposomes dissolve to release the DNA. This is the technique that looks most hopeful at the moment.

Switching on the CFTR gene

Once inside the cell, the gene seems to switch itself on – perhaps the lack of CFTR does this itself. However, genes do not last forever unless they are repaired by the cell. The 'foreign' DNA, like the CFTR gene here, is not repaired by the cell. Within a short time the treatment needs to be repeated. There is a worry that the body's immune system may start to reject the gene-carrying virus particles if they are used too often.

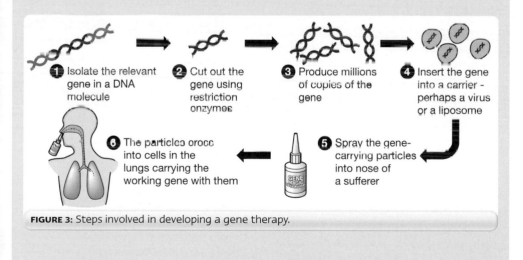

FIGURE 3: Steps involved in developing a gene therapy.

1. Isolate the relevant gene in a DNA molecule
2. Cut out the gene using restriction enzymes
3. Produce millions of copies of the gene
4. Insert the gene into a carrier – perhaps a virus or a liposome
5. Spray the gene-carrying particles into nose of a sufferer
6. The particles cross into cells in the lungs carrying the working gene with them

QUESTIONS

5 Give **two** problems with gene therapy for cystic fibrosis.

6 Why is the liposome method of getting DNA into cells probably better than the viral method?

7 Gene therapy is not easy or guaranteed to work. Why are doctors so hopeful about the system compared with existing treatments?

Stem cell treatments

Stem cells are cells harvested from very young embryos. They seem to be able to become any type of cell in the body when given the right treatment. Some doctors suggest that a sample of stem cells could be injected into a cystic fibrosis sufferer.

The stem cells could be made to produce a constant stream of the CFTR gene and would multiply. One treatment would last for many years – possibly for life. It would be as if the body had developed its own, internal, gene therapy unit. But there are still problems.

- Stem cells currently need to be harvested from embryos.
- Stem cells may be rejected in the same way as virus particles.
- Getting stem cells to produce the CFTR gene may not be easy.
- The CFTR gene still needs to get into the lung cells.

Breast cancer is another disease that is affected by our genes. Women with a particular genotype seem more likely to develop cancer, but it is not a simple connection as with cystic fibrosis. Stem cells will not help them. But more genetic research could find other ways forward. How might a woman who knows she has the breast cancer gene feel about new genetic research?

QUESTIONS

8 What is special about stem cells compared with normal body cells?

9 From where are stem cells normally collected at the moment?

10 What is the major advantage of using stem cells in gene therapy for cystic fibrosis?

Designer beasts

You will find out:
- How genetic engineers transfer genes between species
- Why transgenic organisms are useful
- Why some sheep are producing human chemicals

Designer beasts

It is not easy or cheap to produce animals with genes from other organisms – but it can be done. Some people talk about new ways to produce essential medicines. Others just see another chance for a biological catastrophe. Who is right? And who should decide?

Strange beasts   (H)

Humans have been changing the genotypes of farm animals for thousands of years. **Selective breeding** has produced cows that give more milk or put on meat more quickly. But only modern **genetic engineering** allows us to put genes from one species into a completely different one. The creatures made by genetic engineering are known as **GMOs** or **genetically modified organisms**.

Some of the GMOs alive now on farms include:

- Cows that have been genetically modified to produce low-cholesterol milk. **Cholesterol** is a chemical that increases the chances of some blood and circulation diseases in humans. Less cholesterol in our diet means less cholesterol in our blood.

- Pigs with human genes so that their organs are not rejected when transplanted into human hosts. There is a massive shortage of donor organs for kidneys, hearts and so on. Could these genetically modified pigs save thousands of human lives?

- Sheep that produce human antibodies in their milk. These antibodies can be used to treat sick patients. Drugs for a range of blood diseases are now made by sheep and goats.

GMOs can be created from organisms that could never breed together. The glofish contains a gene from a sea coral. Glofish have been developed to detect pollution – they actually change colour in polluted waters!

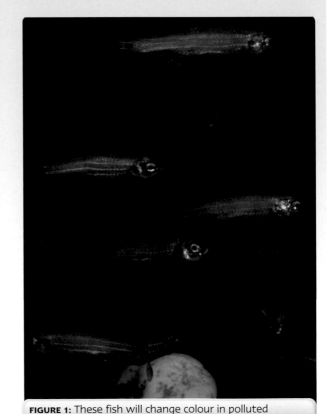

FIGURE 1: These fish will change colour in polluted marine environments. They act almost like swimming universal indicator papers.

QUESTIONS

1. What is cholesterol?
2. Why is genetic engineering different from selective breeding?
3. Why can't we transplant pig hearts into humans from pigs that have not been genetically modified?

Glofish have been developed to detect pollution

...cholesterol ...DNA ...enzyme ...genetically modified organism (GMO)

Building your designer beast (H)

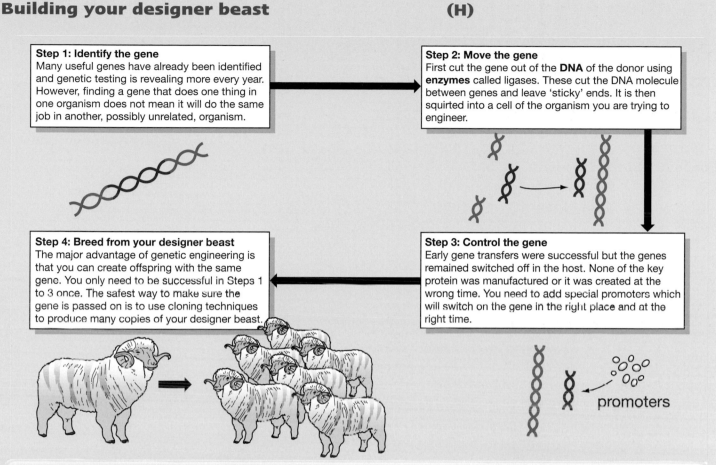

Step 1: Identify the gene
Many useful genes have already been identified and genetic testing is revealing more every year. However, finding a gene that does one thing in one organism does not mean it will do the same job in another, possibly unrelated, organism.

Step 2: Move the gene
First cut the gene out of the **DNA** of the donor using **enzymes** called ligases. These cut the DNA molecule between genes and leave 'sticky' ends. It is then squirted into a cell of the organism you are trying to engineer.

Step 4: Breed from your designer beast
The major advantage of genetic engineering is that you can create offspring with the same gene. You only need to be successful in Steps 1 to 3 once. The safest way to make sure the gene is passed on is to use cloning techniques to produce many copies of your designer beast.

Step 3: Control the gene
Early gene transfers were successful but the genes remained switched off in the host. None of the key protein was manufactured or it was created at the wrong time. You need to add special promoters which will switch on the gene in the right place and at the right time.

promoters

FIGURE 2: Use the process above to create your designer beast.

Genetic hybrids – a mixed blessing? (H)

It all looks perfect. Pigs producing human organs for **transplants**. Cows with cholesterol-free milk and sheep that give valuable biochemicals to treat human illnesses in their milk. What could go wrong?

Imagine a virus that targets pigs. It creates a serious and fatal disease. Normally humans are immune to this disease. If we have had a transplant from an engineered pig, will we now be susceptible to that disease? And once it's got into human tissue, will it be able to spread to humans without the pig organs? A **xenotransplant** is a transplant from a different species. This possibility of catching a foreign virus as well is called the **xenovirus** issue. In 2005 we have no experience of animal–human transplants but we do know of one virus which has jumped between species. Asian bird flu now seems to be able to infect humans and has caused deaths across the world. Is this a warning of things to come?

FIGURE 3: Everyone entering Hong Kong is scanned for temperature rises that might suggest bird flu.

▥▥ QUESTIONS ▥▥

4 What are the key steps in creating a genetically modified animal?

5 Which enzymes are used to cut open DNA molecules to produce individual genes?

6 Give **two** ways genes can be inserted into foreign cells.

7 Why is cloning probably a better way to produce more animals rather than normal breeding from a parent with the desired genes inserted?

8 What is the xenovirus issue?

9 Is it fair to suggest that the natural 'species jumping' of bird flu would be made worse by human–animal

HUGO knows

You will find out:
- About the Human Genome Project
- Why the human genome is so useful
- Why the human genome information may have some unexpected drawbacks

HUGO knows your genes

The Human Genome Project, run by The **Human Genome Organisation** (**HUGO**), has mapped all of the genes in the **human genome**. The genome includes all of the genes present in a species. We now know the sequence of the bases for most of the DNA in your cells. But is this useful?

Pros and cons

As scientists identify particular genes that cause disease, say the cystic gene, they can develop chemical probes which will look for the gene in your cells. If you have the damaged gene you might decide not to have children – or check to see if your partner also has the gene.

This seems helpful, but imagine a gene that means you are more likely to suffer from cancer or heart disease or die early. Now imagine you want to buy life insurance. If your insurance company can check your genotype for these 'high risk' genes, they may refuse to sell you insurance.

Perhaps you want a demanding, but well-paid, job. Can your employer ask to check your genes to see if you will suffer from stress? Could they refuse you the job because your genes show you are likely to suffer from a heart attack? Is it a good thing that you are kept out of these high-stress jobs?

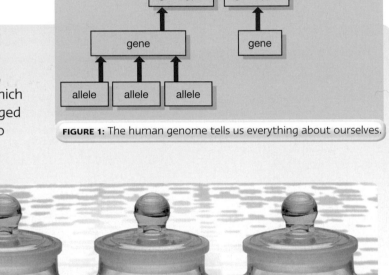

FIGURE 1: The human genome tells us everything about ourselves.

FIGURE 2: How will genetic technology shape our future?

:: QUESTIONS ::

1 What do the letters HUGO stand for?
2 What is a genome?
3 Make a list of the things that you would agree to have checked in your genes.
4 Make a list of the things you do not think should be checked in your genes.

...chromatography   ...DNA fingerprinting   ...DNA fragment

Applications of the genome

So is the **human genome** a bad idea? No, it offers a range of very important benefits.

Medicines that work for some people seem to be useless for others. Doctors sometimes have to try two or three different drugs before they find the right one for a particular patient. Is this because of different genes in the patients?

One of the hopes of HUGO is that scientists will be able to catalogue these genetic differences. Patients can then be prescribed medicines matched to their particular genotype. This should make treatment much quicker and reduce the chance of unpleasant or dangerous side effects.

Forensic scientists often have to identify suspects from small amounts of DNA left behind at a crime scene. A tiny speck of blood carries enough information to identify you. Even the invisible cheek cells left behind on a used toothbrush can give a positive identification. With such tiny clues, criminals have to be much more careful than they used to be. The first criminal case that used genetic evidence to catch and convict a criminal in the UK was in Leicester. The work was done by Professor Alec Jeffries who helped the police to identify a rapist.

DNA fingerprinting

DNA fingerprinting, the technique developed by Professor Jeffries, has been used to prove that children belong to a parent. Indeed, Professor Jeffries' main work involved proving that families were related when immigration officials called this into question.

Most of the DNA in our cells is not used for genes. Lengths of DNA between genes are made of repeating patterns of nonsense called 'junk'. These junk areas vary a great deal and can be used to create a genetic fingerprint.

The light bands in the picture correspond to chunks of 'junk' DNA. The smaller chunks travel further and the heavier ones lag behind. By comparing the distribution of these bands, scientists can tell if a DNA sample comes from a particular person. Since we inherit our DNA from our parents we will have some of the same bands as they do. This allows scientists to link children to parents.

Giant DNA molecule

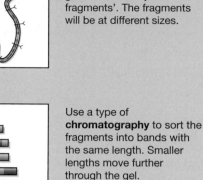

Cut the DNA between the genes to create 'junk fragments'. The fragments will be at different sizes.

Lighter fragments

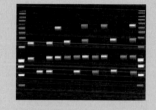

Use a type of **chromatography** to sort the fragments into bands with the same length. Smaller lengths move further through the gel.

Stain the fragments and take a picture. Each band corresponds to a particular length of **DNA fragment**. Areas with lots of DNA show up lighter on the picture.

FIGURE 3: Creation of a genetic fingerprint.

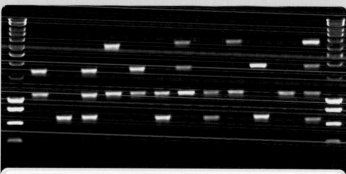

FIGURE 4: Photo of a genetic fingerprint.

===== QUESTIONS =====

5   Give **three** benefits of the Human Genome Project.
6   What is 'junk' DNA?
7   There is very little or no variation between genes for important enzymes but a great deal of variation in junk DNA between these genes. Why?

WOW FACTOR!

Twins have the same DNA fingerprint – even if they look completely different!

Brave new world?

You will find out:
- That decisions about science and technology involve ethics as well as scientific facts
- That genetic technology brings a range of new and difficult decisions

Future heaven or hell?

Genetic technology is advancing rapidly. What does the future hold? A genetic heaven with massively increased food production and treatment for a range of illnesses? Or a genetic hell where some people are genetically unfit and artificially created pests create new problems? Only one thing is certain. Scientists alone cannot make the decisions about what sort of research should be allowed.

Human cloning

On page 36 we talked about the possibility of human **cloning**. No-one is sure whether this has been done yet. Every year, a new group claims a breakthrough. It may be that while you were working on this unit a cloned baby was born somewhere in the world. Is this going too far?

So, can we 'un-invent' the technology and stop all future research? Can we shut down the laboratories, destroy all the records and pretend it never happened? In the USA, President Bush has cut back on some biological research because of pressure from fundamentalist Christian groups. Is this wise? Or even possible?

Most people are very nervous about human cloning. Many are completely opposed to it. It is currently illegal in most countries but this could change.

And human cloning is only one part of the new **biotechnology**. Every year new advances make things possible that seemed like miracles a short time ago. But just because we can do something, does that mean we should?

FIGURE 1: Genetic technology could be good or bad!

▥ QUESTIONS ▥

1 List the technologies you know about that involve genetics (look back through this unit to get some clues).

2 Sort these technologies into two groups:
 low risk – these have almost no bad points
 high risk – these have a number of serious disadvantages.

3 Decide which sorts of research should continue. Give a reason for each of your choices.

4 Do you think we can 'un-invent' some technologies? Should we try?

...biotechnology ...cloning ...genetic technology

Designer babies (H)

One of the most difficult areas is the creation of humans with a particular **genotype** – the so-called 'designer babies'. But why do people want these babies?

"I want a fair-haired, blue-eyed child. There is no difference between genetic technology and any other technology. To ban this research infringes on my human rights. Technology is about providing choices. All new technologies are frightening but we have to learn to live with them."

"My son suffers from a genetic illness that will kill him. He needs a kidney **transplant**. If I can have another child who is genetically identical a transplant is possible. I don't care about blue eyes or fair hair – I am concerned only with my son's life. If this research is banned you are condemning my son to an early death."

"Genetic technology promises so much – but the dangers are real. What happens when human beings are created just to provide 'spare parts' for other humans? How will the donor feel – they only exist to save another's life."

"The world is already divided into rich and poor. Only the rich will be able to afford this new technology and the divide will get even wider. The 'genetically fit' will look down on the others. This is a kind of racism. We are not mature enough to handle this technology. It should be banned now."

"Genetic technology is not the only solution. We can find other ways to solve food supply and medicine problems that do not have the risks of genetic technology. We should slow down on this very expensive research and spend the money on other types of science."

"What happens when trends change? Will the fair-haired, blue-eyed babies be unloved if dark hair and brown eyes come into fashion?"

"I suffer from a genetic illness. I want the technology to make sure my children are healthy."

QUESTIONS

5   Which of the people above do you agree with? Give reasons for your choice.

6   Which of the people above do you think has the worst view? Why?

7   Pick **one** of the technologies here and list the arguments for and against it: human cloning, genetic testing of humans for diseases, creation of human beings to particular genotypes (designer babies).

Business as usual? (H)

There are risks with the new genetic technology. Many people think that we are heading for a nightmare brave new world where some of the population are 'genetically unfit'. They may not be able to get certain jobs or even be allowed to have children.

However, genetic technology offers many benefits in terms of food production and medicine. A person waiting for a kidney transplant may have a very different view of research into growing human organs compared with someone with a healthy kidney. Millions of people die every day because of lack of food or diseases that could be cured by genetic technology. These are real problems today, not potential problems in the future. So, do we stop genetic research and carry on as we are?

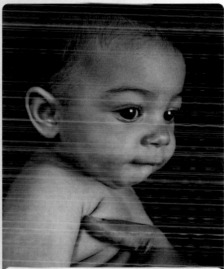

FIGURE 2: Designer babies may be just the tip of the iceberg.

QUESTIONS

8   List the kinds of genetic research that you think should continue.

9   List the kinds of genetic research you think should be banned.

10   On balance, do you think the future looks hopeful or frightening? Give reasons for your answer.

Unit summary

Concept map

Genes

Genes are made of a chemical called DNA. DNA can reproduce, or replicate, itself.

Genes control the characteristics of an organism. The genotype is the selection of genes in a particular organism.

A mutation is a sudden, random change in a gene. Most mutations are detrimental.

Many genetic diseases are caused by gene mutations.

Variation is the natural differences between members of the same species. It can have genetic or environmental causes.

Environment

The environment of an organism includes all the living and non-living components where it lives.

Changes in the environment can increase or reduce the population of organisms in that area – even leading to extinction.

Energy enters an ecosystem as sunlight. It is used by plants to build biomass.

A pyramid of biomass shows the mass of organisms at different feeding levels in an ecosystem.

Unit quiz

1. What is the scientific name for human beings?

2. What is the name given to the small differences between members of the same species?

3. Why is the top level in a pyramid of biomass always smaller than the bottom levels?

4. What do we call an animal which eats plants?

5. List **three** things an animal uses energy for, other than growth.

6. Name **three** things an animal needs to survive.

7. What does a pesticide do?

8. What does the word 'extinct' mean?

9. Are identical twins clones?

10. What do the letters DNA stand for?

11. How many genes for eye colour do humans have?

12. Name **two** diseases caused by faulty genes.

13. What is special about stem cells?

14. Where are stem cells collected from?

15. What do the letters GMO stand for?

16. Why might it be useful to put human genes in a sheep?

17. How many chromosomes does a human skin cell contain?

18. How many chromosomes does a human sperm contain?

19. Why should a criminal be careful not to leave a speck of blood, a hair or even a few cheek cells in some spit, at the scene of a crime?

Literacy activity

Harvesting stem cells ethically

An ethical argument against harvesting stem cells from embryos is that the embryo dies in the process. Fertility treatments for sterile human mothers typically produce more embryos than are required. After a successful pregnancy some of these 'spare embryos' can be donated for research – including harvesting stem cells. The cells are collected from the centre of a 100-cell embryo with a syringe and are put in in special flasks. The embryo dies.

A technique pioneered in rats extracts a single cell from a much younger embryo – the 8-cell stage. One of the cells is removed and placed with a colony of other stem cells. These stem cells seem to switch on the embryo cell which grows to produce a complete new colony of embryonic stem cells – and the embryo survives. The remaining seven cells seem to develop normally to produce a healthy baby.

Does this solve the ethical concerns? Well, maybe some, but who owns the stem cells harvested from the embryo – the scientists, the embryo when it becomes a baby and finally an adult or the company performing the operation? It may be that lawyers would advise potential users of stem cells to destroy the embryo anyway – to avoid an appearance in court!

Another advantage of this technique is that it produces stem cells with the same genetic make-up as the baby. Parents could have cells harvested from an embryo and then frozen to use in later life in case of serious illness or an accident. Of course, this 'biological insurance' would only be available to the rich.

QUESTIONS

1. What does the word 'ethical' mean?
2. Should scientists be involved in ethical decisions? Give reasons for your answer.
3. State **two** advantages of the new stem cell harvesting technique.
4. Who owns the stem cells produced by this technique? If they are used to develop a profitable medical technique, should the original donor be given some of the money?

Exam practice

1. Thousands of caterpillars feed on the leaves of an oak tree. The caterpillars are eaten by ground beetles, which are themselves eaten by shrews. Some of the shrews are eaten by a lone fox.

   Which of the diagrams below shows the pyramid of biomass for this food chain? [1]

   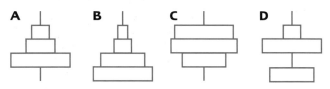

2. There is a large population of caterpillars in the wood. Which one of the following defines the word 'population'?
   A   All the organisms of the community within the ecosystem.
   B   All the organisms of co-existing species in the ecosystem.
   C   All the organisms of a species in a given space and time.
   D   All the organisms occupying this particular habitat. [1]

3. Cystic fibrosis is an inherited disease. It occurs only in individuals who have inherited two recessive alleles (f) for the disease. Mr and Mrs Brown are both carriers of the cystic fibrosis allele. They have two children, Jack and Jill.

   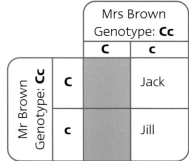

   Use the information in the genetics diagram to decide which one of the following statements is correct.
   A   Jack is a sufferer of cystic fibrosis.
   B   Jill is a sufferer of cystic fibrosis.
   C   Both Jack and Jill suffer from cystic fibrosis.
   D   Neither Jack nor Jill suffer from cystic fibrosis. [1]

4. Cystic fibrosis is caused by a recessive allele. What is an allele?
   A   A type of gene.
   B   A type of DNA.
   C   A type of RNA.
   D   A type of chromosome. [1]

5. The following table gives brief descriptions of three ways in which genetic material can be changed in organisms.

Method 1	Method 2	Method 3
Desirable genetic material is selected artificially by humans, who control which organisms reproduce. The offspring have the new genetic material.	Natural change (mutation) in genetic material, which benefits the organism and allows it to reproduce. Sexual reproduction results in an organism with the new genetic material.	Desirable genetic material is manipulated directly by humans. Sexual reproduction is not needed to produce an organism with the new genetic material.

   Which one of the following statements is correct?
   A   Method 1 is natural selection; Method 3 is genetic engineering.
   B   Method 1 is genetic engineering; Method 2 is selective breeding.
   C   Method 2 is natural selection; Method 3 is genetic engineering.
   D   Method 1 is genetic engineering; Method 3 is natural selection. [1]

6. Genetic information is passed on to offspring during reproduction. In many species, organisms can reproduce either sexually or asexually. Which one of the following statements is correct?
   A   Offspring from asexual reproduction are genetically identical to parents.
   B   Offspring from asexual reproduction are genetically different to parents.
   C   Offspring from both sexual reproduction and asexual reproduction are genetically identical to parents.
   D   Offspring from both asexual reproduction and asexual reproduction are genetically identical to parents. [1]

(Total 6 marks)

The peppered moth has two contrasting forms of appearance. One is pale and speckled which provides camouflage against the lichen-covered bark of trees growing in clean air. The other is dark, which provides good camouflage on trees growing in polluted air. Air pollution prevents many lichens from growing and can blacken the bark of trees.

a Birds tend to eat the form of moth that is most visible. Which one of the following statements is true?

   A In polluted air, more of the pale form are eaten than the dark form of moth.

   B In clean air, more of the pale form are eaten than the dark form of moth.

   C In polluted air, both forms of moth are eaten in similar numbers.

   D In clean air, both forms of moth are eaten in similar numbers. [1]

b The pale and dark forms of the peppered moth are controlled by a single gene, which has two alleles. The dominant allele (D) is for the dark appearance. The recessive allele (d) is for the pale form.

Two moths, both with the genotype Dd, reproduce. The genetics diagram below shows the possible offspring.

	Female		
	Sex cells	D	d
Male	D	DD	Dd
	d	Dd	dd

Which one of the following statements is true?

   A All the possible offspring are the dark form.

   B All the possible offspring are the pale form.

   C The possible offspring include both dark and pale forms.

   D The possible offspring include neither dark nor pale forms. [1]

c In a rural wood, not affected by air pollution, which would be the most common genotype for the peppered moth?

   A DD

   B Dd

   C dd

   D DD and dd [1]

This answer is correct. In polluted air, the pale form is less well camouflaged than the dark form.

This is the wrong answer. In a wood not affected by air pollution, there would be more of the pale form of moth (dd). The correct answer is C.

a) A ✔

b) A ✗

c) A ✗

This is the wrong answer. The genotype dd is for the pale moth form. The correct answer is C.

How to get an A

You need to practise questions on genotypes and their corresponding phenotypes.

DISCOVER VECTORS!

Mosquito is a Spanish word meaning 'little fly'. They evolved around 170 million years ago during the Jurassic era. Mosquitos are principally nectar feeders with only the females requiring a meal of blood.

The mosquito is about to use its proboscis to pierce the skin. It will inject some saliva containing anticoagulant to stop the blood from clotting. Then it will suck up blood. The saliva might contain *Plasmodium*, which causes malaria. The mosquito is, therefore, a vector of the disease.

Malaria infects approximately 350-500 million people annually, mainly in the tropics, and causes approximately 1.3 million deaths.

The female mosquito uses the blood as a source of protein to make eggs.

CONTENTS

Nervous system

You will find out:
- That reflex actions help to protect us from serious injury
- How the nervous system connects the sensory organs to effectors and enables us to respond to a stimulus
- How pain is important in protecting the body from further injury

Danger all around

Like all animals, we need to know what is going on around us at all times. We need to sense danger and find food, shelter and a mate! Once we know what is happening, we need to respond. This might involve making ourselves safe, getting a good meal or smiling at someone of the opposite sex!

FIGURE 1: These meerkats are using all of their senses to be aware of danger.

Protecting yourself

James doesn't know that the pan he is about to pick up is very hot. When he touches it, he gets a shock. He drops it pretty quickly! He is protecting himself from danger. James doesn't even have to think about dropping the pan. It is a **reflex** or **involuntary action**. James's body detected a stimulus. The stimulus was the heat of the pan, which could have burnt him. He very quickly made a **response**, by letting go of the pan. In the skin of James's hand there are pain receptors. The muscles in his arm moved his fingers. The muscles in his arm made the response happen. We call the muscles an effector.

YEOWW!

FIRE FIRE

I'll connect you to the fire service

| stimulus | coordinator | response |

QUESTIONS

1. Name the five senses.
2. Name the sense organs and match them to the senses.
3. What is meant by a reflex action?

WOW FACTOR!

In some parts of the body impulses travel at over 250 km/h.

The nervous system

How did the pain **receptors** in James's hand manage to tell his arm muscles to open his hand? What would happen in the example where James phoned the fire brigade? He wouldn't speak directly to the firefighters. He would speak to an operator. The operator will tell the fire brigade where to go. The operator is a coordinator.

In the body, the nervous system works a bit like a telephone system allowing different parts of the body to communicate with each other. The nervous system consists of two parts:

- the **central nervous system** (**CNS**), which is made up of the **brain** and **spinal cord**
- the peripheral nervous system, which is made up of nerves that connect the central nervous system to all parts of the body.

The skull protects the brain; and the backbone protects the spinal cord.

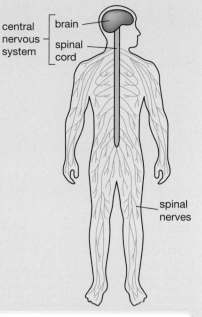

FIGURE 2: The nervous system.

The brain

The brain is a very complicated organ. It has three main parts.

- The cerebral hemispheres connect senses such as hearing and seeing with muscles for movement. They are used for memory, intelligence, thinking and emotions.
- The cerebellum controls balance and muscles.
- The medulla controls automatic actions such as breathing and heartbeat.

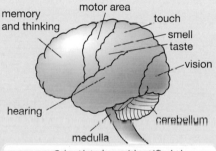

FIGURE 3: Scientists have identified the function of many parts of the brain.

Voluntary responses

These are the things we think about and then do. Picking up a cup and drinking from it is a **voluntary action**. Your brain sends **impulses** to control your muscles. You don't think about breathing, however, you just do it – it is an involuntary or reflex action.

EXAM HINTS AND TIPS

Make sure you can remember the path of a nerve impulse from stimulus to response.

QUESTIONS

4 Put these in the correct order: receptor, stimulus, effector, response.
5 Name the two main parts of the nervous system.
6 How is the central nervous system protected?
7 Give **three** facts about reflex actions that help us to minimise injury.

Feeling pain

It is only after a reflex action has been completed that impulses travel up the **spinal cord** to your **brain**. You do not feel pain until the impulse reaches your brain!

FIGURE 4: This skater will hopefully give himself a chance to recover before doing any more damage! The pain will remind him!

Fighting pain

Childbirth is a very painful experience. There are many ways of reducing the pain. One recent method is a Transcutaneous Electrical Nerve Stimulation (TENS) machine. This gives out small electrical impulses from pads on the woman's back. The theory is that these electrical impulses cause the body to produce natural painkilling chemicals called endorphins.

Other senses

As well as sensing external stimuli we also constantly monitor internal changes, such as body temperature. If our body temperature rises or falls, we respond to ensure it stays at the optimum.

QUESTIONS

8 Why is it important that we feel pain after we have been injured?

9 a How does your body respond to a fall in temperature?

   b How does your body respond to an increase in temperature?

   c Are these voluntary or involuntary actions?

Fast reflexes

You will find out:
- That reflex actions are fast
- How the structure of a reflex arc makes reflexes fast
- About the structure of neurones and how they are adapted for coordination

Speedy reactions

It only takes about 0.3 seconds for the ball to reach a batsman once a fast bowler has let go of it! That doesn't give the batsman a lot of time to decide where he is going to hit the ball.

Our nervous system is designed to make our **reflex actions** happen as quickly as possible. For example, the ducking reaction may save you from a flying cricket ball. As well as helping you to score the winning runs, fast reflexes can help save your life.

FIGURE 1: Batsmen must have quick reflexes.

Fast reflexes can help save your life

A reflex arc

Figure 2 shows the path of a nerve **impulse** in a reflex action. Only three nerve cells are involved. That's one reason why a reflex action can happen very quickly. A very fast **reaction time** means that damage to James's hand will be reduced. This type of reflex is called a withdrawal reflex.

WOW FACTOR!

The highest electronically measured speed for a ball bowled in cricket is 161.3 km/h.

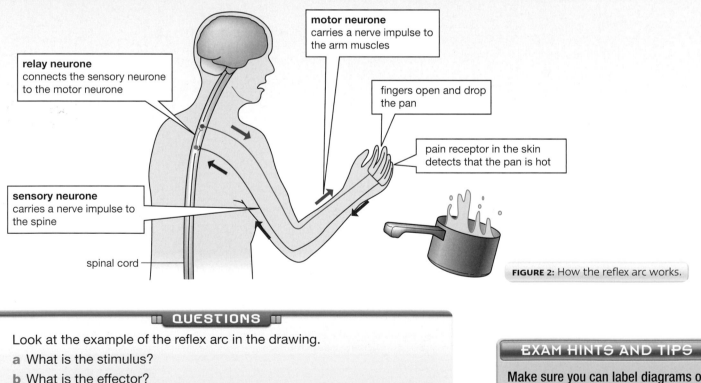

relay neurone
connects the sensory neurone to the motor neurone

motor neurone
carries a nerve impulse to the arm muscles

fingers open and drop the pan

pain receptor in the skin
detects that the pan is hot

sensory neurone
carries a nerve impulse to the spine

spinal cord

FIGURE 2: How the reflex arc works.

▥ QUESTIONS ▥

1 Look at the example of the reflex arc in the drawing.
 a What is the stimulus?
 b What is the effector?
 c What is the response?
2 Think of another example of a withdrawal reflex.

EXAM HINTS AND TIPS

Make sure you can label diagrams of a sensory neurone and a motor neurone and know which is which!

Neurones and nerves

Relay neurones are found only in the **central nervous system**. Sensory and motor neurones are connected to the relay neurones and go to all other parts of the body. The photograph shows a section through the **spinal cord**. The brown area is made of relay neurones. It is called grey matter.

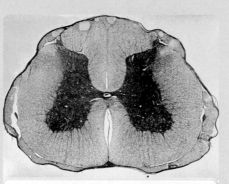

FIGURE 3: Section through the spinal cord.

Each neurone is very long and thin. Fifty neurones side by side would measure just 1 mm. Many neurones are bound together in a bundle. Each bundle forms a nerve.

Like all cells, neurones have a membrane, nucleus and cytoplasm but they have a different shape from other cells. The **axon**, in the middle of the neurone, carries the impulse. In a sensory neurone from a toe to the spine, the axon can be up to a metre long. At the ends of each neurone there are hundreds of branches called dendrites. Each dendrite forms a connection to a different relay neurone. Each relay neurone can then connect to many different motor neurones. This means that an impulse from one **receptor** can result in messages being sent to many different effectors. For example, if you saw a small insect about to hit your eye you would blink, but if it was a cricket ball, you would quickly get your head out of the way!

Each nerve impulse is an electrical signal. Impulses pass along the axon.

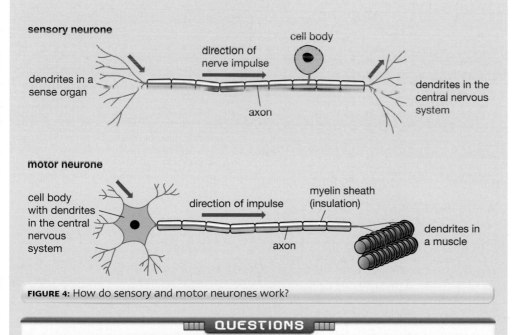

FIGURE 4: How do sensory and motor neurones work?

QUESTIONS

3   Each neurone ends in many dendrites. Each dendrite is attached to a different neurone. How does this help the nervous system to carry out its function?

4   Describe the similarities and differences you can see in the structure of a sensory neurone and a motor neurone.

Multiple sclerosis

The axon is surrounded by a layer called the **myelin sheath**. This is made of layers of fatty material. It acts as an insulating layer to ensure that the impulse stays in the axon. It also helps the impulse to travel more quickly along the axon.

FIGURE 5: This shows the myelin sheath (brown) surrounding the axon (red).

Multiple sclerosis is an **auto-immune** disease. The body's immune system normally fights infections. Multiple sclerosis causes the myelin sheath to gradually break down. Nerve impulses slow down or can even stop completely. People with this disease eventually lose the use of their muscles because impulses do not reach them or because messages pass to the wrong nerve. Imagine switching on the kettle but finding that the toaster comes on instead!

QUESTIONS

5   Why do nerve impulses need to travel faster in a human than in an earthworm?

6   Read about what happens in multiple sclerosis. What do you think the symptoms are? Explain your answer.

7   Jack stands on a drawing pin. Draw a flow diagram to show the route of the nerve impulse from stimulus to response.

Synapses

You will find out:
- How reaction time can be affected by drugs
- How **neurones** are connected to each other by synapses
- How synapses help the nervous system to work

Nerve poisons

Hunters in South America use nerve poisons to help them catch prey. They extract a poison called curare from the bark of trees. They cover the tips of darts with curare and use a blowpipe to fire them at their prey high up in the trees. When the poison gets into the body of the prey, it is paralysed and falls from the tree.

Slowing down reaction time

As we have seen, a fast **reaction time** is important in protecting us from danger. We can use different methods of measuring reaction time. One experiment involves standing in a circle holding hands. One person squeezes the hand of the person on their left. At the same time he or she starts a stopwatch. As soon as each person feels the right hand being squeezed they pass on the squeeze to the next person. When the squeeze gets back to the timekeeper, the stopwatch is stopped. The average time for each person to sense the stimulus and respond can be worked out using the formula:

$$\text{average reaction time} = \frac{\text{total time}}{\text{number of people in the group}}$$

FIGURE 2: Hunters using poison darts in South America.

Reaction time is slowed down by drinking alcohol. That's why drinking and driving is very dangerous.

FIGURE 1: Drinking slowed the reaction time of this motorist.

Reaction time is increased by drinking alcohol

WOW FACTOR!

There are about 12 000 000 000 neurones in the human body! Most of them are in the central nervous system.

QUESTIONS

1. A class of 20 pupils stand in a circle holding hands. It takes 10 seconds for a 'hand squeeze' to go round. What is the average reaction time for the class?
2. How does using poisoned darts make hunting easier?
3. Which part of the body is affected by alcohol to increase reaction time?

...brain   ...chemical transmitter   ...grand mal   ...impulse   ...mitochondria

Synapses connect neurones

Look at figure 2 on page 64. In reality the three **neurones** are not actually touching. There is a small gap between each pair of neurones. This is called a **synapse**.

- When an **impulse** arrives at the end of the neurone a **chemical transmitter** or **neurotransmitter** is released from tiny structures, called **vesicles**.

- The **mitochondria** provide the energy to make the chemicals.

- Special receptor cells in the membrane of the next neurone pick up the chemical transmitter.

- They then start a new electrical impulse.

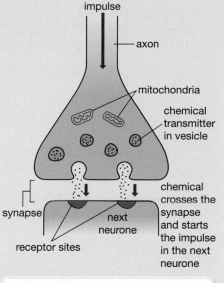

FIGURE 3: How a synapse works.

Synapses are also found where neurones join muscles. These are called **motor end plates**. The muscle contracts when the chemical transmitter crosses the synapse.

Impulses can move both ways along neurones but synapses ensure that they move in the correct direction from neurone to neurone.

Disrupting the brain (H)

There are several conditions that can affect the **brain**.

- Parkinson's disease causes trembling of the arms and legs, stiffness of the muscles and slowness of movement. It is caused when neurones in the part of the brain that coordinates movement die and stop producing a chemical transmitter called dopamine.

- A stroke is caused when part of the brain is deprived of oxygen, usually by a blood clot. This causes some brain cells to die and can affect movement and speech.

- Brain tumours are due to abnormal growth of neurones. One effect of a brain tumour can be to cause epilepsy.

- Epilepsy is due to abnormal electrical activity in the brain. This can cause convulsions when impulses are simultaneously sent to many different muscles.

- The most serious epileptic seizure is called **grand mal**. A grand mal seizure can cause loss of consciousness and convulsions.

QUESTIONS

4. Why are there lots of mitochondria at the ends of neurones?

5. Draw a flow diagram to show how electrical impulses pass from one neurone to another.

Synapses

Synapses help to ensure that the nervous system works properly.

- They only allow impulses to travel in one direction as only one side of the synapse can make the chemical transmitter and only the other side can respond to it.

- They ensure that the nervous system does not send out impulses too readily. A neurone needs to receive the chemical transmitter from several impulses before it produces a new impulse. This could be several impulses from the same neurone or from a few different neurones.

- Synapses can be used to send impulses to several different effectors at the same time. (This is a bit like the emergency services operator calling both the fire service and an ambulance.)

FIGURE 4: Martial arts experts have to coordinate arm, leg and head muscles at the same time. Synapses are sending impulses to several different effectors at the same time to allow them to do this.

QUESTIONS

6. Draw a diagram to explain why synapses only allow impulses to travel one way through a reflex arc.

7. Explain why it is important that several impulses are needed before a message is passed across a synapse.

Seeing the light

You will find out:
- How the iris and pupil are coordinated by the retina and optic nerve to control the amount of light that enters the eye
- How the ciliary muscles change the shape of the lens to focus on near and distant objects

Changing light

You are fast asleep on a dark winter morning. Then some cruel person comes into your room and turns on the light! Ow, that's bright! Your eyes hurt and you want to crawl under the covers! Yet a few seconds later the light is fine and you are ready to get up.

If you go outside at night from a brightly lit room you cannot see very much. After a few minutes your night vision improves and you can see much more. These simple examples demonstrate that our eyes need time to adjust to changes in light intensity. But how do they do this?

FIGURE 1: Light can be too bright when you first wake up!

Your eyes

Get a partner and look closely at one of his or her eyes. The black bit in the middle is called the **pupil**. The pupil is like a window that lets light into your eye. The coloured ring around the pupil is called the **iris**.

The iris controls the size of the pupil. The eyelids move over the eye every time you blink. This washes the eye with tears.

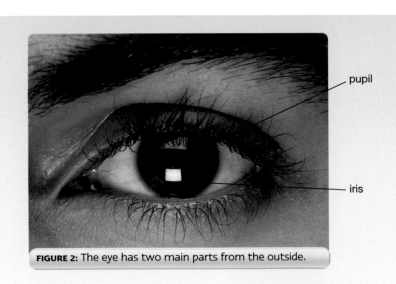

pupil

iris

FIGURE 2: The eye has two main parts from the outside.

QUESTIONS

1 Draw a diagram of your partner's eye. Label the iris and pupil.
2 Why do you think we have eyelashes?
3 Why do you think we have eyebrows?

WOW FACTOR!

The giant squid has the biggest eye. It is about 25 cm in diameter.

...accommodation ...brain ...constricted ...cornea ...dilated ...impulse

Using your eyes

Figure 3 shows a cross-section through the eye. Light passes through the **cornea** which focuses it. It then goes through the pupil and is focused further by the lens. An image is formed on the light-sensitive cells found in the retina. The retina then sends **impulses** to the **brain** along **sensory neurones** in the **optic nerve**. The brain converts these impulses into the 'picture' we see.

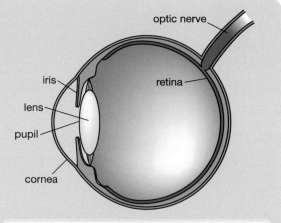

FIGURE 3: The eye has more parts than meets the eye!

Controlling the light

Try this simple experiment:

Work with a partner. Turn the lights off and close the curtains. Wait for about two or three minutes, then shine a torch in your partner's eyes and observe what happens.

- When the light is dim the pupil gets bigger. We say it becomes **dilated**. This lets as much light as possible into the eye.
- When the light is bright the pupil gets smaller. We say it becomes **constricted**. This prevents too much light getting into the eye.

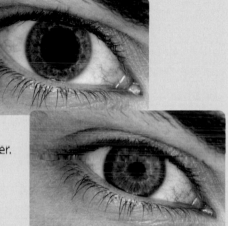

FIGURE 4: The eye responds to different levels of light.

- Adjusting the size of the pupil like this is called the iris reflex. It is controlled by the nervous system. The **retina** is a **receptor** that detects the light entering the eye. The iris is the effector that controls the size of the pupil.

How does the iris work?

The iris is made of muscle. There are two sets of muscles in the iris:

- radial muscle
- circular muscle.

Circular muscle contracts in bright light making the pupil smaller. Radial muscle contracts in low light making the pupil larger.

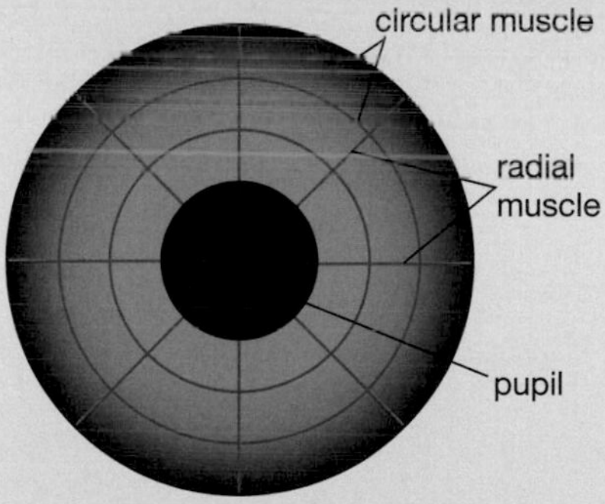

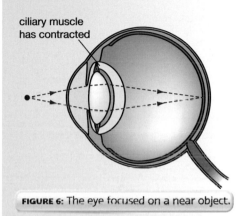

FIGURE 5: The muscles in the iris.

Accommodation

This has nothing to do with where you live! Light is focused as it passes through the cornea. Your lens is used to fine focus on objects depending on how far away they are. This is called **accommodation**.

To focus on near objects the lens needs to be thicker. The ciliary muscle contracts and the suspensory ligaments become slack. The lens' elasticity makes it go fatter.

FIGURE 6: The eye focused on a near object.

To focus on distant objects the lens needs to be thinner. The ciliary muscle relaxes and the suspensory ligaments tighten. The lens is pulled into a thinner shape.

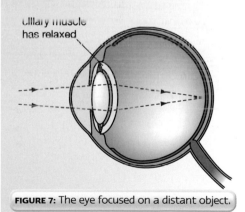

FIGURE 7: The eye focused on a distant object.

QUESTIONS

4 Describe the path of a ray of light as it travels from an object to your retina.

5 Describe the path of the nerve impulse from your retina to produce a picture of what you can see.

6 Draw a diagram to explain how the size of the pupil is controlled by the iris.

QUESTIONS

7 Draw flow charts to show how the eye focuses on near and distant objects.

8 What shape would the lens be if it was removed from the eye?

# Blood

You will find out:
- That blood is the transport system of the body
- About the composition of blood
- The roles of the different blood cells

Vital stuff

Blood is really important stuff. If someone has an operation or an accident they may lose a lot of blood. A blood transfusion would be needed to replace the blood that has been lost.

Blood transfusions come from blood donors, people who volunteer to give about half-a-litre of blood. It is safe to give this amount of blood as the body will soon replace it

What does blood do?

Your blood has two main jobs:
- it transports things around your body
- it helps you to fight disease.

Your body contains about 4–5 litres of blood. It looks like a liquid but if it is left to stand for a while you can see it is not all liquid. The blood in the photograph has separated into two layers. At the top is the pale yellow liquid called **plasma**. Below is a layer of cells, most of which are red blood cells.

Instead of leaving blood to stand in order to separate the layers, it can be centrifuged. A **centrifuge** is a machine which spins the tubes of blood at high speed. This makes the heavier cells sink to the bottom of the tube while the plasma stays at the top.

FIGURE 1: Blood transfusions save lives.

There are about 5 000 000 red blood cells in 1 mm³ of blood

FIGURE 2: Centrifuged blood.

:: QUESTIONS ::

1 What is the name of the yellow liquid part of the blood?
2 What is a centrifuge?
3 What are the two main jobs of the blood?
4 How much blood can safely be given by a blood donor?

...adrenaline ...anaemia ...centrifuge ...endocrine gland ...haemoglobin

Blood for transport

Plasma is mostly water with various chemicals dissolved in it. Plasma transports several substances:

- Urea which is a waste material made in cells is transported to the kidneys where it is removed from the blood.
- Foods, such as glucose, amino acids, vitamins and minerals, which are absorbed into the blood in the intestine and carried to different parts of the body.
- **Hormones**, such as **adrenaline**, which are carried from the **endocrine glands** to all parts of the body. These carry messages to target organs in the body.
- Proteins, such as antibodies which help fight diseases and fibrinogen which helps blood to clot.
- Carbon dioxide, which is carried from all of the cells of the body to the lungs where it is breathed out.
- Heat energy which is carried mainly from the muscles and liver. Normally this heat maintains the body temperature although when we exercise it is carried to the skin where it is lost to the environment.

> ### WANT TO KNOW MORE?
> To find out more about how blood helps to fight disease see the section on 'Immunity' on pages 90–91.

Blood cells

There are three main types of cells in the blood.

- **White blood cells** – these cells help fight disease.
- **Platelets** – these are tiny fragments of cells that help to clot blood if you get cut.
- **Red blood cells** – their main function is to carry oxygen from the lungs to all parts of the body. They have no nucleus and are filled with a red pigment called **haemoglobin**. Red blood cells also carry some carbon dioxide.

FIGURE 3: Red blood cells.

QUESTIONS

5   Make a table to summarise the substances transported by blood.
6   What gives red blood cells their colour?
7   Why are white blood cells difficult to see through a microscope?
8   What is fibrinogen used for?

Red cells and oxygen

There are about 5 000 000 red blood cells in 1 mm³ of blood. Each cell is shaped like a squashed disc, called a biconcave disc. This increases the surface area so that they can absorb oxygen efficiently.

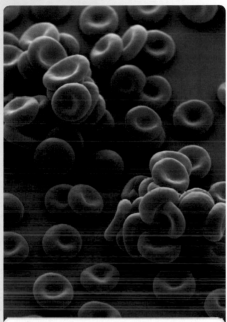

FIGURE 4: Did you know your blood really looked like this?

Oxygen is attracted to haemoglobin and combines with it to make oxyhaemoglobin.

haemoglobin + oxygen ⇌ oxyhaemoglobin

This is a reversible reaction. When there is a lot of oxygen the reaction goes to the right. When there is little oxygen it goes to the left.

Haemoglobin contains iron. If you lack iron in your diet then you cannot carry enough oxygen in your blood and you will feel tired. This is called **anaemia**.

QUESTIONS

9   How does their shape help red blood cells to do their job?
10 How does the reversible reaction between oxygen and haemoglobin help to get plenty of oxygen from the lungs to the body's cells?

Adrenaline

You will find out:
- That the adrenal glands produce a hormone called adrenaline
- That adrenaline prepares the body for 'fight or flight'

On your marks!

The athlete is on his starting blocks ready for the race of his life. **Adrenaline** is flowing through his body, and his heart is pounding as he waits for the gun to start the race.

'On your marks, get set.' BANG! He's off. Ten seconds later the race is over. Did he win? The adrenaline he produced will have helped to ensure he was ready to run as fast as possible

FIGURE 1: On your marks...

Adrenaline

Adrenaline is a special kind of chemical called a **hormone**. It is produced by two glands that are found on top of the kidneys. These are called the **adrenal glands**. Adrenaline is carried around the body in the blood. Adrenaline gets your body ready for action. This is sometime called 'fight or flight'. You are ready to face up to or run away from danger. Adrenaline affects different parts of your body:

- you breathe faster
- the tubes in your lungs get wider
- your heart beats faster
- your skin goes pale as blood is diverted to essential organs.

FIGURE 2: When faced with a bear, this man thought that flight was a better idea than fight!

Adrenaline is flowing through his body, his heart pounding as he waits for the gun ...

▪▪ QUESTIONS ▪▪

1. Whereabouts in your body are the adrenal glands?
2. Why do you breathe faster when you are running?
3. Why does your heart beat faster when you are doing exercise?
4. Name some of the parts of the body that are affected by adrenaline.

EXAM HINTS AND TIPS

Sorting information into a table will help you with learning.

Ready for action

In the 'fight or flight' response, your body is ready for action. Your muscles must be able to work at maximum efficiency. You need to be able to think quickly and clearly. You must keep injuries to a minimum. The effects of adrenaline on different parts of the body ensure that you are able to do these things.

- **Glycogen** is converted to glucose to use as an energy supply. Glycogen is a substance used to store energy in your liver.

- You breathe faster so that you get more oxygen into your body and get rid of the extra carbon dioxide you produce.

- **Bronchioles** are the tubes that go into your lungs. They open up so that you can get more air in and out of your lungs.

- Your heart beats faster to carry extra glucose and oxygen to your muscles.

- Blood vessels to the muscles and brain widen or **dilate**. This ensures that extra blood can carry glucose and oxygen to where it is needed most.

- Blood vessels to the intestines and skin narrow or constrict. This makes more blood available to where it is needed most. Reduced blood flow to the skin reduces the risk of bleeding if you are injured.

- In hairy animals, the hair stands on end. This makes them look bigger so that they frighten off an attacker.

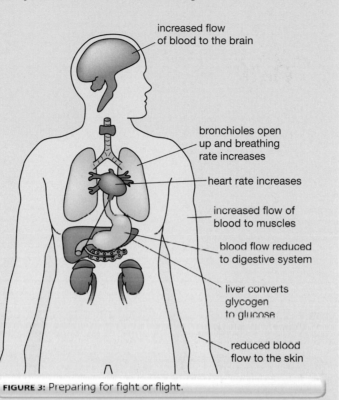

increased flow of blood to the brain

bronchioles open up and breathing rate increases

heart rate increases

increased flow of blood to muscles

blood flow reduced to digestive system

liver converts glycogen to glucose

reduced blood flow to the skin

FIGURE 3: Preparing for fight or flight.

You can't imagine how much adrenaline I am making right now!

███ QUESTIONS ███

5   Draw a table to summarise the effects of adrenaline on different parts of the body and to explain why they help us in the 'fight or flight' response.

6   Why do people often look pale when they are frightened?

7   Why do you often get goose bumps when you are frightened?

Using adrenaline

Some people suffer from very severe allergies. Certain foods or insect bites can cause them to go into **anaphylactic shock**. This is a life-threatening condition where the bronchioles get narrower and breathing becomes very difficult. In some cases the person may die. As you have already found out, one of the effects of adrenaline is to open up the bronchioles. These people can carry an automatic injection device. This can be used to give a dose of adrenaline immediately.

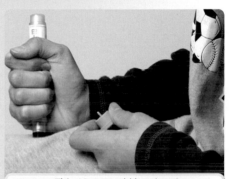

FIGURE 4: This 10-year-old boy is using an EpiPen to inject himself with adrenaline.

Some people who have heart problems or high blood pressure may be given drugs called **beta-blockers**. These reduce the effects of adrenaline. Beta-blockers are banned in sports such as shooting and archery.

FIGURE 5: Archers are not allowed to take beta-blockers.

███ QUESTIONS ███

8   Produce a leaflet to give advice to people who suffer from severe allergies.

9   Why are beta-blockers banned in sports such as shooting and archery?

...bronchiole ...dilate ...glycogen ...hormone

Hormones

You will find out:
- That hormones are chemicals
- That hormones act as signals to cells and organs
- The names of some of the endocrine glands and the hormones they produce
- The effects of some hormones on the body

Endocrine glands

This man is suffering from goitre. This is caused by an enlarged thyroid. One of the causes of goitre is a lack of the mineral iodine in the diet. Most of us get enough iodine from soil via the vegetables we eat or from eating sea fish. In some places there isn't very much iodine in the soil. If these places are far from the sea then there is a greater chance of developing goitre. A small amount of iodide is added to table salt to ensure that we get enough.

FIGURE 1: A very severe case of goitre.

What do your endocrine glands do?

The adrenal glands and the thyroid are **endocrine glands**. These glands make **hormones**, which carry messages around the body. Like the nervous system, the endocrine system is a way in which parts of the body can communicate.

The nervous system is much faster than the endocrine system. It's a bit like the difference between making a telephone call and posting a letter. If your house was on fire you wouldn't send a letter to the fire brigade! It would, however, be normal to get a party invitation by post.

Better get a letter in the post dear - the kitchen's on fire!

FIGURE 2: A letter will arrive much too late!

WOW FACTOR!

Robert Wadlow was the tallest person ever. When he died in 1940 aged 22 he was 2.72 m tall. That's 8 feet 11 inches. His pituitary gland made too much growth hormone.

▪▪ QUESTIONS ▪▪

1 Which mineral is needed for the thyroid gland to function properly?
2 What condition might you get if you lack iodine in your diet?
3 How are hormones carried around the body?
4 In what way is the endocrine system similar to the nervous system?

...adrenaline ...endocrine gland ...glucagon ...hormone ...human growth hormone (HGH) ...insulin

Where are the endocrine glands and what do they do?

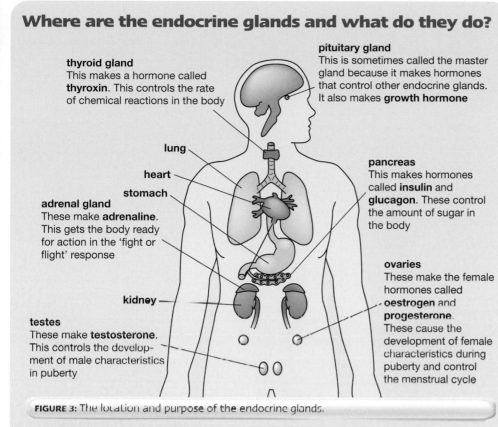

thyroid gland
This makes a hormone called **thyroxin**. This controls the rate of chemical reactions in the body

pituitary gland
This is sometimes called the master gland because it makes hormones that control other endocrine glands. It also makes **growth hormone**

lung

heart

stomach

adrenal gland
These make **adrenaline**. This gets the body ready for action in the 'fight or flight' response

pancreas
This makes hormones called **insulin** and **glucagon**. These control the amount of sugar in the body

kidney

ovaries
These make the female hormones called **oestrogen** and **progesterone**. These cause the development of female characteristics during puberty and control the menstrual cycle

testes
These make **testosterone**. This controls the development of male characteristics in puberty

FIGURE 3: The location and purpose of the endocrine glands.

Secondary sexual characteristics

Figure 4 shows some of the changes that happen during adolescence. These differences between men and women are called **secondary sexual characteristics**. They start to develop when the pituitary gland sends hormones to the testes and ovaries signalling increased production of sex hormones.

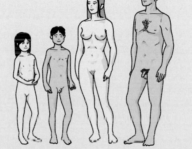

FIGURE 4: Adolescence causes our bodies to change.

Secondary sexual characteristics in women	Secondary sexual characteristics in men
ovaries start to produce eggs	testes grow and start to produce semen, the liquid which contains sperms
periods start	facial, body and pubic hair starts to grow
development of breasts	the voice 'breaks' and becomes deeper
widening of the hips	muscles develop
extra fat produced around buttocks and thighs	
growth of pubic hair and extra hair on the legs and under the arms	

▪▪▪▪ QUESTIONS ▪▪▪▪

5   Summarise the differences between the nervous system and the endocrine system.

6   Which endocrine glands are not found in both men and women?

Drugs and sport

FIGURE 5: Some athletes cheat by using HGH.

Some athletes are thought to have cheated by using **human growth hormone** (**HGH**) to build more muscle and improve their performance. Other, honest, athletes rely on the fact that HGH is produced during sleep and after exercise. Early nights and exercise really do help.

FIGURE 6: Sleep is a natural way of regenerating HGH.

▪▪▪▪ QUESTIONS ▪▪▪▪

7   How does HGH help athletes to improve their performance?

The menstrual cycle

You will find out:
● How oestrogen causes the lining of the uterus to thicken in the menstrual cycle
● How progesterone maintains the lining of the uterus in the menstrual cycle and in pregnancy

First period

One change that happens in puberty is that girls start to have periods. This usually happens between the ages of 10 and 14. A girl's first period can be a very exciting event but it can also be quite frightening. It means that a girl's ovaries are producing eggs. She is able to get pregnant.

FIGURE 1: Women use tampons to soak up the blood produced during menstruation.

What happens in the menstrual cycle?

In each **menstrual cycle** important changes happen in a woman's body.

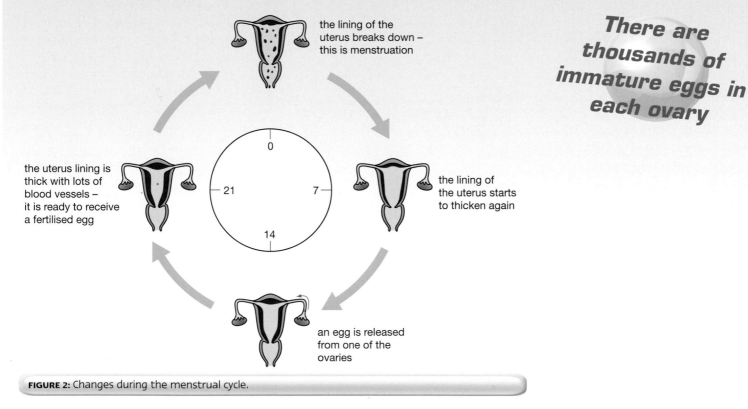

the lining of the uterus breaks down – this is menstruation

the uterus lining is thick with lots of blood vessels – it is ready to receive a fertilised egg

the lining of the uterus starts to thicken again

an egg is released from one of the ovaries

There are thousands of immature eggs in each ovary

FIGURE 2: Changes during the menstrual cycle.

QUESTIONS

1   Why is the menstrual cycle called a monthly cycle?
2   Which part of the body makes eggs?
3   What happens to an egg if it gets fertilised?
4   What is a 'period'?

EXAM HINTS AND TIPS

Draw a flow chart of a biological process to help you remember it.

...feedback ...follicle stimulating hormone (FSH) ...hormone ...luteinizing hormone (LH)

Controlling the menstrual cycle (H)

The menstrual cycle is controlled by two **hormones** called **oestrogen** and **progesterone**.

There are thousands of immature eggs in each ovary. One egg starts to develop inside a Graafian follicle. This protects the developing egg and releases oestrogen.

The oestrogen is carried in the blood and causes the uterus lining to thicken with more blood vessels. Oestrogen also prevents the ovaries from releasing any more eggs.

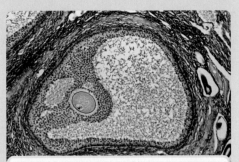

FIGURE 3: This photograph, taken using a microscope, shows an egg developing inside a Graafian follicle.

On about day 14 of the menstrual cycle the follicle bursts open and releases its egg. This is called **ovulation**. The empty follicle turns into a yellow body or corpus luteum. This stays in the ovary and starts to produce progesterone. Progesterone makes the uterus lining thicken even more and stops it from breaking down. The yellow body gradually withers away and stops making progesterone. By about the 28th day there is no more progesterone being made and the uterus lining breaks down again and the woman has a period.

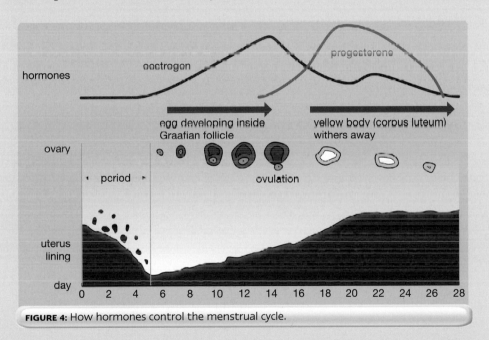

FIGURE 4: How hormones control the menstrual cycle.

If an egg is fertilised then the yellow body does not disappear. It carries on making progesterone. This ensures that the uterus lining does not break down. It also prevents further eggs being released.

QUESTIONS

5   What is ovulation?

6   Why does the uterus lining need lots of blood vessels?

7   Draw a flow diagram to summarise the changes that happen during the menstrual cycle. Add a time scale down the side of your flow chart.

The pituitary and the menstrual cycle

Follicle stimulating hormone (FSH) is secreted by the pituitary at the end of menstruation. It tells the ovary to prepare a new egg. The oestrogen produced by the Graafian follicle stops the pituitary from making any more FSH. We say that the oestrogen inhibits FSH production. When the oestrogen in the blood reaches a certain level, it tells the pituitary to produce another hormone, called **luteinizing hormone (LH)**. LH makes the ovary release an egg and it changes the empty follicle into a corpus luteum. The progesterone produced by the corpus luteum inhibits LH production. The way these different hormones interact is an example of negative **feedback**. When the baby is about to be born the pituitary produces another hormone called **oxytocin**. This stimulates the muscles in the uterus to start contracting.

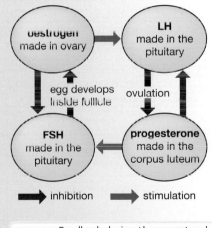

FIGURE 5: Feedback during the menstrual cycle.

QUESTIONS

8   Add information about luteinizing hormone and follicle stimulating hormone to the flowchart you did in question 7.

9   What do you think tells the pituitary to start making oxytocin?

Controlling fertility

You will find out:
- How artificial sex hormones can be used for contraception
- How artificial sex hormones can be used to treat women who are unable to have children

Test tube babies

Lord Robert Winston helped to make history in 1978. He was part of the team of scientists that created the world's first 'test tube baby', Louise Brown. The picture on the right shows him surrounded by photographs of some of the children born by the in-vitro fertilisation (IVF) method that he helped to develop.

FIGURE 1: Have I really helped to create that many babies?

Birth control

We also use **hormones** so that people can choose not to have children. The **contraceptive pill** is a tablet taken by women. It is a reliable method of contraception as long as it is taken every day of the month (except for a week while the woman has a period). The pill should only be given to women by a doctor. There are some health risks for women, especially if they take the pill for many years. The pill stops women from producing eggs. When a woman stops taking the pill she will start making eggs again so she can choose when she becomes pregnant.

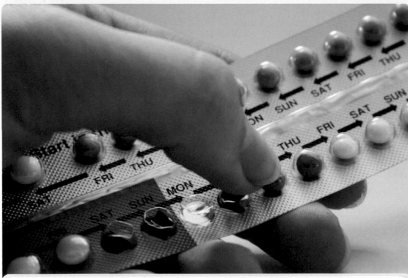

FIGURE 2: The pill is very reliable.

Danger

Not all women are able to take the pill because, like all **drugs**, there are some dangers involved:

- women with liver disease or diabetes should not take the pill
- women who smoke are at greater risk of having heart problems, headaches and blood clots if they take the pill.

WOW FACTOR!

The oldest mother on record is Adriana Iliescu, a Romanian, who gave birth in January 2005, aged 66. She had been given IVF treatment. How old will she be when her daughter is 15?

⁂ QUESTIONS ⁂

1. What is the proper name for 'the pill'?
2. Why does a woman have to see a doctor before she can be given the pill?
3. What could happen if a woman forgot to take her pill?
4. Make a list of the good and bad points of using the pill.

...contraceptive pill ...drug ...follicle stimulating hormone (FSH) ...hormone

How does the pill work?

The pill contains **oestrogen** and sometimes **progesterone**. Remember that oestrogen inhibits the production of **follicle stimulating hormone (FSH)**. This means that the ovaries do not release any eggs. This happens when a woman is pregnant. The pill 'tricks' the woman's body into acting as if she is pregnant.

Treating infertility

Some women do not produce an egg every month. This means that they have difficulty getting pregnant. This is called **infertility**. Doctors can give the woman an injection of FSH. This makes the ovary produce eggs. One effect of using this type of fertility treatment is that the ovary can produce more than one egg. Women having this treatment are more likely to have twins or even more babies at once!

FIGURE 3: Fertility treatment increases the chances of a multiple birth.

In-vitro fertilisation

Some couples cannot have children because the man does not make enough sperm or because the woman's fallopian tubes are blocked. Both of these problems make it difficult for eggs and sperms to meet. **In-vitro fertilisation (IVF)** can help these people. The woman is given FSH to make her produce eggs. The eggs are then removed from her ovary in a small operation.

They are kept alive in a Petri dish. Sperm is collected from the father and mixed with the eggs. Medical staff use microscopes to observe the eggs for a few days. When they can see that an embryo is developing properly it is put into the mother's uterus where it develops as normal.

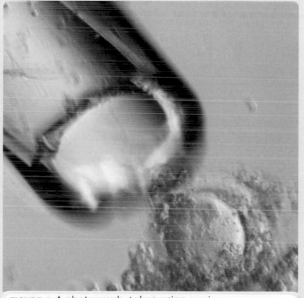

FIGURE 4: A photograph, taken using a microscope, showing a tiny pipette being used to prepare an egg for in-vitro fertilisation. The egg is about the size of a full stop on this page!

Morning-after pill

If a woman has sex without using a contraceptive she can take the 'morning-after pill' to prevent pregnancy. It contains high doses of oestrogen and progesterone and prevents the fertilised egg from implanting in the uterus. Although called the morning-after pill it works for up to three days after having sex. The sooner it is used the greater the chance that it will work however. The morning-after pill is available over the counter in chemists' shops. It is known as a form of emergency contraception because it contains high doses of hormone and so should not be taken too often.

The morning-after pill can have some unpleasant side-effects but these are not common. These can include headaches, abdominal pain, tender breasts and dizziness.

QUESTIONS

5 How does the pill prevent women from becoming pregnant?

6 Which women are most at risk of harm due to taking the contraceptive pill?

7 List some reasons why people cannot become pregnant.

8 Draw a flow chart to summarise how in-vitro fertilisation is carried out.

QUESTIONS

9 Make a list of the advantages and disadvantages of using hormones in fertility treatment.

10 Should doctors have used IVF treatment on Adriana Iliescu?

...infertility   ...in-vitro fertilisation (IVF)   ...oestrogen   ...progesterone

Diabetes

You will find out:
- How insulin regulates the concentration of glucose in the blood
- That insulin is made in the pancreas
- About the advantages of using human insulin produced by genetically modified bacteria

Daily injections

Are you afraid of injections? Imagine having to give yourself injections every day. Some people have an incurable condition called **diabetes**. They do not make enough of the **hormone**, **insulin**. They have to inject insulin every day.

Do you like sweets, cakes and biscuits? Diabetics have to limit the amount of sugar in their diet or they can become very ill.

What is diabetes?

Normally, when we eat sugar, most of it is converted into a chemical called **glycogen**. Glycogen is stored, mainly in the liver. People with diabetes have a faulty **pancreas**. The pancreas is the gland that makes insulin. After eating a meal, diabetics cannot reduce the amount of **glucose** in their blood. If the amount of glucose gets too high a person could go into a coma and die.

Controlling diabetes

Although diabetes cannot be cured it can be controlled in three ways:

- by controlling the amount of sugar in the diet
- if the condition is not too severe, then a tablet can control the blood sugar
- if the condition is severe, then daily insulin injections are needed.

How do you know if you have diabetes?

Diabetics have too much glucose in their blood. This makes them feel tired and very thirsty. The person loses weight. The kidneys try to get rid of the extra glucose. The most reliable sign of diabetes is finding glucose in the urine and high levels of blood sugar.

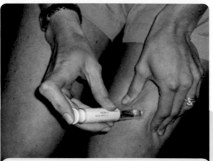

FIGURE 1: Diabetics have to inject insulin every day.

FIGURE 2: Diabetics have to limit the amount of sugar in their diet.

QUESTIONS

1 Why do our cells need glucose?
2 What could happen if the amount of glucose in the blood got too high?
3 Where is the hormone, insulin, made?
4 Where is glycogen mostly stored?

WOW FACTOR!

Before there was a reliable chemical test for sugar, some doctors would taste a patient's urine to check if it contained sugar!

Regulating blood sugar

There are actually two hormones involved in regulating the concentration of glucose in the blood. As well as insulin, the pancreas also makes a hormone called **glucagon**. These two hormones have the opposite effects. The pancreas monitors the blood glucose level and either:

- makes insulin to reduce the amount of blood glucose
- makes glucagon to increase the amount of blood glucose.

Glucagon and insulin control this chemical change (see figure 3).

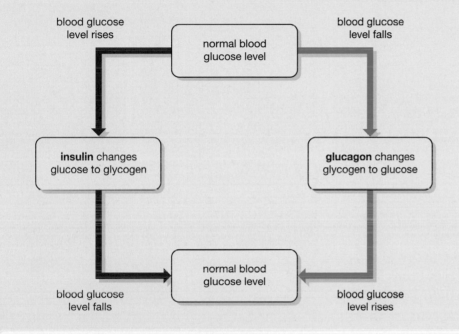

FIGURE 3: Insulin and glucagon control the glucose level.

Out of control

In a normal person the amount of insulin produced by the pancreas varies depending on the amount of glucose in the blood. Diabetics cannot give themselves the exact amount of insulin that they need. Sometimes they have too much insulin or not enough food. The blood glucose level becomes too low. This causes the diabetic to become confused and to sweat and tremble. He or she would soon fall into a coma due to a lack of glucose reaching the brain. Fortunately, most diabetics and their families learn to recognise these signs early and eat sweets or have soft drinks to raise the glucose level in the blood.

Until the 1920s there was no treatment for diabetes. Patients who developed the condition had to follow a near-starvation diet. They did not grow properly and eventually died as a result of their weight loss.

QUESTIONS

5   What causes the blood glucose level to rise?
6   What causes the blood glucose level to fall?
7   Why would a very low blood glucose level cause confusion and coma?

Ideas and evidence

Insulin was first discovered in 1922 by Sir Fred Banting and Charles Best at the University of Toronto. They removed the pancreas from dogs so that the dogs developed diabetes. They extracted different substances from the pancreas. They injected these into the dogs until they found the one which successfully prevented diabetes.

FIGURE 4: Sir Fred Banting and Charles Best with the first dog they kept alive using insulin injections.

In 1922 a diabetic boy was successfully treated with insulin. At last, using insulin from pigs and cattle, doctors were able to control diabetes.

In 1982 a further breakthrough in the treatment of diabetes was achieved when scientists used **genetically modified (GM)** bacteria to produce human insulin. The **gene** for making insulin in humans was identified, extracted from human **DNA** and inserted into the DNA of bacteria. The bacteria produce insulin that is exactly the same as human insulin.

QUESTIONS

8   Should scientists be allowed to use animals in research?
9   Why is GM human insulin better than that from cows and pigs?

Controlling the sugar rush

SELF-CHECK ACTIVITY

Alex is a student who is studying Biology at College. She wants to find out about a condition called diabetes because a friend of hers has just been diagnosed as having it. She knows that this is something to do with a substance called insulin.

She goes on the internet and finds out that insulin is produced in an organ called the pancreas. There's quite a clear diagram that she downloads to see where the pancreas is.

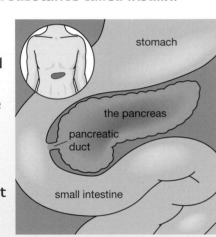

Alex then finds out that insulin is made as a response to glucose in the bloodstream. She knows from her work at College that glucose comes from certain types of food. If there's more glucose, the insulin level will then rise. A few hours later when the glucose level in the blood drops, so does the insulin level.

She is interested in finding out how the insulin deals with the glucose, and learns from the web site that the insulin stimulates all kinds of cells around the body to take in the available glucose and use it in respiration. This reduces the glucose level in the bloodstream.

CHALLENGE

Read the text above. Draw and label a picture of a meal that would, when digested, produce a lot of glucose in the bloodstream.

The graph shows how the glucose level in the bloodstream fluctuates. Copy the graph and sketch a line on it to show how you think the insulin levels will change in response to the glucose.

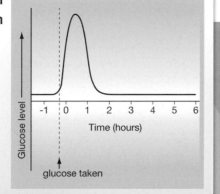

glucose taken

Now, using your notes, a book or the internet, find a diagram of an animal cell and the word equation for respiration. Draw a cell diagram and use the words from the word equation to show what is entering the cell and what is leaving it.

Maximise your grade

These sentences show what you need to include in your work to achieve each grade. Use them to improve your work and be more successful.

Grade	Answer includes...
F	Recall that glucose is a sugar.
	Recall that a large range of foods is broken down to sugars by the body.
	Describe how glucose levels change following a meal.
	Describe what insulin does.
C	Explain how insulin production responds to, or how it regulates, glucose levels in the blood.
	Describe what insulin does and explain how insulin production responds to and regulates glucose levels in the blood.
A	Explain how insulin production responds to and regulates glucose levels in the blood.
	As above, but with particular clarity and detail.

What effect does insulin have on the speed of this respiration equation?

Microbes and disease

You will find out:
- That a pathogen is a disease-causing organism
- That the main pathogenic organisms are bacteria, viruses, fungi and protozoa

Smallpox

This man is suffering from smallpox, a disease caused by a virus. Smallpox used to kill millions of people worldwide every year. Many scientists have been involved in the battle against smallpox over the years. The World Health Organisation announced in 1977 that it had eradicated the disease. There was a further case in Birmingham University in 1978 when a worker caught the disease from viruses kept for study.

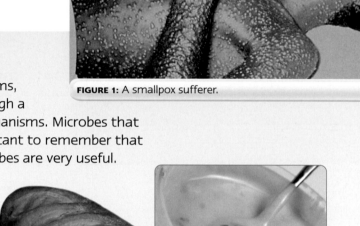

FIGURE 1: A smallpox sufferer.

Microbes

Viruses are a type of **microbe**. These tiny organisms, which we often call germs, can only be seen through a microscope. Microbes are also known as micro-organisms. Microbes that cause **diseases** are called **pathogens**. It is important to remember that most microbes do not cause diseases. Many microbes are very useful.

FIGURE 2: Beer, cheese, bread, yoghurt and medicines like antibiotics are all made using microbes.

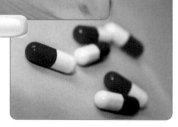

There are also many diseases that are not caused by microbes. Diseases are caused by several different types of pathogenic microbe:

- **bacteria** cause bacterial infections
- **fungi** cause fungal infections
- **viruses** cause **viral infections**
- **protozoa** cause protozoal infections.

QUESTIONS

1 List the types of microbe that may cause diseases.
2 Give an example of a disease that is not caused by a microbe.
3 List some products that are made using microbes.
4 What does 'pathogen' mean?

WOW FACTOR!

Queen Mary II of England, Emperor Joseph I of Austria, King Luis I of Spain, Tsar Peter II of Russia, and King Louis XV of France all died of smallpox.

Bacteria

- Bacteria are just big enough to be seen through a light microscope.
- They respire and reproduce.
- Some have a flagellum that they use to move around.
- Bacteria are found just about everywhere – on your skin, in your body, in the air, in water and in the soil.
- Many bacteria are very useful and are used to make yoghurt, cheese, medicines and enzymes in biological detergents.
- Bacteria cause diseases such as tuberculosis, food poisoning, pneumonia and cholera.

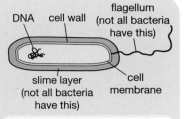

FIGURE 3: Bacterial structure.

Fungi

- Fungi include organisms like mould, mushrooms and yeast.
- **Yeasts** are single-celled organisms.
- Yeasts are used in making bread, beer and wine.
- Thrush is an **infection** of the mouth and vagina and is caused by a yeast.
- Other fungi consist of a network of threads called hyphae that branch out in all directions.
- Mushrooms and moulds reproduce by making tiny spores, which are carried by the wind.
- Fungi cause diseases such as ringworm and athlete's foot.

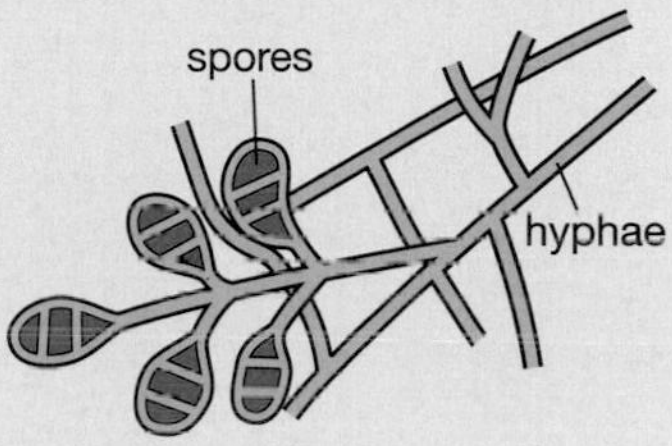

FIGURE 4: Fungal structure.

Viruses

- They do not have a cell membrane or a nucleus.
- They are made of a few genes surrounded by a protein coat.
- Viruses are much smaller than bacteria and can only be seen with an electron microscope.
- Viruses can only reproduce when they enter a living cell.
- Viruses cause diseases such as flu, colds, measles, smallpox and AIDS.

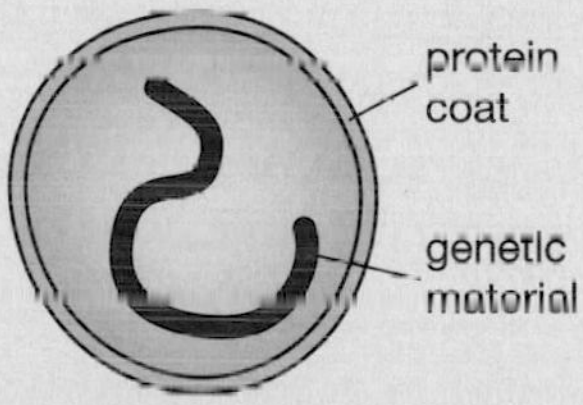

FIGURE 5: Viruses have a very simple structure.

Protozoa

- Protozoa are single-celled 'animals'.
- They cause diseases such as malaria and sleeping sickness.

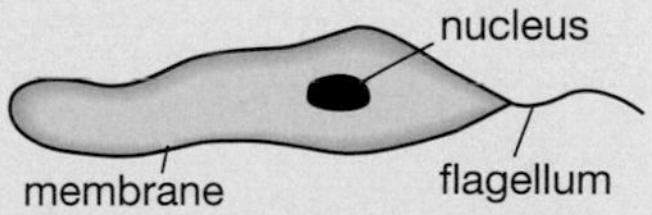

FIGURE 6: This is the protozoan that causes malaria.

EXAM HINTS AND TIPS

Avoid using the word 'germ' when answering examination questions – examiners prefer you to say 'microbe' or 'micro-organism'.

Diseases from proteins

In 1986 a new disease of cattle was seen in the UK. News bulletins showed cattle staggering around and collapsing. The press called it 'mad cow disease'. Its correct name is Bovine Spongiform Encephalopathy (BSE).

FIGURE 7: A cow, which died of BSE, is carried away to be burned.

The brains of the dead animals were found to have become spongy. This disease was similar to other diseases such as scrapie in sheep and Creutzfeldt–Jakob disease (CJD) in humans. The disease was spread by cattle food containing brain and spinal cord from other cattle. People have caught, and died of, a new form of CJD after eating infected meat.

These diseases are not caused by a microbe. They are caused by a protein called a **prion**. These proteins are able to replicate themselves. They are not destroyed by being heated, frozen or dried.

QUESTIONS

5   Make a table like the one below to summarise the information about microbes.

Type of microbe	Diagram	Uses	Diseases	Other information

QUESTIONS

6   Imagine you are a journalist on a science magazine in 1986. Write a report with the headline 'Mad Cow Disease'.

7   What is a prion?

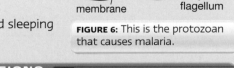

...prion ...protozoa ...viral infection ...virus ...yeast

Spreading disease

You will find out:
- About the different ways In which disease-causing microbes can be passed from person to person
- About how we can take precautions to reduce the risk of infection

Coughs and sneezes spread diseases

Aaaa ... tishoo! Oh, dear, you've got a cold. How did you get it? Look at the picture. Microbes can enter our body when we breathe in. When the man sneezes, a shower of tiny droplets spreads out in the air. The droplets might contain microbes and you might breathe them in.

Airborne droplets

Breathing in droplets is just one of many ways in which microbes can enter your body. Diseases like colds, flu, pneumonia, diphtheria, and tuberculosis are spread by droplets. We call them **airborne diseases**. They spread particularly well in places where there are lots of people close together, such as schools and offices. These diseases are more likely to spread in the winter when we spend more time indoors, with the windows and doors closed and the heating turned up high.

Airborne droplets are just one of many different ways in which microbes can be spread, or **transmitted**, from one person to another. These include:

- touching infected people (**direct contact**)
- touching things which infected people have used (**indirect contact**)
- insects and other animals that carry microbes (**vectors**)
- food and water
- using infected hypodermic needles.

FIGURE 1: Coughs and sneezes ...

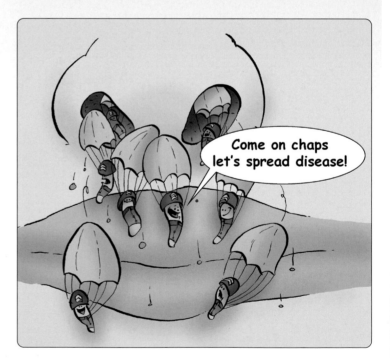

Come on chaps let's spread disease!

QUESTIONS

1 Why should you cover your nose and mouth when you cough or sneeze?
2 Would flu spread so easily if it didn't make you sneeze?
3 Why are you more likely to catch a cold in the winter?
4 What is the difference between spreading diseases by direct and indirect contact?

 When scientists say 'vehicle-borne', they do not just mean motor vehicles. 'Vehicles', are any means of carrying infection – shoes, coats, packaging etc.

...*airborne diseases ...direct contact ...contagious diseases ...horizontal infection ...indirect contact*

Contagious diseases

Some diseases are transmitted by touching an infected person. These are called **contagious diseases**. **Sexually transmitted diseases** like gonorrhoea and syphilis can only be spread by direct contact. The bacteria that cause these diseases die very quickly outside the body.

Foot and mouth

Foot and mouth

A farmer is seen here disinfecting his car before leaving a farm in Northwest England.

Precautions have been introduced to prevent the spread of the disease, which can be vehicle-borne, carried on the wheels of farm vehicles.

Meanwhile all animals which show signs of the disease, or have been in contact with animals suffering from the disease are to be killed and the bodies burnt.
Cattle and pigs on a farm in Northern England are burnt after being slaughtered. The animals were confirmed as being infected with the foot and mouth virus. The disease can spread rapidly through a herd of animals.

Rabies

Dog passports to end rabies quarantine

A dog owner is seen here at Dover with her two Labradors. The dogs have been vaccinated against a number of diseases including rabies. The information to prove that they have been vaccinated is stored on a microchip embedded in the animal's skin. Rabies is caused by a virus carried by dogs, foxes and wolves amongst others. Dogs without a 'passport' will still have to be kept in quarantine for six months to check that they do not have the disease.

QUESTIONS

5   What is meant by a contagious disease? Give an example.
6   Why do cars leaving farms where there is foot and mouth have to be disinfected?
7   Why are the bodies of animals with foot and mouth burned?

Vertical and horizontal infections

Vertical infections happen between a mother and her baby. This can happen when the foetus is in the womb or by breast-feeding. It is most likely to occur during birth, because the baby is in contact with blood and other body fluids. The microbe that is most likely to be passed on in this way is HIV, which causes AIDS. **Horizontal infections** occur when a person is in contact with someone carrying a microbe.

Malaria

Malaria is a **vector-borne** disease which means that it is passed on by a vector, in this case the mosquito. Malaria is caused by a protozoan called *Plasmodium*. The female mosquito feeds by sucking blood. When a mosquito sucks blood from an uninfected person the Plasmodium can enter their bloodstream. Malaria kills about 2 000 000 people each year.

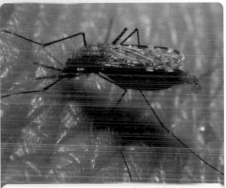

FIGURE 2: A mosquito sucking blood.

Malaria kills about 2 000 000 people each year

QUESTIONS

8   What is the difference between vertical and horizontal infection?
9   In what way is rabies similar to malaria?

Keeping microbes out

You will find out:
- About ways in which microbes get into your body
- About ways in which your body keeps out microbes

Microbes all around

This photograph on the right has been taken using an electron microscope. It shows the point of a pin magnified about 500 times! Those little orange things are bacteria! We are surrounded by microbes. They are on our skin, in our body, in air, water and soil and in food. So why don't we catch diseases all the time? Most microbes are harmless. Our body is designed to keep microbes out. Even if they do get in, we have ways of fighting them.

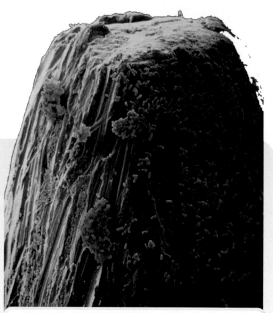

FIGURE 1: Bacteria on a pin.

Ways in

- Your skin is tough and **microbes** cannot get through it. If you cut yourself, however, or even get a scratch, microbes can get in through the wound. That's why you should always keep yourself clean. If you do get a cut, you should clean the wound and keep it covered.

- There are microbes in our food and water. Microbes can get into your body when you eat and drink. **Food hygiene** is important to make sure there are not too many microbes in our food.

- There are microbes in the air. They can enter your body when you breathe in. Always cover your mouth and nose when you cough or sneeze.

- Microbes can get into the body through sexual contact. Condoms can prevent microbes being passed on.

It's no good, chaps. This skin is too tough. We'll have to look for another way in.

▌▌ QUESTIONS ▌▌

1 Write a paragraph to explain what to do if you get a cut.
2 Write down **three** important food hygiene rules.

...ciliated cells   ...clot   ...enzyme   ...food hygiene   ...goblet cells   ...lysozyme

Barriers

Your body has several ways of keeping microbes out. These work against all types of microbes and so are described as non-specific.

eyes
Your eyes make tears which contain two chemicals that kill microbes – salt and **lysozyme**. Every time you blink these chemicals are spread over your eyes.

lungs
Your air passages are lined with two types of cell. **Goblet cells** make **mucus**, a sticky liquid. Microbes and dust stick to the mucus. **Ciliated cells** have microscopic hair-like structures, called cilia, which sway back and forth, carrying the mucus out of your lungs. When it reaches your throat you swallow it.

bacteria trapped in mucus   mucus

ciliated cells   goblet cells

FIGURE 3: Mucus and ciliated cells help get rid of microbes in the lungs.

nose
Your nose is lined with hairs and mucus which trap dust and microbes.

skin
The outer layer of your skin is a tough barrier that stops microbes. Hair follicles make **sebum**, an oily substance that kills microbes.

stomach
Your stomach lining contains cells that make hydrochloric acid, which kills microbes.

blood
If you get cut your blood clots and forms a microbe-proof scab.

FIGURE 2: Your body has many ways of keeping microbes out.

Blood clots

If you get cut, you bleed. Soon the blood thickens, forming a **clot** and the bleeding stops. The clot forms a scab. The scab keeps microbes out of your bloodstream. A series of changes in the blood stops blood clotting inside the body.

In your blood there is a soluble **protein** called fibrinogen. This forms an insoluble protein called fibrin, which joins onto tiny structures called **platelets** forming a mesh which traps **red blood cells**. This is a clot.

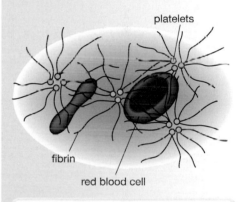

platelets

fibrin

red blood cell

FIGURE 4: Forming a blood clot

Fibrinogen is converted to fibrin by an **enzyme** called thrombin. Undamaged vessels do not contain thrombin – they have an inactive form of the enzyme called prothrombin. Undamaged vessels contain a chemical called heparin. Heparin stops prothrombin changing to thrombin. Damaged vessels release an enzyme, thrombokinase. This stops heparin from working.

QUESTIONS

3   You swallow mucus from your air passages. Why don't the microbes in the mucus cause diseases?

4   Make a table to summarise the ways microbes are kept out of your body.

5   Smoking cigarettes damages the cilia in the lungs. Why do smokers often develop a cough?

QUESTIONS

6   Draw a flow chart to show the chain of events that occurs when a blood vessel is damaged.

...*microbe*   ...*mucus*   ...*platelet*   ...*protein*   ...*red blood cells*   ...*sebum*

Immunity

You will find out:
- That phagocytes protect against disease by 'eating' microbes
- That inflammation helps to protect against diseases
- That lymphocytes protect against disease by making antibodies which give immunity

The microbe eaters

The body has many barriers to keep microbes out but some will still manage to get past this 'first line of defence'. Fortunately there is a 'second line of defence'. White blood cells 'eat' and digest microbes. They also make chemicals that help fight microbes.

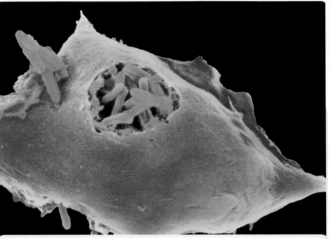

FIGURE 1: A phagocyte (yellow) is eating bacteria (green).

Watch out lads, they're eating us now!

Phagocytes

Blood is carried by the **circulatory system**. Blood contains red cells which carry oxygen. It also contains different types of white cell. One type of white cell is called a **phagocyte**. These cells travel around the body. When they find **microbes** they ingest or eat them. Then they digest the microbes, killing them. This is called phagocytosis. White cells 'eat' all types of microbe. They are non-specific.

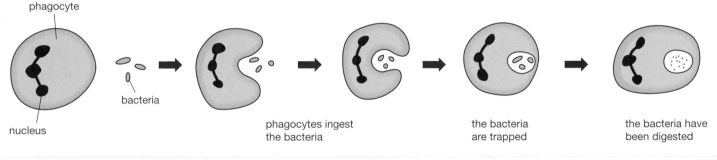

phagocyte

bacteria

nucleus

phagocytes ingest the bacteria

the bacteria are trapped

the bacteria have been digested

FIGURE 2: How phagocytes 'eat' microbes.

Sometimes you get an infected cut which fills up with yellow liquid called pus. This contains white cells and the remains of bacteria. Areas which are infected become hot and red because of the extra blood carried to them. This is called **inflammation**. Extra white cells and the higher temperature help to kill microbes.

> ## ❚❚ QUESTIONS ❚❚
>
> 1. Draw a flow chart to explain what happens in phagocytosis. Draw a diagram for each stage.
> 2. What is a phagocyte?
> 3. What is pus?

...antibodies ...antigen ...antitoxin circulatory system ...disease ...immune ...inflammation

Antibodies

Lymphocytes are another type of **white blood cell**, which provide a 'third line of defence' against microbes. When a microbe gets into the body, the lymphocytes recognise chemicals, mainly proteins, on the surface of the microbe. We call these **antigens**. Different microbes have different antigens. Lymphocytes make chemicals called **antibodies**, which stick to antigens. Each antigen has a different antibody. There are different types of antibody, which attack microbes in different ways.

- Some antibodies make the microbes stick together in clumps. This makes it easier for phagocytes to ingest them. It also prevents microbes from reproducing.

- Some antibodies stick to the microbes which makes it easier for the phagocytes to find them.

- Some antibodies stick to toxins, poisons produced by microbes. This makes the toxins harmless. These antibodies are called **antitoxins**.

- Some antibodies stick to microbes and make them burst open.

- Each antibody only works against a particular microbe. They are described as specific.

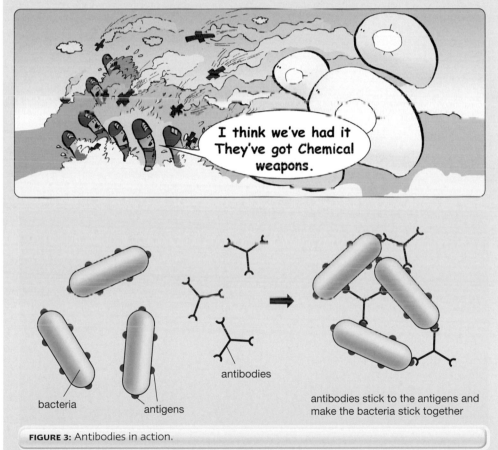

FIGURE 3: Antibodies in action.

People get measles and chickenpox in childhood and never get them again

Allergies

Lymphocytes make antibodies to help fight off pathogens. Allergies are caused when the body tries to fight off harmless 'foreign bodies' such as pollen.

Lymphocytes

There are two types of lymphocyte – B cells and **T cells**. T cells have receptors on their surface which recognise antigens, stick to them and destroy them. T cells also stimulate the B cells, which make antibodies, to multiply.

Special B cells are called **memory B cells**. They stay in the blood for many years and 'remember' different antigens. If you get a particular infection again the B cells make antibodies quickly, so the microbe is killed before you get the **disease**.

Once you have had a disease you are **immune**, often for life. That is why people get measles and chickenpox in childhood and never get them again. Antibodies are specific. The measles antibody fights off measles, but it has no effect on other diseases.

QUESTIONS

4   Make a concept map to summarise the information on 'lymphocytes'.

5   Farhat got measles. She was ill but she soon got better. The next year Abid got measles, but Farhat did not get it again. Explain why.

6   What is an antigen?

QUESTIONS

7   What are the functions of the T cells?

8   What is the function of a memory B cell?

Immunisation

You will find out:
- That vaccination can be used to produce artificial immunity
- How immunisation works
- What passive immunity is

Getting the needle

Ouch, that hurts! How many times have you had an injection? Most of the injections you have are to give you immunity to diseases so it is well worth a bit of pain. Many diseases that killed large numbers of people 100 years ago are almost unknown in the UK today because today most people have been immunised against them and hygiene and diet have improved.

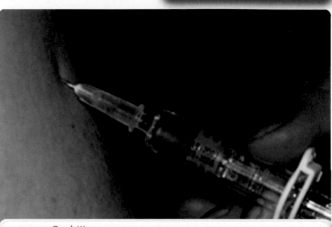

FIGURE 1: Ouch!!!

Immunisation

People in the UK are given **immunisation** to protect them against a number of different **diseases**. Most of these immunisations are given when you are quite young.

Age	Immunisations given
2–4 months	diphtheria, tetanus, whooping cough, polio, meningitis
13 months	measles, mumps and rubella (German measles)
3–5 years	diphtheria, tetanus, whooping cough and polio
10–14 years	tuberculosis
13–18 years	diphtheria, tetanus and polio

TABLE 1: Ages at which vaccinations are given.

Mary Montague and smallpox

In the 18th century, smallpox was a very serious disease, killing thousands of people. Lady Mary Montague was the wife of the British ambassador to Turkey. She lived there for many years. While in Turkey she got smallpox. She recovered but was left badly scarred. She discovered that in Turkey, people were often inoculated with smallpox from someone who seemed to have a mild form of the disease. If they recovered they did not get smallpox again but many people died from the treatment. Mary Montague brought this idea back to Britain and many doctors tried it out.

Many diseases that killed large numbers of people 100 years ago are now almost unknown in the UK

⫍ QUESTIONS ⫎

1 Make a list of all of the immunisations you have had. Ask your parents if you are not sure.
2 Write a newspaper report about Lady Mary Montague for an 18th century newspaper.

EXAM HINTS AND TIPS

Make sure you do not confuse the words 'antigen' and 'antibody'.

...antibodies ...antigen ...bacteria ...booster ...disease ...immune

Edward Jenner – ideas and evidence in science

Edward Jenner was a doctor in Gloucestershire in the 1790s, when many people died of smallpox. He tried to persuade people to be inoculated. Many of them refused, saying that they had had cowpox and couldn't get smallpox. Jenner decided to test this idea. Cowpox is a mild disease, caught from cattle. People who worked with cattle often caught it.

In 1796 Jenner took a small boy, called James Phipps and a milkmaid, called Sarah Nelmes, who had caught cowpox. Jenner scraped pus from a 'pock' on Sarah's hand and smeared it on a scratch he made on James' arm. James got cowpox and recovered. Jenner then gave James smallpox. James did not get smallpox. Jenner inoculated James with smallpox many times in the next 20 years but he didn't get smallpox. He was **immune** to it. Jenner named his new technique **vaccination**, from the Latin word for cow. We now use the word immunisation.

FIGURE 2: Jenner vaccinates his own son with cowpox. Of course, he had already tested his idea out on James Phipps!

How does immunisation work?

Cowpox has very similar **antigens** to smallpox. When the cowpox **virus** gets into the blood, the **lymphocytes** make **antibodies** against the cowpox antigens. If the person then gets infected with smallpox, the antibodies help the body to fight the smallpox virus.

Immunisation involves injecting microbial antigens into the body. The lymphocytes make antibodies. If a person gets infected by that **microbe** at some point in the future they already have antibodies to fight the disease. The injection will consist of one of the following:

- antigens extracted from a microbe
- dead microbes
- live weakened microbes.

SMALLPOX

The last case of naturally acquired smallpox was in Somalia in 1977.

Passive immunity

Babies get antibodies via the placenta and breast milk, giving the baby immunity to the same diseases as its mother. This is **passive immunity**. Once the baby stops breast-feeding these antibodies disappear and the baby starts building up its own immune system.

Passive immunity can be given artificially. Tetanus is a disease which can be picked up in cuts, especially if soil gets into the wound. Tetanus **bacteria** make a toxin that can kill. Doctors give people an injection of tetanus antibodies, which neutralises the toxin.

This antibody is made by injecting tetanus toxin into horses. The horses make antibodies which are extracted from its blood. These antibodies do not last as long as natural ones, so **boosters** are needed every few years.

FIGURE 3: Gardeners are at particular risk from tetanus and need to make sure they have anti-tetanus boosters.

QUESTIONS

3 Do you think Jenner would have been allowed to carry out his experiment today? Explain your answer.
4 Draw a cartoon strip to explain Jenner's experiment and how it worked.
5 Draw a flow chart to summarise the modern day technique of immunisation. Include the cells that play a part in the process.

QUESTIONS

6 Should we use animals to make antibodies for use by humans?
7 Why are gardeners at particular risk of getting tetanus?

...immunisation ...lymphocyte ...microbe ...passive immunity ...vaccination ...virus

Helping the immune system

You will find out:

- That antiseptics are substances that kill microbes
- That antibiotics are medicines made by microbes that prevent the growth of other microbes

Surgery – then and now

Compare the two pictures showing doctors performing operations. There doesn't seem to be a lot in common between the operating theatre in the 1870s and the one from the present day but there is one similarity. In the picture from the 1870s there is an antiseptic spray near the patient. Joseph Lister was a surgeon who, in 1863, discovered that some chemicals, such as carbolic acid, would kill microbes. He called these chemicals antiseptics.

FIGURE 1: Surgery then and now.

Antiseptics and aseptic technique

Surgery before the time of Joseph Lister was a pretty gruesome business. Anaesthetics had recently been discovered which meant that patients were at least spared the pain of having operations while awake. (They were often given gin to get them drunk!) Having an operation was still a risky business, however, and many patients died of infected wounds. After Lister, as well as spraying the air around the wound, the doctors' instruments were also cleaned with carbolic acid to kill **microbes**. Before the invention of **antiseptics**, doctors would perform one operation after another without even washing their instruments! Later doctors realised that **aseptic technique** was more important than using antiseptics. The operating theatre is kept well-ventilated and all medical staff wear sterile masks and gloves. Antiseptics still have a vital part to play in killing microbes in wounds.

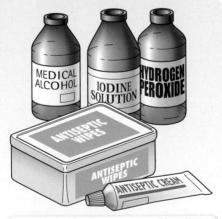

FIGURE 2: There are many antiseptics in use today.

QUESTIONS

1 Imagine that Joseph Lister is about to operate on you. You ask about the carbolic acid spray. Write what he would tell you about it.

2 Write down the names of some antiseptics we use today.

3 What does aseptic mean?

WOW FACTOR!

Eating a mouldy orange was an old Chinese remedy for a sore throat! Fleming wasn't the first person to have his idea about antibiotics.

...antibiotic ...antiseptic ...aseptic technique ...broad spectrum ...erythromycin ...infection

Looking for magic bullets

Antiseptics helped to kill microbes but **infections** still happened. Antiseptics cannot be used on infections inside the body as they damage the body's tissue. Paul Ehrlich was a German scientist who tested hundreds of chemicals, looking for what he called 'magic bullets'. Eventually he discovered a chemical that cured syphilis, without harming the patient.

We might as well surrender – they've got magic bullets!

A fortunate error!

In 1928 Alexander Fleming was studying bacteria in London. In one experiment he spread Staphylococcus bacteria over agar in Petri dishes. After the Petri dishes were incubated, he expected to see bacteria all over the surface of the agar. One of the Petri dishes had been left out without a lid and had been contaminated with some mould, called *Penicillium notatum*. Fleming was about to throw the Petri dish away when he noticed that there were no bacteria growing in the area around the mould. He realised that the mould had made a chemical that killed bacteria. Fleming wrote about his discovery but could not identify and extract the chemical, which he called **penicillin**.

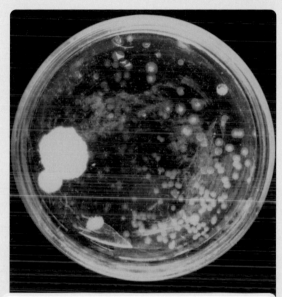

FIGURE 3: Fleming's actual Petri dish.

It took 12 more years before Howard Florey and Ernst Chain were able to produce enough penicillin to test it out. They injected it into mice with bacterial infections and found that it cured the mice and left no ill effects. By this time the Second World War had started. Many soldiers' lives were saved by using penicillin to treat infected wounds.

Penicillin was the first **antibiotic**, a substance made by living organisms, usually fungi, which stops the growth of microbes.

Antibiotics have no effect against viruses.

QUESTIONS

4 What did Paul Ehrlich mean by a 'magic bullet'?
5 Write a sentence to explain what we mean by an antibiotic.
6 Explain how Florey and Chain tested penicillin.
7 Why would a doctor not give you antibiotics if you had flu?

How do antibiotics work?

We now have hundreds of antibiotics. An antibiotic must stop bacteria growing without harming the patient. The antibiotic needs to affect some part of the bacteria that humans don't have.

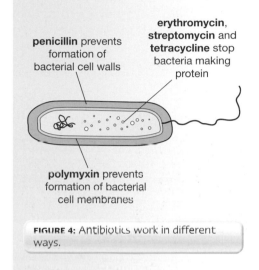

penicillin prevents formation of bacterial cell walls

erythromycin, streptomycin and **tetracycline** stop bacteria making protein

polymyxin prevents formation of bacterial cell membranes

FIGURE 4: Antibiotics work in different ways.

Tetracycline works well against a wide range of bacteria so we call it a **broad spectrum** antibiotic. Other antibiotics only work well against a few bacteria so they are called **narrow spectrum** antibiotics.

- Penicillin is used to treat sore throats, diphtheria and some types of meningitis.
- Streptomycin is used to treat tuberculosis and meningitis.
- Polymyxin is used to treat eye infections.
- Erythromycin is used to treat acne, pneumonia and tooth infections.

QUESTIONS

8 Make a table to summarise how antibiotics work and the diseases they are used to treat.
9 What is the difference between broad and narrow spectrum antibiotics?

Tuberculosis (TB)

You will find out:
- What causes tuberculosis
- How the spread of TB can be prevented and controlled
- About strains of TB that are resistant to drugs
- Why TB is becoming more common in the UK
- Why it is very expensive to develop new drugs

Fighting TB

What is a photograph of Nelson Mandela doing in a book about science? In 1986, while in prison, he became seriously ill with **tuberculosis (TB)**, a **disease** which mainly affects the lungs. Nelson Mandela was cured of the disease and, after his release, he went on to become president of South Africa.

However, TB has not always been curable. In the 19th century, 25% of all deaths in Europe were caused by TB.

FIGURE 1: Nelson Mandela.

What is tuberculosis and what causes it?

Tuberculosis is caused by **bacteria** called *Mycobacterium tuberculosis*. When a person who has TB coughs, sneezes or even just breathes out, they produce small droplets that contain the bacteria. These droplets can float around in the air for hours. They can easily be breathed in by someone else.

Most people who breathe in TB bacteria do not develop tuberculosis. The **immune system** goes into action and fights off the bacteria. The person might just have a cough or even have no symptoms at all. Only about 5% of people who get an infection of TB bacteria actually get the disease tuberculosis. The disease mainly develops to the active stage in people who are elderly, have a poor diet or have AIDS.

Active tuberculosis

Sometimes the bacteria keep on multiplying and become active. It can happen that someone has had a tuberculosis **infection** which was fought off by the immune system. The bacteria were not all killed and some survived in the scar tissue in the lungs. Years later, if the immune system is not working so well, these bacteria can start to multiply again and become active. Only people who have active TB can pass on the disease.

Only people who have active TB can pass on the disease

QUESTIONS

1. Why is TB less common than it was 100 years ago?
2. Name some other diseases that are spread by airborne droplets.
3. How would the immune system fight off the tuberculosis bacteria?
4. Which groups of people are most likely to get TB?

WANT TO KNOW MORE?

It is estimated to cost up to £1 billion to develop a new drug. Go to http://wistechnology.com/article.php?id=377 to find out how this cost is reached.

...antibiotic ...antigen ...bacteria ...disease ...drug ...gene

What are the symptoms of tuberculosis?

The main symptom is a cough which goes on for weeks and weeks and which can produce bloodstained phlegm. Patients feel tired, feverish and short of breath. They may have chest pains, lack of appetite and lose weight.

How do I know if I have tuberculosis?

- Heaf test – a tuberculosis **antigen**, tuberculin, is scratched into the skin. If it becomes red and itchy after a few days it shows that you have had a TB infection sometime in your life. It does not show if you have active TB.
- Chest X-ray.

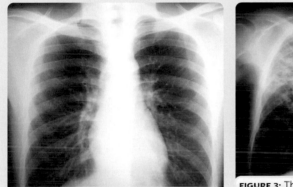

FIGURE 2: These are healthy lungs.

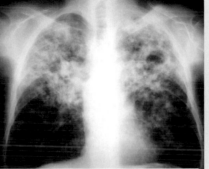

FIGURE 3: The white patches show where these lungs are affected by TB.

- Bacterial culture – scientists grow bacteria from patients' phlegm then look at them through a microscope. *M. tuberculosis* grows very slowly. It might be 6–10 weeks before the bacteria can be identified. Treatment starts before TB has been confirmed.

How can we prevent and treat tuberculosis? (H)

In the 19th century, tuberculosis was widespread. Many people lived in overcrowded houses and had a poor diet, which helped the bacteria to spread.

In the 1850s rich people with TB went to a sanatorium, usually in mountainous areas. People believed that sunshine, fresh air and exercise cured TB. This is not true but sanatoria helped to prevent the spread of the disease by isolating infected patients. Poorer people were also treated in this way though they went to sanatoria in the countryside near home rather than the Swiss Alps!

In 1921 a **vaccine** against TB was developed. This is a weakened form of the bacteria called *Bacillus Calmette-Guerin* (BCG) which is still used today.

In 1943 streptomycin, the first **antibiotic** effective against *M. tuberculosis*, was developed. Since then many more anti-TB **drugs** have been developed. TB is a difficult bacterium to kill, requiring several different antibiotics to be taken for several months. It can cost about £1 billion to develop a new drug.

QUESTIONS

5 Why were you given a Heaf test before you had your BCG vaccination?

6 How does the Heaf test show that a person has had a TB infection?

7 Why don't doctors wait for the results of the bacterial culture test before starting to give antibiotics for TB?

Why is tuberculosis on the increase again? (H)

Most people who get infected with *M. tuberculosis* do not develop TB because the immune system fights it but if the immune system is not working the disease may develop. Many people with AIDS get TB.

TB is common in some parts of the world. About 30% of the world's population carries the bacterium. Increased travel means that more people travel to areas with TB.

A tiny proportion of TB bacteria are naturally resistant to a particular antibiotic. When a patient takes an antibiotic, it kills most of the bacteria but not the resistant bacteria which multiply and pass on **resistance** in their **genes**. Patients are given different drugs so that the bacteria do not become resistant to any one of them. Recently multi-drug resistant tuberculosis has emerged, caused by bacteria that are resistant to several drugs.

Drug companies may be unwilling to invest in the high cost of developing drugs that will mainly be used in poorer countries that cannot afford to pay for them.

FIGURE 4: This TB patient is being treated in a sanatorium. To get most benefit from sunlight she is naked and outdoors!

QUESTIONS

8 Why are people with AIDS more likely to get TB?

9 Draw a flow chart to explain how bacteria can become resistant to an antibiotic.

Drugs

You will find out:
- How drugs cause abnormal behaviour
- How drugs can increase the risk of getting infections
- How drugs can affect the nervous system
- About the use of painkilling drugs and the risk of overdose

What is a drug?

Drugs are substances that affect the way the body works. Many drugs are useful and are used as medicines, such as antibiotics and painkillers. Other substances such as alcohol, tobacco and caffeine in cola and coffee are drugs.

Drug abuse or **misuse** is where people use drugs without getting any benefit from them. Some useful drugs are used by people who do not actually need them. Some drugs, such as cocaine and cannabis, are used by people for enjoyment.

Using drugs has many dangers

FIGURE 1: Many everyday substances are drugs.

Drug abuse

Several different types of drug are misused. They are grouped depending on how they affect your body.

- **Stimulants** speed up the nervous system. They include cocaine, crack, ecstasy and speed.
- **Depressants** slow down the nervous system. They include alcohol, solvents, aerosols and tranquillisers.
- **Hallucinogens** alter the way you see and hear things. They include cannabis, magic mushrooms and LSD.
- **Analgesics** are painkillers. They include heroin.

QUESTIONS

1 What is meant by a drug?
2 Write down the names of **five** drugs that are helpful.
3 What is meant by drug misuse?
4 Make a table to show the different groups of drugs, how they affect the body and some examples of each group.

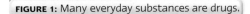

...*analgesic* ...*barbiturate* ...*caffeine* ...*cannabis* ...*depressant* ...*drug*

Injecting drugs

Using drugs has many dangers. Injecting drugs, however, has an extra danger due to the risk of infection when using hypodermic needles. Many drug users share needles and there is a huge risk of passing on viral infections such as AIDS and hepatitis.

Drugs for pain relief

Paracetamol is a mild painkiller which affects the nervous system but, despite having been used for around 50 years it is still not understood how it works! Just because it is a mild drug, it should not be treated carelessly. Overdoses of paracetamol can cause liver damage, especially when taken with alcohol.

Cannabis is another drug that seems to give pain relief to people suffering from cancer and other diseases. Some doctors believe that terminally ill patients should be allowed to use cannabis as a painkiller. Others think that more research should be done on cannabinoids, the substances in cannabis. This would enable doctors to find the exact ingredients that give pain relief and to be able to prescribe them more precisely.

Morphine (one of the **opiate** drugs) is used as a very powerful painkiller for people who are terminally ill or who have undergone major surgery. It works by blocking receptors in the post synaptic membrane so that when an impulse reaches a synapse it is unable to go any further. Contrary to what many people believe, morphine is not addictive when used to treat pain, nor does it shorten the patient's life.

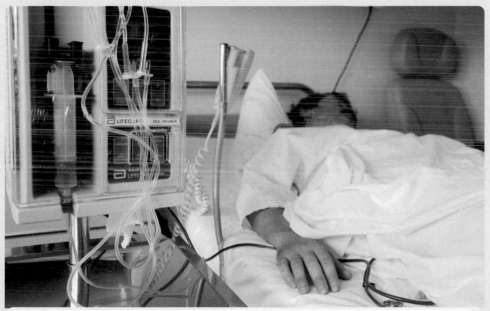

FIGURE 2: This patient is connected to a morphine pump that can deliver measured doses of morphine as he needs them.

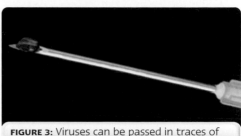

FIGURE 3: Viruses can be passed in traces of blood if needles are shared.

WANT TO KNOW MORE?

Look at the website
www.mindbodysoul.gov.uk

Drugs and the nervous system

Barbiturates are a group of sedative drugs used to reduce stress and as sleeping pills. They are not so widely used now as they are highly addictive. They are depressants, acting on the neurones in the brain. Nerve impulses are created when sodium ions cross from just outside to just inside the axon. They do this by moving through special channels in the cell membrane. Barbiturates work by blocking these channels, stopping nerve impulses being formed.

Caffeine is found in tea, coffee, cola and many 'energy drinks'. It is a mild stimulant, affecting the nervous system. It makes people feel more alert and decreases reaction time. It does this by stimulating the release of neurotransmitters in the synapses of neurones in the brain.

QUESTIONS

5   What is the particular danger involved in injecting drugs?

6   Should terminally ill patients be prescribed cannabis by their doctor?

7   Draw a diagram to show how morphine works.

QUESTIONS

8   Write a short paragraph to explain how barbiturates work.

9   Find some examples of products that contain caffeine.

...hallucinogen ...misuse ...morphine ...opiate ...paracetamol ...stimulant

Smoking

You will find out:
- About the effects of smoking on the respiratory system
- About the effects of smoking on the blood system
- About the effects of smoking on a foetus

Dying for a smoke

You probably know that smoking can cause lung cancer, but it also causes many other illnesses.

- Smoking kills around 114 000 people in the UK each year.
- 42 800 are from smoking-related cancers.
- 30 600 are from cardiovascular disease.
- 29 100 are from emphysema and other chronic lung diseases.
- Smoking cigarettes reduces your life expectancy by about eight years.

Cigarette smoke – a lethal combination

Cigarette smoke contains a combination of harmful chemicals. When cigarette smoke is inhaled many of these chemicals get into the blood. They are carried around the body.

- **Nicotine** in tobacco is an addictive drug. That is why smokers find it difficult to give up. It makes people feel calm by affecting the brain. It also makes the heart beat faster and increases blood pressure.
- **Tar** is a mixture of thousands of chemicals. They collect in the lungs when smoke is inhaled. Some of the chemicals in tar cause cancer.
- **Carbon monoxide** is a gas that is produced when tobacco burns. It reduces the amount of oxygen that the blood can carry. It makes smokers short of breath, especially when they do exercise.

Passive smoking

You do not actually need to smoke to inhale the substances listed above. **Passive smoking** is where you breathe in the smoke from other peoples' cigarettes. It is estimated that passive smoking kills nearly 12 000 people a year.

FIGURE 1: Most smokers start young.

Smoking and pregnancy

Smoking during pregnancy reduces the amount of oxygen available to the foetus. Women who smoke during pregnancy are more likely to have babies that are underweight, born prematurely or stillborn (born dead). Smoking can also affect a couple's chance of getting pregnant. Men who smoke have a lower sperm count, have sperm that cannot swim as well as normal, and make sperm that are deformed.

Even after birth, babies born to women who smoke are more likely to be ill and are twice as likely to suffer cot death.

⚏ QUESTIONS ⚏

1. What is meant by an addictive drug?
2. A packet of 20 cigarettes costs £5. How much does it cost to smoke 10 cigarettes a day for a year?
3. Why do smokers get short of breath when they run?
4. What is passive smoking?

...bronchitis ...cancer ...carbon monoxide ...cardiovascular disease ...emphysema

SOUTHALL & WEST LONDON COLLEGE

Smoking and health

Bronchitis

This is a disease where air passages become inflamed. Cigarette smoke causes the goblet cells to make large amounts of mucus. Tar from cigarette smoke clogs the cilia in your lungs, stopping them from moving. Carbon monoxide also prevents cilia from moving. Mucus does not get removed from the lungs. Bacteria multiply in the mucus. People with bronchitis develop a cough to get rid of the mucus.

Emphysema

Gaseous exchange occurs in the alveoli. These are tiny air spaces, surrounded by capillaries. Oxygen diffuses from the air space into the blood while carbon dioxide diffuses in the opposite direction. The alveoli have a huge surface area to allow plenty of oxygen into the blood. Smoking damages the walls of the alveoli, causing emphysema. This reduces the surface area of the lung, so much less oxygen can pass into the blood.

All that coughing will put you in a coffin!

Cancer

Many of the chemicals in the tar in cigarette smoke are carcinogenic. This means that they cause cancer. The main form of cancer caused by smoking is lung cancer as well as cancer of the oesophagus, bladder, kidneys, pancreas and cervix.

Cardiovascular disease

Nicotine increases the blood pressure and narrows the arteries. Carbon monoxide reduces the amount of oxygen that the blood can carry. These factors combine to cause cardiovascular disease. This causes blocked arteries, which can cause heart attacks and strokes.

Erectile dysfunction

Men get an erection due to extra blood being pumped into the penis. Smoking can cause damage to blood vessels, preventing a man from getting an erection. This is called erectile dysfunction.

WOW FACTOR!

In a non-smoker, the surface area of all of the alveoli is about the same size as a tennis court! Emphysema reduces this surface area, making it more difficult to absorb oxygen.

EXAM HINTS AND TIPS

A lot of biology questions involve explanations. 'Emphysema reduces the amount of oxygen diffusing into the blood' is a better answer than 'emphysema stops oxygen getting into the blood'.

Haemoglobin

You should remember that red blood cells carry oxygen round the body. They contain **haemoglobin**, which combines with oxygen in a reversible reaction to form oxyhaemoglobin.

haemoglobin + oxygen ⇌ oxyhaemoglobin

Carbon monoxide and oxygen molecules are a similar size and shape. Carbon monoxide combines with haemoglobin molecules about 300 times more readily than oxygen does. This reduces the amount of haemoglobin available to carry oxygen. Unlike the reaction between haemoglobin and oxygen, the reaction between haemoglobin and carbon monoxide is irreversible. Very high concentrations of carbon monoxide can cause death. This is why a faulty gas fire is so dangerous. Cigarettes do not produce enough carbon monoxide to kill a person but it is enough to contribute to several conditions caused by smoking.

QUESTIONS

5   Why do smokers develop a cough?

6   What damage can be caused by continual coughing?

7   Make a poster to summarise the risks to your health caused by smoking.

8   What does carcinogenic mean?

QUESTIONS

9   Draw a flow chart to explain why smokers are often short of breath.

...erectile dysfunction   ...haemoglobin   ...nicotine   ...passive smoking   ...tar

Alcohol

You will find out:
- How alcohol affects the liver and brain
- How alcohol increases reaction time and how this can affect activities such as driving

Socially acceptable?

Alcohol is a socially acceptable drug in the UK. It is legal for people over the age of 18 to buy alcohol. In some countries you have to be 21 to drink, while in other parts of the world alcohol is totally illegal.

Alcohol is classed as a drug because it alters the way the body works. One part of the body that is affected is the nervous system. This causes lack of coordination, lack of judgement and slower reaction times. The consequences can be serious.

FIGURE 1: A quiet drink with friends can turn into something more serious …

Alcohol is a poison

… unless you are sensible!

Alcohol – an addictive drug

Most people drink **alcohol** socially and because they enjoy the taste. However, drinking too much alcohol can make people become **addicted**. Their bodies develop a **tolerance** to alcohol. That means they need to drink more alcohol to get the same effect. An **alcoholic** is someone who cannot get through life without drinking.

Richard and his mates liked to hang out in the park and have a few drinks.

After drinking a lot of alcohol, Richard found it difficult to get up to go to school.

He realised how much work he had missed when he did his exams.

Richard did badly in his exams. His grades were not good enough for college or 6th form.

QUESTIONS

1. What is meant by an addiction?
2. What is an alcoholic?
3. What do you think might happen to Richard? What advice would you give him?

DANGEROUS HABIT

Heavy drinking causes 33 000 deaths every year in the UK.

…addicted …alcohol …alcoholic …cirrhosis

Units of alcohol

The more alcohol a person drinks, the more and the quicker they are affected. Different alcoholic drinks contain different amounts of alcohol. One way to compare the strength of different drinks is to compare how many units of alcohol they contain.

The recommended maximum is:

- men – 21 units per week and no more than four units per day
- women – 14 units per week and no more than four units per day.

It takes about one hour to remove one unit of alcohol from the body.

small bottle of beer   1 small glass of vodka   1 bottle of alcopop   1 glass of wine   pint of cider

FIGURE 2: Each of these drinks contains one unit of alcohol.

A good night out!

When you drink alcohol it is quickly carried to your brain. At first you feel cheerful and relaxed. Then you might start to feel more emotional, your speech starts to become slurred and your vision is affected. A couple more drinks and you lose coordination – you cannot walk without stumbling. Your judgement is not so good and you might do things you regret. As you drink more, the good feelings wear off and depression sets in. You might be sick and could choke. A few drinks more and you are in a state of **stupor**. You do not know where you are or what you are doing.

FIGURE 3: Your judgement is not so good and you might do things you regret.

This can be followed by coma. Any of these stages will leave you feeling ill the next morning, suffering from a **hangover**. Then you wonder if you can remember everything you said or did.

Reaction time

Alcohol increases your **reaction time**. It takes an average driver about 0.75 seconds from seeing danger to hitting the brakes. Four units of alcohol will increase this time by about 0.25 seconds.

QUESTIONS

4. Joel drank four pints of beer, a glass of wine and two small vodkas. How many units did he drink?

5. How much further would a car travelling at 20 m/s (about 45 mph) travel before the driver hits the brakes if he has just drunk two small bottles of beer?

Long-term effects

Alcohol is a poison. One function of the liver is to break down poisons. Too much alcohol, over many years, can damage the liver causing **cirrhosis** of the liver. Healthy liver cells are replaced with fat and fibrous cells. The liver is less able to remove alcohol and other poisons from the body.

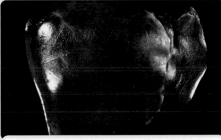

FIGURE 4: A healthy liver.

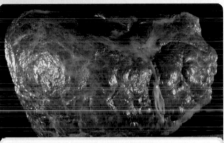

FIGURE 5: A liver with cirrhosis.

Drinking over many years can cause brain damage. Alcohol destroys brain cells and breaks down dendrites that connect brain cells, leading to memory loss. Stopping drinking allows the brain to recover.

Drinking heavily also increases the risk of developing:

- cancer of the mouth, oesophagus, liver, large intestine and breasts
- heart disease
- obesity
- an inability to get an erection
- depression
- high blood pressure.

Alcohol also increases your risk of having accidents.

QUESTIONS

6. Draw a labelled diagram of the body summarising the long-term effects of alcohol.

7. Describe the differences you can see between the healthy liver and the liver with cirrhosis.

Unit summary

Concept map

The central nervous system comprises the brain and spinal cord. The function of the brain can be disrupted by strokes, brain tumours, Parkinson's disease and epilepsy.

Receptors detect stimuli and effectors (muscles and glands) respond to them. They are connected by neurones, which carry electrical impulses.

Reflex actions are automatic, very fast and help to protect the body. The nerve impulses involved in a reflex action pass along a reflex arc, which contains a sensory neurone, a relay neurone and a motor neurone, with synapses between them.

Electrical and chemical signals

Body processes are coordinated using nerves and hormones.

Hormones are produced by the endocrine glands and act as chemical messages. They are carried in the blood. Blood consists of liquid, called plasma, and red and white blood cells.

The menstrual cycle is controlled by oestrogen, progesterone, FSH and LH. Sex hormones are used artificially for contraception and fertility treatment.

Insulin is a hormone, produced by the pancreas, which regulates blood glucose concentration. Insulin, produced by genetically modified bacteria, is used to treat diabetes.

Depressants, such as alcohol and barbiturates, increase reaction time and can damage the liver and brain; stimulants, such as caffeine, decrease reaction time.

Solvents affect behaviour and can damage the brain and lungs.

Drugs

Drugs are chemicals which affect the way the body works. Many are used as painkillers although these can be misused. Developing new drugs is a costly process involving thorough testing.

Smoking tobacco causes cancer, bronchitis, emphysema and heart disease.

'Hard drugs', such as cocaine and heroin, can cause severe health problems. Injecting drugs can cause infection by microorganisms.

Microorganisms can be passed from person to person by direct contact, indirect contact, in the air, by animals and in food and water.

The skin, mucus and blood clotting help to stop pathogens getting into the body. Some white blood cells ingest pathogens, while others produce antibodies and antitoxins.

Disease

Infectious diseases are caused by pathogenic microorganisms, such as bacteria, viruses, fungi and protozoa. Bacteria and viruses make people ill by producing toxins and damaging cells.

Painkillers help relieve symptoms but do not cure diseases.

Antibiotics are used to kill bacteria in the body, but bacteria can become resistant to antibiotics.

Immunisations and vaccinations protect against infectious diseases.

Unit quiz

1. What is meant by the peripheral nervous system?

2. Put the following terms in the correct order for a reflex arc:
   effector, stimulus, response, relay neurone, sensory neurone, receptor, motor neurone.

3. What is a synapse?

4. How are nerve impulses transmitted across a synapse?

5. Which set of muscles contracts to make the pupil of the eye bigger?

6. Name **three** substances that are carried by blood plasma.

7. What is *in vitro* fertilisation?

8. What effect does insulin have on the blood sugar level?

9. Which hormone, also produced by the pancreas, has the opposite effect to insulin?

10. Why is it helpful for adrenaline to convert glycogen to glucose?

11. Write down **three** other effects of adrenaline on the body.

12. Name a sex hormone made by the ovaries.

13. Name the gland where FSH and LH are made.

14. What is meant by a pathogen?

15. How is malaria spread from person to person?

16. What kind of microorganism causes flu?

17. Which component of blood helps it to clot?

18. What do **a)** phagocytes and **b)** antibodies do?

19. What is meant by passive immunity?

20. Which component of tobacco smoke **a)** is addictive and **b)** can cause cancer?

21. How does alcohol affect reaction times?

Literacy activity

Blood transfusions

If someone loses a lot of blood, they may need a blood transfusion. Doctors cannot just give any blood, however. If the wrong blood is given then the cells will stick together. This could be fatal if it blocked blood vessels.

Blood group	A	B	AB	O
Antigens on red cells	A	B	A and B	none
Antibodies in plasma	anti B	anti A	none	anti A and anti B

Table 1: Antigens and antibodies in each blood group

There are four blood groups – **A**, **B**, **AB** and **O**. The blood group depends on antigens on the red cells. There are two antigens called **A** and **B**. The plasma also contains antibodies called anti A and anti B. Table 1 summarises the antigens and antibodies in each blood group.

A person with blood group A cannot be given group B blood because the antibodies in the blood group A blood would cause the group B red cells to stick together.

People with group AB have antigens A and B yet they can safely receive group A or B blood despite the fact that they contain anti B and anti A antibodies respectively. This is because the amount of antibody is small and will be diluted in the recipient's blood.

QUESTIONS

1. Copy and complete the following table to show which blood groups can be safely transfused.

2. Why is group O called the 'universal donor' group?

3. Which group is called the 'universal recipient' group?

Blood group	Can receive blood from	Can donate blood to
A		
B		
AB	All groups	
O		

Exam practice

1 Chloe accidentally places her hand near a candle flame. She quickly jerks her hand away. The electrical signal for this action forms a reflex arc. The reflex arc starts with a stimulus, ends with a response and involves several structures:

1 effector   2 motor neurone
3 relay neurone   4 sensory neurone
5 receptor.

The correct order of structures in the reflex arc through which the signal travels is:

A 5 1 4 3 2
B 5 3 4 2 1
C 5 4 3 2 1
D 5 2 3 1 4   [1]

2 Chloe's quick response to pain is an example of a reflex action. Which one of these statements about a reflex action is true?

A It involves the brain.
B It does not involve the brain.
C It involves hormones.
D It does not involve nerves.   [1]

3 Apart from the candle flame, the room is dim. In Chloe's eye, which part of the retina responds to dim light?

A Rod cells.
B Cone cells.
C The blind spot.
D The fovea.   [1]

4 Which one of the following statements is true?

A Lysozymes are proteins on micro-organisms, which are attacked by antigens produced by white blood cells.
B Pathogens are proteins on micro-organisms, which are attacked by antigens produced by white blood cells.
C Antigens are proteins on micro-organisms, which are attacked by antibodies produced by white blood cells.
D Antibodies are proteins on micro-organisms, which are attacked by antigens produced by white blood cells.   [1]

5 a 'Stopping distance' is the shortest distance that a driver can bring a car to a stop. It is a measure of reaction time. The following graph shows the speed of a car in relation to its stopping distance. Which of the following statements is correct?

A At 30 mph, the stopping distance is six car lengths.
B The stopping distance is 16 car lengths when the speed is 45 mph.
C The stopping distance is 18 car lengths at 50 mph.
D From 45 mph to 70 mph, the stopping distance increases by eight car lengths.   [1]

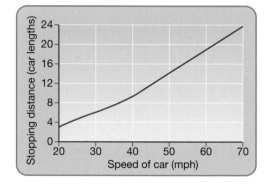

b The following table shows stopping distances for a sober driver (has not drunk any alcohol) compared to a drunk driver (has had several units of alcohol).

Speed of car (mph)	Stopping distance (number of car lengths)	
	Sober driver	Drunk driver
20	3	5
40	9	14
60	18	24

Which one of the following statements is correct?

A At lower speeds, it takes longer to stop the car.
B The drunk driver stops the car twice as quickly as the sober driver.
C The sober driver stops the car twice as quickly as the drunk driver.
D The drunk driver always has a slower reaction time than the sober driver.   [1]

(Total 6 marks)

The following graph shows relative amounts of hormones associated with changes during a woman's menstrual cycle.

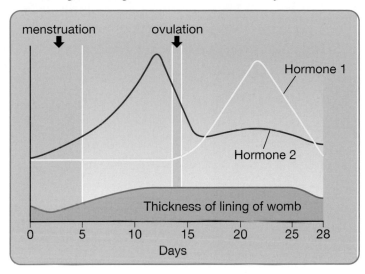

a Which one of the following statements is correct?
- **A** Hormone 1 is luteinising hormone; Hormone 2 is follicle-stimulating hormone.
- **B** Hormone 1 is follicle-stimulating hormone; Hormone 2 is luteinising hormone.
- **C** Hormone 1 is oestrogen; Hormone 2 is progesterone.
- **D** Hormone 1 is progesterone; Hormone 2 is oestrogen.   [1]

b Which one of the following statements is **false**?
- **A** Menstruation causes thickening of the lining of the womb.
- **B** Hormone 2 causes ovulation to take place.
- **C** Hormone 1 causes thickening of the lining of the womb.
- **D** Hormone 1 maintains thickening of the lining of the womb.   [1]

c What happens to the lining of the womb between day two and day eight?
- **A** The lining of the womb is maintained at a constant thickness.
- **B** The thickness of the lining of the womb increases then decreases.
- **C** The thickness of the lining of the womb increases.
- **D** The thickness of the lining of the womb decreases.   [1]

This answer is correct.

a D ✓

b C ✗

c C ✓

This is the wrong answer. Statement 'A' is false, because menstruation does not <u>cause</u> thickening of the lining of the womb.

This answer is correct. The answer can be worked out by looking carefully at the graph.

How to get an A

Multiple choice options may be very similar at first glance. Make sure you read each option very carefully, and check your work when you've finished.

DISCOVER THE BLAST FURNACE!

Man has been extracting iron from iron ore for over 3000 years. Until the 18th Century, the ore was smelted using charcoal. Since then we have used coke.

White-hot molten iron at 1500 °C flows from a blast furnace into a railway wagon called a 'torpedo ladle'. This carries the iron to another furnace, where it is converted into steel.

The UK's largest blast furnace is at Redcar on Teesside. It can produce 10 000 tonnes of iron per day.

These clothes are coated with aluminium, to reflect the heat.

CONTENTS

Starting small

You will find out:
- That atoms make up everything in the universe
- That atoms are very small and cannot be seen with the naked eye
- That atoms are made up of other smaller particles

Very small but important

When looking at a very impressive building, like one of the Great Pyramids (see figure 1), we notice the wonderful shape that the building has – it also looks as if it has very smooth sides.

However, it is only when we move closer to the pyramids, that we notice that the pyramids are themselves made up of very large blocks of stone – these blocks are placed one on top of the other to produce a very large, and very strong building that has lasted for many years.

FIGURE 1: A great pyramid – even great objects like this are made up of simple building blocks.

Tiny building blocks

Atoms are like these building blocks.

They make up everything in the universe from the incredibly small to the absolutely massive.

The amazing thing about atoms is that they cannot be seen with the naked eye – they are far too small.

There is a very powerful microscope called an electron tunnelling microscope that can magnify up to a billion times – it can see atoms. Figure 2 shows the surface of some silicon – each dot is a real atom.

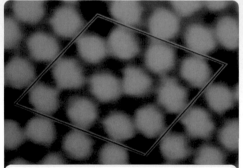

FIGURE 2: The surface of silicon showing the atoms as dots.

Building up atoms

Experiments were carried out over a century ago that show that atoms are made up of even smaller particles called **protons**, **neutrons** and **electrons**. The neutrons and protons exist inside a central part of the atom called the **nucleus**. The electrons fly around the nucleus, like bees around a honey pot. Figure 3 shows the protons, neutrons and electrons present in an atom.

 Although atoms are made up of charged particles, they are not charged themselves.

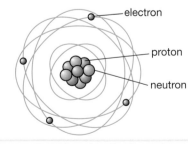

FIGURE 3: An atom, showing its nucleus and the electrons (not to scale).

◼◼ QUESTIONS ◼◼

1 Why can't atoms be seen with the naked eye?
2 What are the names of the particles that are found in the nucleus of an atom?
3 Where are electrons found in an atom?

...atom ...atomic number ...electron ...element ...mass number

A closer look

There are some important things to realise about the particles that make up an atom.

- The nucleus contains protons and neutrons.

- Protons have a relative mass of 1 and a positive charge.

- Neutrons have a relative mass of 1 and a neutral charge.

- Electrons have a very small mass – about 1/2000 of a proton or a neutron.

- Electrons have a negative charge.

This information is summarised in the table below.

Name of particle	Relative mass	Relative charge
proton	1	+1
neutron	1	0
electron	1/2000	-1

TABLE 1: The mass and charge of atomic particles.

What's the difference between one atom and another?

Atoms of different chemical **elements** contain different numbers of protons in the nucleus – this number is called the **atomic number** of that element.

The atomic number tells us the number of electrons as well as the number of protons, since in an atom they are always equal to each other.

The **mass number** tells us the total number of protons and neutrons in an atom.

Electrons move around the nucleus in **shells**. There is a maximum number of electrons each shell can hold.

Shell Number	Number of electrons allowed
1st shell	2
2nd shell	8
3rd shell	8

TABLE 2: Number of electrons in each shell.

Electrons enter the first shell. When this is filled they then enter the second shell, and so on. For example, an atom of potassium has 19 electrons – these enter the shells as 2, 8, 8, 1, that is, 2 in the first shell, 8 in the second shell, and so on.

QUESTIONS

4 Explain why all atoms have a zero charge, if the number of protons and electrons are equal.
5 Which particles contribute most to the mass of an atom?
6 Suggest why it took a lot longer to discover the neutron in an atom.

WOW FACTOR!

If one million atoms were placed in a line, the line would only measure about 1/10 of a millimetre. Look on your ruler to see how small this would be.

Let's look at some real examples

All elements have two numbers – an atomic number and a mass number. For example, aluminium has an atomic number of 13 and a mass number of 27, it is often written as:

$$^{27}_{13}\text{Al}$$

- A nucleus of aluminium has 13 protons in it (since the atomic number is 13).

- There must also be 14 neutrons in the nucleus since the mass number is 27 and we already know that 13 protons are present.

- 13 electrons orbit the nucleus in shells.

- 2 electrons enter the first shell; 8 in the next shell and 3 in the outer shell.

QUESTIONS

7 How many protons are there in an atom of the element lithium if it has an atomic number of 3?
8 How many neutrons are there in the nucleus of an atom of lithium if the mass number is 7?
9 How would the electrons be arranged into shells around an atom of lithium?

...*neutron* ...*nucleus* ...*proton* ...*shell*

It's all elemental!

You will find out:

● What is meant by a chemical element
● What the difference is between a chemical element and a chemical compound
● How to name some simple compounds

Nature's building blocks

When we look around and see the world, and when we gaze up at the night sky, it looks as if life is very complicated – there are so many different things.

However, when we look at things very closely and see how they are made up, we realise that substances are built up of a small number of chemical building blocks called **elements**. Elements make up all of the **substances** around us.

What are elements?

Some important facts about elements are as follows.

■ Elements are substances that cannot be broken down to form simpler substances.

■ Elements are made up of **atoms** that are all the same.

■ The elements are sometimes shown in a special chart called a **periodic table** – this is a very important arrangement of elements. This will be discussed later.

■ Some examples of chemical elements include hydrogen, oxygen, carbon, sulphur – none of these substances can be broken down to form anything simpler by heating.

■ Elements have **symbols** – a kind of shorthand – and chemists often use these symbols when talking about a particular element. For example, the symbol for an element called sulphur that is found in volcanoes is S and the symbol for magnesium, a metal used to make alloy wheels, is Mg. The symbol for lead is Pb. This might seem a bit weird, but lead's old name is plumbum – a plumber is someone who fixes lead pipes!

FIGURE 1: A galaxy of stars.

QUESTIONS

1 What is a chemical element?
2 Give the names of **two** chemical elements from the passage.
3 When a substance is heated, it breaks down to form a new substance. Was the substance being heated an element, or not?
4 What is special about the atoms found in an element?

 All elements have symbols that begin with a capital letter.

...atom ...compound ...element ...periodic table

Elements joining together

Some elements, such as gold, can be found in the Earth as shiny lumps in rock. This is because they are so unreactive that they do not react with anything. However, more reactive metals such as calcium are never found in this form.

FIGURE 2: A gold nugget.

Many elements are very **reactive** – this means that they react with other elements to form new substances called **compounds**.

EXAM HINTS AND TIPS

When a compound is made of only two elements, it normally ends in –ide. When a compound contains oxygen (and contains more than two elements), it normally ends in –ate.

Figure 3 shows a section of some human bone – this is made of a compound called calcium phosphate. It is made of three elements – calcium, phosphorus and oxygen.

Here are a few facts about compounds.

- Compounds can be broken down to form simpler substances.

- Compounds have names that depend on the elements that they contain, for example, sodium chloride is a compound of the elements sodium and chlorine.

- When elements make a compound, they are said to be chemically combined – this means that the atoms of each element in the compound are strongly glued or bonded together.

- Compounds, and elements, are single substances – they are made of the same types of atoms all the way through the substance. For example, copper sulphate is a compound of copper, sulphur and oxygen, and nothing else.

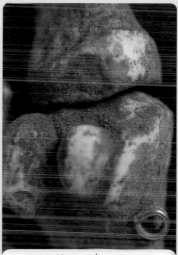

FIGURE 3: Human bone – a chemical compound.

QUESTIONS

5 What is the difference between a chemical element and a chemical compound?

6 What is the name of the compound which contains copper, sulphur and oxygen?

7 Why are some elements found in the Earth uncombined with any other elements?

8 Is the air an element, a compound, or a mixture of elements and compounds?

What's in a name?

When elements form a compound, the compound is given a name that depends on the elements from which it is made. An example of a **reaction** which forms a compound is when hydrogen explodes with chlorine gas to form hydrogen chloride:

hydrogen + chlorine → hydrogen chloride

Copper reacts with sulphur to form copper sulphide:

copper + sulphur → copper sulphide

Notice that the ending of a compound containing two elements normally ends in –ide.

When a compound contains oxygen, often when a total of three elements are present, the compound normally ends in –ate. Copper sulphate is an example of a compound containing oxygen.

Figure 4 shows Michelangelo's David, a statue made of the compound called calcium carbonate – this compound contains calcium, carbon and oxygen.

FIGURE 4: David – made of calcium carbonate.

QUESTIONS

9 What is the difference in the elements that the following compounds contain – sodium sulphide and sodium sulphate?

10 Which elements are present in calcium carbide and calcium carbonate?

11 A compound is made from a reaction between iron and sulphur – suggest a name for it.

It's all symbolic

You will find out:
- That all chemical elements have a symbol
- What the chemical symbol of an element or the chemical formula of a compound tells us about the atoms it contains

From drink to pop

You may have come across a drink called J_2O – it is a fruit drink, but notice the name of it. Similarly, U2 is the name of a famous pop band that has sold millions of records worldwide.

The names J_2O and U2 look like some kind of code, or formula. Chemicals too are often referred to by a chemists' code called a chemical **formula**.

FIGURE 1: Is J_2O a real chemical formula?

Starting with elements

Figure 2 shows a large diamond.

It is now known that a diamond is made up of pure carbon, and carbon is an **element** that has a **symbol** – the capital letter C.

Gold is also a chemical element but it has a strange symbol – Au. This is because the Latin word for gold is *aurum*, hence Au.

All of the elements have symbols; some examples are given below:

Hydrogen – H	Lithium – Li	Lead – Pb	Magnesium – Mg
Helium – He	Oxygen – O	Nitrogen – N	Fluorine – F

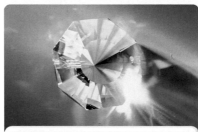

FIGURE 2: A beautiful diamond.

Note the following points when writing symbols of elements.

- All symbols for elements are made up of one or two letters, but never more than two.

- The first letter is always a capital letter.

- The second letter, if there is one, is always a small letter.

A modern light bulb contains many elements. For example, the gas that fills up the light bulb is argon which has the symbol Ar. The very fine metal coil inside the bulb that produces the light is made of tungsten which has the symbol W. The glass contains two more elements, silicon (Si) and oxygen (O).

FIGURE 3: A tungsten filament is used in this light bulb – tungsten is a chemical element.

■ QUESTIONS ■

1 What are the symbols for the elements called nitrogen and oxygen?

2 What element has the symbol C?

...*compound* ...*diatomic* ...*element* ...*endothermic* ...*exothermic*

From elements to compounds

Coal is also made of the same stuff that diamonds are made of – carbon. When coal burns, heat is produced by the chemical **reaction** involved. Reactions which generate heat are called **exothermic** reactions. Other reactions can take in heat and they are called **endothermic** reactions.

FIGURE 4: Burning coal.

When coal burns, the carbon that makes up the coal joins with the oxygen in the air to form a **compound** called carbon dioxide, which is a gas. The chemical formula of carbon dioxide is CO_2. When we look at a formula like this one, it can tell us some important things.

- It is a compound because it is made up of two or more elements chemically combined.

- It is made up of carbon and oxygen atoms.

- It tells us that in every one carbon dioxide **molecule** there is one carbon atom and two oxygen atoms. Remember that a molecule is a group of atoms bonded, or joined, together.

Other very important **substances** together with their chemical formulae are given below:

CO	carbon monoxide	H_2O	water
H_2SO_4	sulphuric acid	NaCl	sodium chloride
HCl	hydrochloric acid	NaOH	sodium hydroxide
CH_4	methane	NH_3	ammonia

When two of these substances (ammonia and hydrochloric acid) are added together, a violent reaction takes place to produce dense white fumes.

FIGURE 5: A violent chemical reaction.

> ### EXAM HINTS AND TIPS
> Make sure that you remember these formulae – they are very useful to know.

▓▓▓▓ QUESTIONS ▓▓▓▓

3 What gas is formed when coal is burnt in air?

4 Give the chemical formulae for water and sodium hydroxide.

5 H_2SO_4 is the formula of a well-known acid – what is it called?

6 The formula of ammonia is NH_3 – give **two** things that the formula tells us about the compound.

Safety in numbers

Although atoms make up all substances, most atoms like to bond together to form a small group of atoms called a molecule.

Elements like oxygen, hydrogen and chlorine are all gases at room temperature and they like to form molecules in which two atoms are bonded together. These types of molecules are called **diatomic** molecules.

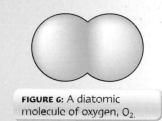
FIGURE 6: A diatomic molecule of oxygen, O_2.

Notice that the number of atoms in a molecule is written into the formula for that substance. An oxygen molecule has the formula O_2 since its molecule is made up of two atoms bonded together.

Sulphuric acid has the formula H_2SO_4. This means that in one molecule of sulphuric acid there are two hydrogen atoms, one sulphur atom and four oxygen atoms. A chemist's model of sulphuric acid is shown below.

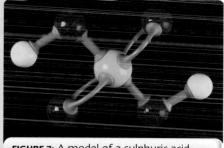
FIGURE 7: A model of a sulphuric acid molecule.

▓▓▓▓ QUESTIONS ▓▓▓▓

7 How many different elements are in a substance that has the formula HNO_3?

8 How many atoms are there in a molecule of water?

9 What is the meaning of the word: diatomic?

10 Ozone is a triatomic molecule. What does this mean?

All change!

You will find out:

- What is meant by a chemical reaction
- What happens to atoms in a chemical reaction
- What is meant by a chemical equation

Fire!

We are all familiar with the idea of striking a match and then using the heat from the flame to set fire to a piece of wood. When something burns, it is a chemical reaction – this means that the substances that were there before the reaction took place are changed into new substances.

Chemical reactions do not just take place in a chemistry laboratory – they are everywhere we look. In fact, we would not be alive if there weren't millions of chemical reactions going on in our bodies every day.

FIGURE 1: Fire – a chemical reaction.

What's in a reaction?

If we take a piece of magnesium ribbon and heat it in a Bunsen flame, a fast chemical **reaction** takes place. The magnesium will start to catch fire and produce a bright white flame. This is a fast reaction but the rates of reactions can often be very different.

- When things burn, they join with the oxygen gas in the air via a chemical reaction to form new things which look different.

- We can write a **word equation** to show the reaction taking place.

- This is done by writing down the names of things which react (known as **reactants**) and then writing down the names of the new things that are made (called the **products**). A typical word equation looks like this:

  reactant + reactant → products

  When magnesium burns, the word equation would be:

  magnesium + oxygen gas → magnesium oxide

- In a chemical reaction, the products often look very different from the reactants. For example, magnesium is a silvery looking metal, oxygen is a colourless gas but the product of the reaction (magnesium oxide) is a white solid. The atoms are still there but they are joined to different partner atoms.

FIGURE 2: Magnesium burning in air.

▮▮ QUESTIONS ▮▮

1. What do you understand by the term 'chemical reaction'?
2. What are the reactants in a chemical reaction?
3. What is the name of the compound formed when magnesium reacts with oxygen?
4. Write a word equation that shows what happens to a lump of coal burning in air.

EXAM HINTS AND TIPS

Don't forget that in all chemical reactions, the mass before and after the reaction is the same.

...*atom*   ...*bonded*   ...*compound*   ...*mass*   ...*product*

What happens to the atoms in a chemical reaction?

What happens when a candle burns? Before the reaction, we have the stuff that burns (the wax) and the gas in which it is burning (oxygen from the air).

If we set light to the candle, when it burns in a jar with the lid on, the candle flame will eventually go out since the oxygen level in the jar decreases.

What happens when wax is burnt?

The wax is a **compound** of hydrogen and carbon, and when it burns, each of the hydrogen and carbon atoms join with oxygen to form carbon dioxide and water vapour.

This can be written as:

wax + oxygen gas → carbon dioxide gas + water vapour

What would happen if the flame was lit and then the jar placed on a balance?

It is very interesting to see that the **mass** reading on the balance does not change during the reaction, even though new substances have formed. This is an important thing to know about all chemical reactions – the total mass before is always the same as the total mass afterwards. This is sometimes called the conservation of mass.

But why does the mass in a chemical reaction stay the same? What does this mean about the atoms?

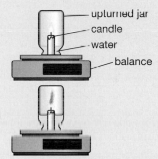

FIGURE 3: Jar and candle before and after burning.

Since the mass is the same before and after a reaction, this must means that the **atoms** are still there but they are joined to different partner atoms. This occurs when atoms from each reactant collide with each other.

FIGURE 4: In this square dance, people swap dance partners in the same way that atoms sometimes do within a chemical reaction.

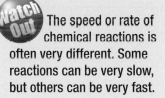
Watch Out The speed or rate of chemical reactions is often very different. Some reactions can be very slow, but others can be very fast.

▚▚▚ QUESTIONS ▚▚▚

5   What happens to the atoms in a chemical reaction?
6   If a reaction is carried out inside a sealed container, what happens to the mass of the container during the reaction?
7   A candle appears to lose mass when it burns. Why is this?
8   Magnesium ribbon increases in mass when it is burnt in air. Why?

Making compounds

Many simple compounds can be made easily by taking a mixture of two elements and heating them. For example, iron sulphide can be made by heating a mixture of iron and sulphur together:

iron + sulphur → iron sulphide

Figure 5 shows what happens on the atomic level when iron and sulphur are heated. Notice that the atoms join up to form a new **substance** – the atoms are chemically **bonded** together.

FIGURE 5: The formation of iron sulphide (not to scale).

Other examples of compounds that can be made by heating elements include the following shown as word equations:

hydrogen gas + oxygen gas → water

carbon + oxygen gas → carbon dioxide

sodium + chlorine gas → sodium chloride

magnesium + oxygen gas → magnesium oxide

▚▚▚ QUESTIONS ▚▚▚

9   What is the name of the compound formed when copper is heated with sulphur?
10   What happens to atoms when they react together?
11   Write a word equation for when potassium reacts with nitrogen gas.

...reactant ...reaction ...substance ...word equation

The chemical code

You will find out:

● What is meant by a chemical formula

● How to write a symbol equation

● What is meant by balancing an equation

Off into space!

People have been able to travel into space for a long time now. This is possible because of a powerful chemical reaction that takes place in rocket engines between oxygen and hydrogen - both of these are chemical elements.

Scientists who designed the Space Shuttle's engines needed to know how hydrogen and oxygen react together in order for the Shuttle to take off. They can describe the reaction using a chemical equation - this is like a chemical code and it is very useful to know.

FIGURE 1: The Shuttle launches into space.

What are the atoms up to?

We now know that all chemicals around us are made up of atoms. We also know that chemical **reactions** take place everywhere and, if it wasn't for reactions, life would not exist as we know it.

We also know that if we do a reaction and weigh it before and afterwards, the **mass** will not have changed – this is because the same **atoms** were there at the end of the reaction as were there at the beginning – no atoms have vanished or suddenly appeared.

We can write an equation to show what is going on in a reaction.

For example, methane gas may be burnt in oxygen to produce new products, as well as some heat – this heat energy may be used to power a car like the one in figure 2.

We might want to write a **word equation** for this reaction:

methane + oxygen → carbon dioxide + water

When magnesium metal is added to dilute hydrochloric acid, a fast reaction takes place with lots of bubbling.

A word equation for this reaction would be:

magnesium + hydrochloric acid → magnesium chloride + hydrogen gas

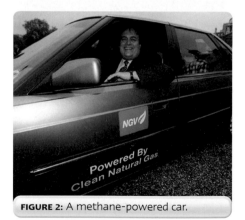

FIGURE 2: A methane-powered car.

‖ QUESTIONS ‖

1   Give the names of the gases used to power the Space Shuttle.

2   What **two** substances are formed when methane burns in oxygen?

3   What is the name of the gas formed when magnesium is added to hydrochloric acid?

EXAM HINTS AND TIPS

Remember that when counting elements in an equation, a number written after the element tells us how many there are. So, in a molecule of water (H_2O), there are 2 hydrogen atoms and 1 oxygen atom.

...atom   ...balanced   ...chemical formula   ...compound   ...element

Symbols in equations (H)

It is possible to show a reaction in many different ways on paper. One way is to write a word equation in which the **reactants** and **products** are written as their names. But we know that **elements** and **compounds** also have formulae. Can we therefore write equations with symbols instead of words?

When hydrochloric acid and sodium hydroxide solution (a well-known alkali) are added together they neutralise each other, and some heat is also released.

STEP 1   We can write a word equation for this reaction if we know the names of the new substances formed.

hydrochloric acid + sodium hydroxide → sodium chloride + water

STEP 2   We can now try to change each name into a **chemical formula** – you may need to recall some of these from page 115 in this book.

HCl + NaOH → NaCl + H$_2$O

STEP 3   Do the count!

Count the number of atoms of each element each side of the equation:

- Hydrogen – there are two on the left-hand side and two on the right-hand side:

   HCl + NaOH → NaCl + H$_2$O

- Oxygen – there is one oxygen atom on the left-hand side and one on the right-hand side:

   HCl + NaOH → NaCl + H$_2$O

- Sodium and chlorine – there is one each on the left and right of the equation:

   HCl + NaOH → NaCl + H$_2$O

The equation is said to be **balanced** since the same numbers of elements are on each side of the equation.

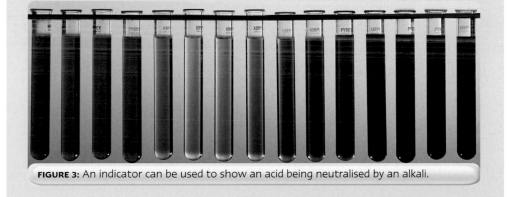

FIGURE 3: An indicator can be used to show an acid being neutralised by an alkali.

━━━ QUESTIONS ━━━

4   What is the name given to a reaction between an acid and an alkali?
5   What is the chemical formula for hydrochloric acid?
6   How many different elements are in sodium hydroxide?

Interesting reaction (H)

Hydrogen gas can burn in chlorine gas to form a new substance called hydrogen chloride.

A word equation for this reaction is therefore:

hydrogen gas + chlorine gas → hydrogen chloride

Now let's replace each name with its correct formula:

H$_2$ + Cl$_2$ → HCl

Notice that there are two chlorine atoms on the left-hand side and only one on the right; the same is true for the hydrogen atoms. Or as a picture:

(not to scale)

We can see that we need to add another HCl to the right hand side so that the same number of atom types is now present.

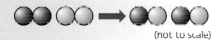

(not to scale)

Or, in symbols:

H$_2$ + Cl$_2$ → 2HCl

This is now balanced.

In a reaction, no atoms vanish or suddenly appear

━━━ QUESTIONS ━━━

7   Balance the equations:
   a H$_2$ + F$_2$ → HF
   b Mg + HCl → MgCl$_2$ + H$_2$
   c Na + H$_2$O → NaOH + H$_2$

...mass   ...product   ...reactant   ...reaction   ...word equation

Energetic chemicals

You will find out:

- That reactions involve energy as well as chemicals
- How to recognise exothermic and endothermic reactions
- That some chemical reactions take place much faster than others

A burst of energy

Natural gas (methane) doesn't react with oxygen until ignited. If gas leaks, nothing happens. The room just fills with gas .... until someone clicks a light switch. Boom! - the whole lot reacts instantly. A very fast reaction causes an explosion, releasing lots of energy very quickly. Fortunately, we can control reactions to release energy gradually. Gas cookers don't normally explode.

FIGURE 1: Pub demolished by a gas explosion.

The ins and outs of chemical energy

Cavemen learned how to make fire. We still depend on it for many needs – including generating most electricity.

- **Combustion** is a chemical reaction. The burning chemicals are reacting with oxygen from the air.

- Chemists call reactions that *give out* heat, like combustions, **exothermic**. Ex = out (like 'exit'); therm = heat. This heat makes the temperature rise.

Exothermic reactions don't always involve burning.

- Our bodies stay warm by using **respiration** to get energy from food.

- Many reactions in solution get hot, such as neutralising acids and alkalis.

Other reactions *take in* heat from their surroundings. So, the temperature drops. These are called **endothermic**. Endo = into.

- Samina eats some sherbet powder. The reaction makes her tongue cold.

FIGURE 2: Bread dough rising.

Controlling reactions

Chemical reactions go faster when heated, and slower when cooled down. Samina makes bread. The mixture ferments, producing carbon dioxide bubbles that make the dough rise.

- Samina keeps the dough warm so it rises faster.

- She bakes the bread. The crust gets hottest and turns brown. The hotter the oven, the faster the reaction, and the darker the crust.

- Samina keeps food in a fridge to slow down reactions that make it 'go off'.

FIGURE 3: This loaf got a bit too hot!

QUESTIONS

1 Is a gas explosion an exo- or endothermic reaction? How did you decide?
2 How can you tell if the reaction between two liquids is exo- or endothermic?
3 Why does food 'go off' more slowly in a freezer than in a fridge?

EXAM HINTS AND TIPS

Remember:
Exo- = exit = heat energy going out
Endo- = into = heat energy taken in

...chemical energy ...combustion ...endothermic ...exothermic

Food, energy and exercise

In 2005, 15-year-old Alicia Hempleman-Adams became the youngest person to reach the North Pole on foot. She had to keep warm in air temperatures as low as −25 °C (colder than a freezer), and pull a sledge 200 miles. Alicia needed lots of energy.

- Food contains **chemical energy**. Respiration changes this into heat, and energy for movement and growth. Respiration is an exothermic reaction.

- Food packets show the chemical energy in the food. It's measured in **kilojoules** (kJ). Alicia ate energy-rich foods, like chocolate, containing sugars and fats.

FIGURE 4: Alicia needed an energy-rich diet for her record-breaking walk.

NUTRITION INFORMATION	
Typical Values	Per 100 g
Energy	2300 kJ
Protein	7.6 g
Carbohydrate	57.0 g
of which Sugars	52.0 g
Fat	32.0 g

TABLE 1: Chocolate. How much chemical energy does 150 g provide?

Where does the energy come from?

All substances contain chemical energy – not just foods. Different substances contain different amounts. So, the products of a reaction may have more chemical energy than the original reactants, or less

- If the products have less energy, the spare is given out; usually as heat, so the temperature rises. The reaction is exothermic.

- If the products have more energy, the extra energy is taken in from the surroundings; again, usually as heat, so the temperature falls. The reaction is endothermic.

FIGURE 5: The 'Thermit' reaction between powdered aluminium and iron oxide produces enough heat to melt the iron. It is used to weld railway lines.

Energy and reaction rate

Rate means speed. If a reaction is fast, the **reaction rate** is high. If it's slow, the reaction rate is low. Gloss paint 'dries' by reacting with oxygen. The reaction rate is very slow, so it takes days. An explosion happens instantly. The rate is extremely high.

All reaction rates increase with temperature. Hotter molecules have more energy, so move faster. They collide more often, knocking bits off each other to form new products. To speed up a reaction, heat it. That's why Bunsens are so useful.

QUESTIONS

4 Name **two** energy-rich foods and **two** low-energy foods.

5 How can you tell that the 'Thermit' reaction is very exothermic?

6 Why does paint dry faster in summer?

WOW FACTOR!

Chemists can measure reactions lasting less than a millionth of a second.

Speed matters

Controlling reaction rates is vital in industry. Time costs money, so manufacturers want to make as much product per hour as possible. They need high rates, but not too high.

- An exothermic reaction releases heat. As the temperature rises, so does the reaction rate. This releases heat even faster, so the rate increases faster still.

- The reaction must be cooled to prevent it running out of control.

FIGURE 6: A reaction rate increased out of control at this chemical factory.

- Conversely, an endothermic reaction cools itself, so its reaction rate will slow down and eventually stop.

- Endothermic reactions need continuous heating to keep them going.

Many chemical processes involve both types of reaction at different stages. They use **heat exchangers** to transfer heat from an exothermic reaction to an endothermic one.

QUESTIONS

7 How can an uncontrolled reaction lead to an explosion?

8 Suggest another heating method besides burning and heat exchange.

9 Why does heat exchange make a process more economic?

...heat exchanger ...kilojoules ...reaction rate ...respiration

Being a detective

You will find out:
- How flame tests can be used to identify some metal compounds
- How colours of precipitates can be used to identify metals in special test-tube reactions

Firework night

Every November 5th, the evening sky is lit up by fireworks.

Fireworks contain chemicals that produce different coloured flames when they react. The red colour of a flame may be due to a metal called strontium, whereas a bright white spark may be due to magnesium metal or iron powder.

What's in a flame?

When a **compound** containing certain metals is placed into the hot flame of a Bunsen burner, the flame can change colour depending on the metal present. For example, a sodium compound will produce a yellow-orange flame whereas a calcium compound will give a red flame.

The colour of a flame can be used to work out which metal is present in a compound. This is called a **flame test**.

Some common metals and their coloured flames are given in table 1.

FIGURE 1: Fireworks are chemical reactions that produce lots of different coloured light.

Name of metal	Colour of flame
sodium	yellow-orange
potassium	lilac
lithium	crimson
copper	green
calcium	orange-red

TABLE 1: Colours produced by metals in flames.

A crime scene

Imagine that a substance is found at a crime scene and you want to know what metal is present in the compound. A flame test can be used as an **analytical** method. The colour of the flame will tell us which metal is present in the mystery substance.

FIGURE 2: Carrying out a flame test.

QUESTIONS

1. A compound is placed into a flame and a green flame is produced. What is the name of the metal in the compound?
2. How do fireworks produce different coloured flames?
3. What is a flame test used to do?

WOW FACTOR!

A flame is a chemical reaction taking place between lots of very hot gases.

...alkali ...analytical ...compound ...exothermic

Are there other ways of using colour to identify substances?

We can carry out **reactions** in test tubes that produce coloured substances. The colour of these substances can be used to identify the metal present.

Transition metals

These special metals are found in the central part of the periodic table, between groups 2 and 3. The first row of **transition metals** includes metals like copper, nickel, iron and manganese.

Sc	Ti	Cr	Mn	Fe	Co	Ni	Cu
scandium		chromium		iron		nickel	
	titanium		manganese		cobalt		copper

When sodium hydroxide solution – a common **alkali** – is added in drops to a **solution** containing a transition metal, colours are formed that can be used to work out which metal is present in the compound.

Figure 3 shows what happens when sodium hydroxide solution is added to copper sulphate solution. A light-blue solid, or **precipitate**, is formed.

Other colours of precipitates formed when dilute sodium hydroxide solution is added to transition metal compounds are shown in table 2.

Name of transition metal in compound	Colour of precipitate
nickel	pale green
copper	pale blue
iron	green or brown
zinc	white

TABLE 2: Colours of precipitates formed by some transition metals.

FIGURE 3: A light blue precipitate forms when sodium hydroxide solution is added to copper sulphate solution.

FIGURE 4: Coloured precipitates formed from transition metals.

⏲ **QUESTIONS** ⏲

4 What type of chemical is sodium hydroxide?
5 Which transition metal has the symbol Cu?
6 Sodium hydroxide solution is added to a solution and a white precipitate is formed. What is the name of the transition metal which could be present in the compound?

Gunpowder!

Gunpowder has been used for many thousands of years. When it burns, the reaction gets very hot and produces lots of gas very fast. This gas can be used to 'push' a projectile out of a tube, for example a bullet out of a gun or a cannonball out of a cannon.

FIGURE 5: Where does the energy come from to fire a cannon ball?

Gunpowder is a mixture of a compound called potassium nitrate, carbon and sulphur.

When it burns, an **exothermic** reaction takes place and lots of gases and smoke are formed. The chemical energy released is used to move a cannonball, a bullet or a rocket through the air.

When gunpowder burns, a lilac flame is formed.

 Not all metals produce colours when they are added to a flame.

⏲ **QUESTIONS** ⏲

7 What are the names of the **three** substances used to make gunpowder?
8 What is the name of the metal present in gunpowder, given the colour of the flame it produces when it burns?
9 What is meant by an exothermic reaction?

…flame test   …precipitate   …reaction   …solution   …transition metal

The halogens

You will find out:
- What is meant by a halogen
- That halogens are very reactive elements
- That halogens can react with other halogens in compounds

Let there be light!

Figure 1 shows a special type of light bulb called a halogen lamp. This type of light is very bright and is used in many houses.

The **halogens** are a family of elements in the periodic table, and one halogen is called iodine. Iodine is placed into a halogen light bulb – this means that the light bulb can operate more brightly, and often, for longer.

FIGURE 1: Why is this light called a halogen light?

What are the halogens?

The halogens are made up of a family of five chemical **elements** and they are found in group 7 of the periodic table. They are called fluorine, chlorine, bromine, iodine and astatine.

The halogens are all coloured elements. Some are gases, others are solids and liquids. Figure 2 shows what some of the halogens look like.

The table below summarises some properties of the halogens.

Name of halogen	Element symbol	Boiling point (°C)	Appearance of element
fluorine	F	-188	pale yellow gas
chlorine	Cl	-34	green gas
bromine	Br	58	brown liquid
iodine	I	184	dark grey solid
astatine	At	unknown	unknown

TABLE 1: The halogens and their properties.

FIGURE 2: Look at how colourful the halogens chlorine, bromine and iodine are.

Notice that the boiling point of the halogens increases on moving down the group of elements. This is why they are gases at the top of the group and solids at the bottom of the group.

Also, it can be seen that the halogens are pale colours at the top of the group (like fluorine being pale yellow), whereas iodine is a dark grey solid as it is at the bottom of the group.

❚❚ QUESTIONS ❚❚

1. What is the name of the halogen found in a halogen light bulb?
2. Suggest why the boiling point and the appearance of astatine are unknown.
3. Using the data in the table above, predict what astatine may look like.

WOW FACTOR!

Halogens, like fluorine, are so reactive that they can even react with xenon and radon. These two elements are members of the noble gases and are very unreactive.

...alkali metal   ...diatomic   ...displacement reaction

How reactive are the halogens?

The halogens are a **reactive** group of non-metals which form **diatomic** molecules. However, they are not all as reactive as each other – some are very reactive and some are less so. It is important to realise that the halogens are all placed in the same group because their chemistry is very similar, in other words, they all react in the same kind of way.

In an experiment, it is possible to add a halogen to a compound containing a halogen. If the halogen being added is more reactive than the halogen in the compound, a reaction occurs. This reaction is called a **displacement reaction**.

Figure 3 shows what is seen when a solution of chlorine in water is added to a solution containing dissolved iodide.

In this reaction, chlorine 'kicks out' or displaces the iodine from the compound. This means that chlorine is more reactive than iodine.

FIGURE 3: Why is there a colour change when chlorine solution is added to potassium iodide solution?

The word and symbol equations for this type of reaction are as follows:

chlorine + sodium iodide → sodium chloride + iodine

$$Cl_2 + 2NaI \rightarrow 2NaCl + I_2$$

Lots more experiments could be carried out like the one above to see how the reactivity of the halogens varies. We would find out that the most reactive halogen is fluorine, and the reactivity decreases on going down the group.

fluorine
chlorine
bromine   reactivity increases
iodine   going up the group
astatine

EXAM HINTS AND TIPS

Non-metals like the halogens get more reactive going up a group in the periodic table. Metals get more reactive going down a group, so it's the other way round!

QUESTIONS

4 Give the name of the most reactive halogen.
5 What would be the names of the products formed when bromine is added to sodium iodide solution?
6 What is the chemical formula for sodium chloride?

Violent chemistry

Halogens are reactive elements. What happens when halogens are added to other elements that are also reactive?

Group 1 elements are called the **alkali metals**. These include metals like lithium, sodium, potassium, rubidium and caesium. Interestingly, metals become more reactive going down the group, so caesium is the most reactive metal in this group.

Fluorine is the most reactive element in its group, so when fluorine and caesium are added together, an almighty **exothermic** reaction should take place.

The picture below shows what might happen!

FIGURE 4: Could this be what happens when caesium and fluorine are added together?

QUESTIONS

7 What is the name of the compound formed when caesium reacts with fluorine?
8 This reaction is highly exothermic. What does this mean?
9 Which two elements in groups 1 and 7 would react together slowest?

Patterns in nature

You will find out:

- What is meant by the periodic table
- How elements are arranged in the periodic table
- Why the periodic table is considered to be an amazing idea

Depression

When people are depressed, they have moments when they are very unhappy and feel down. Depression is a medical condition and various drugs can be given by a doctor which may help the patient. Sometimes, people can have a serious type of depression called manic depression.

In this serious situation, a person may be given a drug called 'lithium'. We now know that manic depression may be caused by the balance between the sodium and potassium in the brain being upset. Lithium works by copying the behaviour of sodium and potassium in the brain. It seems that lithium, sodium and potassium are chemically similar, and it is useful for chemists to think of them as a **group**.

FIGURE 1: 'The Scream' painted by Edvard Munch. He suffered with manic depression.

Putting elements into classes

Playing cards are made up of cards that are all different. However, some cards are related to other cards in the pack, for example, there are four cards with the number 2 on them, or 13 cards with the same suit, for example hearts.

There are about 90 chemical **elements** that occur in nature, and these are like playing cards – some seem to belong to the same family.

For example, the elements in figure 2 are those mentioned above when talking about depression: lithium, sodium and potassium, known as **alkali metals**.

Why are these elements placed into the same group?

- They are all shiny and soft.
- They are all highly reactive and may explode with some other substances.
- They are all light and float on water.
- They react with water.

FIGURE 2: The elements lithium, sodium and potassium, stored under oil.

QUESTIONS

1 Name an element that is involved in manic depression.
2 Why are lithium, sodium and potassium put into the same group?

WOW FACTOR!

Lithium, sodium and potassium are all metals but all float on water.

...alkali metal   ...element   ...group

The periodic table (H)

The **periodic table** is a special chart that is found on the walls of most chemistry classrooms. It is one of the most important discoveries in the whole of science.

What's the story?

Many people were involved in the putting together of the periodic table, but the father of the table was a Russian man called Dmitri Mendeleev.

Mendeleev was born in 1834. At the time only a few chemical elements had been discovered.

All elements have a special number that could be worked out by an experiment. This number is called the relative atomic mass. As we learnt on page 111, they also have **mass number**.

FIGURE 3: This is Mendeleev.

Mendeleev arranged the elements in order of their mass number and also placed elements with similar chemical behaviour (for example, the halogens) in the same column. The beginning of this table looked like this:

H = 1	Li = 7	Be = 9	B = 11	C = 12	N = 14	O =16
F = 19	Na = 23	Mg = 24	Al = 27	Si = 28	P = 31	S = 32
Cl = 35	K = 39	Ca = 40	? = 44	Ti = 48?	V = 51	

Mendeleev then noticed that each element in the same group was very similar to the other members.

For example, lithium, sodium and potassium were all in the same group. Helium, neon and argon, known as **noble gases**, are all in the same group too – the latter three elements are all very unreactive so do not react with other elements, even really reactive ones.

Mendeleev therefore found a way of classifying (putting into classes) the chemical elements. The modern periodic table is built on Mendeleev's table and his table is now considered to be one of the most remarkable ideas in the whole of science.

FIGURE 4: A use for the noble gases.

Mendeleev accurately predicted the appearance of the missing elements

A good guess

In the early periodic table there were many blanks.

This is because not all elements had been discovered at that time, and Mendeleev had the courage to leave blanks for elements which he believed had yet to be discovered. He was not guessing – he had worked out from the pattern that the elements were missing here.

Within Mendeleev's own lifetime, some of these missing elements were discovered and put in the gaps. These were called gallium (Ga) (discovered in France) and germanium (Ge) (discovered in Germany).

Even more amazing, Mendeleev was able to predict the appearance, density, formulae of the oxide, etc. with a great level of accuracy, even though the elements hadn't been discovered in 1869!

▦▦▦ QUESTIONS ▦▦▦

6 Why were some blanks left in the early periodic table?

7 Give the name of an element discovered in Mendeleev's own lifetime.

8 How was Mendeleev able to use a periodic table to predict the properties of other elements?

▦▦▦ QUESTIONS ▦▦▦

3 What is the name of the famous scientist who built the periodic table?

4 Why are the elements helium, neon and argon placed in the same group of the periodic table?

5 What is the number that was originally used to arrange the elements in the periodic table?

Patterns out of chaos

You will find out:
- Why the periodic table is so useful
- How elements are organised within a modern periodic table
- The names of some groups of elements in the periodic table

Making the world a cleaner place

Many people die of disease every year. Diseases that are found in dirty water are a serious problem – these include cholera, diphtheria and typhoid. Chlorine and iodine are two chemical elements found in the same group (the halogens) in the periodic table that have destroyed many diseases and have saved millions of peoples' lives.

FIGURE 1: A disinfectant like this one is made from chlorine.

Elements organised

Some facts about the chemical **elements** are as follows:

- There are only about 90 elements that make up most of the substances in the universe.

- Elements fit into families or **groups** in which the elements in each group are chemically similar.

- A Russian chemist called Mendeleev produced a special chart of the elements. This chart is called the periodic table.

Why is a periodic table useful?

Elements are arranged in groups, containing elements with similar chemical properties. If we know how one element reacts, we can predict that another element in the same group will react in a similar way.

Tom wants to find out about an element called rubidium. He knows that rubidium has the symbol Rb. Tom can predict the chemical behaviour of this element by looking at the other elements in its group.

Rubidium is in the same group as other elements called lithium, sodium and potassium (**alkali metals**) and these are all very dangerous and reactive metals. Tom can therefore predict that rubidium is also a reactive metal since it is in the same group as other reactive elements.

FIGURE 2: Tom wants to know about rubidium.

QUESTIONS

1. How many elements are found naturally?
2. Name a substance that is added to water to save lots of people's lives.
3. Name another metal that is in the same group as lithium, sodium and potassium
4. Name a disease that may be found in water.

WOW FACTOR!

There are more than three times as many metal elements as non-metal elements.

...alkali metal   ...atomic number   ...element   ...group   ...halogen

The modern-day periodic table

The periodic table that scientists use today is shown below.

Group

Group I	II												III	IV	V	VI	VII	0
					1 1 H hydrogen													4 2 He helium
7 3 Li lithium	9 4 Be beryllium												11 5 B boron	12 6 C carbon	14 7 N nitrogen	16 8 O oxygen	19 9 F flourine	20 10 Ne neon
23 11 Na sodium	24 12 Mg magnesium												27 13 Al aluminium	28 14 Si silicon	31 15 P phosphorus	32 16 S sulfur	35 17 Cl chlorine	40 18 Ar argon
39 19 K potassium	40 20 Ca calcium	45 21 Sc scandium	48 22 Ti titanium	51 23 V vanadium	52 24 Cr chromium	55 25 Mn manganese	56 26 Fe iron	59 27 Co cobalt	59 28 Ni nickel	64 29 Cu copper	65 30 Zn zinc	70 31 Ga gallium	73 32 Ge germanium	75 33 As arsenic	79 34 Se selenium	80 35 Br bromine	84 36 Kr krypton
85 37 Rb rubidium	88 38 Sr strontium	89 39 Y yttrium	91 40 Zr zirconium	93 41 Nb niobium	96 42 Mo molybdenum	99 43 Tc technetium	101 44 Ru ruthenium	103 45 Rh rhodium	106 46 Pd palladium	108 47 Ag silver	112 48 Cd cadmium	115 49 In indium	119 50 Sn tin	122 51 Sb antimony	128 52 Te tellurium	127 53 I iodine	131 54 Xe xenon
133 55 Cs caesium	137 56 Ba barium	139 57 La lanthanum	178 72 Hf hafnium	181 73 Ta tantalum	184 74 W tungsten	186 75 Re rhenium	190 76 Os osmium	192 77 Ir iridium	195 78 Pt platinum	197 79 Au gold	201 80 Hg mercury	204 81 Tl thallium	207 82 Pb lead	209 83 Bi bismuth	210 84 Po polonium	210 85 At astatine	222 86 Rn radon
223 87 Fr francium	226 88 Ra radium	227 89 Ac actinium															

FIGURE 3: A modern day periodic table.

- The elements are not arranged in order of the relative atomic **mass number**, as early scientists would have done, but rather in order of **atomic number**.
- There is a jagged line that separates the metals from the non-metals.
- Metals are on the left-hand side of the table, non-metals are on the right.
- The horizontal rows are called **periods**.
- The vertical columns are called groups.
- Groups are numbered from left to right, from 1 to 8 (sometimes called group 0).
- Groups contain families of elements that react in a similar way. Some families, or groups, are given names.

Group number	Name of element family	What is special about these elements?
1	alkali metals	they react with water to make alkalis
2	alkaline earth metals	they form alkalis and many rocks in the earth have a lot of these metals in them
7	**halogens**	halogens make salts – halogen means 'salt maker'
8	**noble gases**	noble means 'of elevated character' – they can't be bothered to react possibly
between groups 2 and 3	**transition metals**	they can form coloured compounds

TABLE 1: Some element groups and their properties.

QUESTIONS

5 What are the names of the vertical columns in the periodic table?
6 How many main groups are there?
7 What are the names of the horizontal rows?
8 What is the name of the elements in group 1 of the periodic table?

Precious metals

Approximately 80% of elements are metals. Some of these are very reactive and are placed in group 1 of the periodic table. Other metals may react as a group 2 element, and so on. However, there are a large number of metals that do not fit into a normal group, and they are found in the centre of the periodic table. They are called the transition metals.

Sc	Ti	V	Cr	Mn	Fe	Co	Ni	Cu	Zn
Y	Zr	Nb	Mo	Tc	Ru	Rh	Pd	Ag	Cd
La	Hf	Ta	W	Re	Os	Ir	Pt	Au	Hg
Ac									

FIGURE 4: The transition metals.

The precious metals used to make jewellery – like gold, copper and silver – all belong to this group of metals within the periodic table.

Figure 5 shows a catalytic converter. It is used in cars to reduce the amount of pollution caused by harmful exhaust gases like carbon monoxide and nitrogen oxides.

FIGURE 5: Catalytic converters are made using transition metals.

The surface of the catalytic converter is coated with three transition metals – platinum, palladium and rhodium – these are all highly expensive metals.

QUESTIONS

9 Give an example of a transition metal.
10 Name **two** pollutants released by cars.
11 Name **three** metals used in a catalytic converter.

Fascinating elements

You will find out:
- About some very useful elements
- The specific uses of some amazing elements
- How some elements can make hundreds of useful substances

Up, up and away!

Figure 1 shows a huge airship called the Hindenburg.

An airship needs to be able to float in air, so the gas that is used to fill up an airship has to be light. Hydrogen gas (formula: H_2) is the gas that used to be used to fill airships. However, hydrogen gas has a problem – it is highly flammable! One day, unfortunately, the airship caught fire and was completely destroyed. Modern airships are filled with another element called helium (symbol: He) – this gas does not burn like hydrogen.

FIGURE 1: The Hindenburg airship.

From light bulbs to lasers

The **elements** in **group** 8 of the periodic table are called the **noble gases**. The noble gases are helium, neon, argon, krypton, xenon and radon.

- They are very unreactive or **inert**. They do not react with many other substances, even very reactive substances.

- They are unusual since they are happy to be atoms on their own – they do not want to join with others to form new substances.

- They have very low melting points and boiling points. Helium, for example, has a melting point of -272 °C and a boiling point of -269 °C – this is extremely cold.

These elements are very useful, mainly because they are so unreactive. Their uses include:

- neon – neon signs (red), diving equipment

- helium – superconducting magnets, deep-sea diving, weather balloons

- argon – light bulbs, fluorescent tubes, a non-reactive blanket for making reactive metals like titanium, blue laser light to correct some eye problems.

FIGURE 2: Tyres can be filled with argon in some luxury cars to reduce road noise.

QUESTIONS

1. The noble gases are found in which group of the periodic table?
2. Give a use for neon.
3. What is the melting point of helium?
4. Why was filling an airship with hydrogen dangerous?

WOW FACTOR!

A piece of gold the size of a grain of rice can be beaten into a sheet that measures 1 metre across.

...atom   ...element   ...formula   ...group   ...halogen

Properties of some special elements

Chlorine is a chemical element that exists as a gas with the **formula** Cl_2 – this formula means that two chlorine **atoms** join together to form a chlorine **molecule**.

A lot of chlorine is used to make a polymer called polyvinyl chloride (PVC). Making water clean enough to drink is also a very important use for chlorine; it is also used for making bleaches and some solvents.

FIGURE 3: Objects made with PVC, a polymer.

Chlorine can be used to make hundreds of different substances

Iodine, like chlorine, is a **halogen**. It is different from chlorine because chlorine is a gas whereas iodine is a solid; this means that iodine has a higher boiling point than chlorine.

From cars to space satellites

Four very useful metals are:

iron (symbol: Fe)	copper (symbol: Cu)
silver (symbol: Ag)	gold (symbol: Au)

All four metals are found in the **transition metal** part of the periodic table.

Copper, gold and silver are all used to make jewellery. This is because they are all unreactive elements, and so will not react with water or oxygen in the air like many other metals do.

Gold is the metal that can be beaten into sheets the easiest – it is highly malleable. It can be used to make decorative ornaments and is even used to coat some satellites with gold foil.

Iron is more reactive than most transition metals – this can be a problem when using iron since it can rust. However, iron is strong and can be made into many different shapes.

▦▦▦ QUESTIONS ▦▦▦

5   Give **two** uses for chlorine.

6   Give a use for gold.

7   Why is gold useful for the use that you mention in question 6?

8   Give a drawback for using iron in everyday life.

Mixing metals

Metals can be mixed together, when molten, to make mixtures of metals called alloys.

The car below has wheels that are made of an alloy of magnesium and aluminium.

FIGURE 4: Alloy wheels.

Another useful alloy is brass – it is an alloy of the metals copper and zinc. It is used to make musical instruments.

Solder (used for electrical soldering) and pewter are two alloys made from the same metals called lead and tin, although the amount of each metal in each of these alloys is different.

FIGURE 5: This goblet is made of an alloy of lead and tin called pewter.

When making jewellery, gold can be mixed with other metals to make various types of gold alloy:

white gold: 90% gold; 10% nickel

blue gold: 46% gold; 54% indium

black gold: 75% gold; 25% cobalt.

▦▦▦ QUESTIONS ▦▦▦

9   What is the name for a mixture of metals?

10 What are the metals that make blue gold?

11 Give a use for the substance known as solder.

...inert   ...molecule   ...noble gases   ...transition metal

The Hunt for Ekasilicon

SELF-CHECK ACTIVITY

Dimitri Mendeleev was a Russian scientist born in 1834. His father died when he was quite young, which made life difficult for him, his mother and his 13 brothers and sisters. As a result, Mendeleev had to work hard to succeed in life.

One of his areas of interest was sorting elements into groups. Like a number of scientists, he was sure there must be a pattern or order to the elements, but it was difficult to see what it was. One reason why it was difficult to see a pattern was the fact that not all of the naturally occurring elements had been discovered at this time.

Mendeleev wrote details of the various elements on pieces of card and arranged them in different ways. He suggested that elements in the same column were in the same group and there would be similarities in their properties. If the pattern failed he believed this was because there was a missing element. He predicted three unknown elements but his ideas were largely ignored until the three were discovered. At this point he was taken seriously, and the Periodic Table as we now know it is based heavily on his work.

CHALLENGE

STEP 1

Mendeleev used the name 'ekasilicon' for one of the elements he predicted. At the time, four other elements in Group 4 (as it is now called) were known. Look at the pattern going down Group 4:

- What would you expect 'ekasilicon' to look like?
- What would you expect its atomic weight (AW) and density to be?

Group 4
Carbon
Solid non-metal, found as graphite or diamond
AW = 12, Density = 2.3 g/cm^3
Silicon
Solid dark-grey semi-metal, extracted from silica
AW = 28, Density = 2.3 g/cm^3
'Ekasilicon'
?
?
Tin
Solid silver grey metal
AW = 118.7, Density = 7.3 g/cm^3
Lead
Solid, bluish white metal
AW = 207, Density = 11.3 g/cm^3

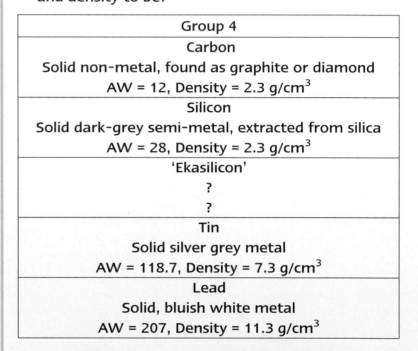

Of course, Mendeleev could also look at the row (the period) it was in.

This was a bit trickier because he'd had to leave another gap right next to it.

Look at Ekasilikon's period, then consider the questions in Step 1 again.

Do you want to change any of your suggestions?

Copper Solid copper metal AW = 63.5 Density = 8.9 g/cm³	Zinc Solid pale grey metal AW = 65.4 Density = 7.1 g/cm³	?	'Ekasilicon'	Arsenic Solid grey semi-metal AW = 74.9 Density = 5.7 g/cm³	Selenium Solid grey non-metal AW = 79 Density = 4.8 g/cm³

STEP 3

Now add a few notes to explain the decisions you made.

STEP 4

You've gone through a similar process to Mendeleev. The big difference is that he had to wait 15 years to see if he had got it right. You can find out by looking up information about an element called Germanium (which is the name Ekasilicon was actually given). How close were you?

Maximise your grade

These sentences show what you need to include in your work to achieve each grade. Use them to improve your work and be more successful.

Grade	Answer includes...
F	Suggest patterns and trends in one property, such as density.
	Spot patterns and trends in one property, such as density.
	Spot patterns and trends in several properties, such as density
	Link patterns in the column (group) with those in the row (period)
C	Use the properties of known elements in the periodic table to predict those of other elements.
	Use and start to explain how the properties of known elements in the periodic table can be used to predict those of other elements.
A	Explain how properties of known elements in the periodic table can be used to predict those of other elements.
	As above, but with particular clarity and detail.

Chemicals at home

You will find out:
- That everything is made up of chemicals
- That some materials we use are natural, but most are artificial
- Some uses of a few simple chemicals around the home

A vital mineral

There's about 100 g of it in your body, but you need to 'top-up' about 4 g a day. You need it to digest food, and make your muscles work. If you don't have enough your heart can't beat properly. Yet eating more than 6 g a day increases the risk of a heart attack. What is this critical chemical? Common salt (sodium chloride) – a simple compound, but essential to life.

Chemicals are everywhere

Your body, and everything around you, including the air, contains millions of different chemicals. Some are simple, like **salt.** Others, like dyes, are more complex. Chemicals aren't just used in laboratories. We all eat, drink and breathe chemicals, use them for work and play, and sleep on them too.

You are what you eat

Your body is made from chemicals in your food. Digestion takes them apart. Your cells then build new substances with the parts – like building with Lego! Foodstuffs contain many complex compounds, and some simple ones.

FIGURE 1: Watch your diet! There's probably more than enough salt in your food without adding extra.

TABLE 1: Chemicals in or related to food.

Chemical	Food
water	in most foods and all drinks; used to cook foods by boiling
salt	added to foods during manufacture and cooking; we sprinkle on even more!
carbohydrates	starch – in cereals, flour, cakes and pasta; sugars – in many foods naturally; added to others
carbon dioxide	gas in fizzy drinks, from cola to champagne; bubbles in bread and cakes
citric acid	natural – sour taste in citrus fruits, for example, lemons; artificial – lemon flavour in food and drinks
ethanoic acid	sour taste in vinegar; preserves food as pickles
phosphoric acid	cola is coloured, flavoured dilute acid; in food additives as phosphate salts
hydrochloric acid	in your stomach to help digestion; too much of it causes acid indigestion

FIGURE 2: This meal contains all the compounds in the table, except stomach acid. Which food contains which?

QUESTIONS

1. What chemicals are all around you, even though you can't see them?
2. Where do the complex chemicals in your body come from?
3. Name **two** types of carbohydrate.
4. Acids are usually harmful. Name **two** acids that are safe to eat or drink.

We all eat, drink, breathe and use chemicals

...*artificial* ...*convert* ...*decompose* ...*extracted*

Using natural materials

A wide range of substances occurs naturally. Yet we use few of them in their **natural** state. Some we just separate out. Others need chemical reactions.

■ Water is a natural material, but tap water isn't. UK water companies purify and sterilise 15 billion litres/day of water to make it safe to drink.

■ Salt occurs naturally as brown, gritty rock salt – good for spreading on icy roads, but not on your dinner. White table salt has been processed to remove the impurities.

■ Gypsum is mined and processed to make plaster for walls and ceilings.

■ Limestone is quarried. Crushed limestone forms the foundations for roads, but most is **decomposed** to make other products (see diagram below).

Improving on nature

Man has always changed natural substances into more useful man-made ones. Thousands of years ago we learned to use fire to:

■ change the taste of food by cooking

■ turn soft clay into pottery

■ obtain iron from rocks.

FIGURE 3: Table salt is rock salt without the other rocks.

More recently man has learned to make completely new materials. We can now make **artificial** substances for almost any purpose we like.

■ We decompose limestone when manufacturing several household materials:

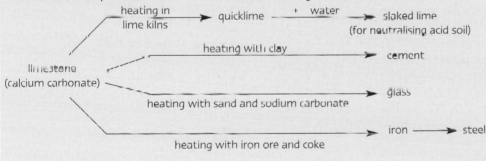

limestone (calcium carbonate)
- heating in lime kilns → quicklime + water → slaked lime (for neutralising acid soil)
- heating with clay → cement
- heating with sand and sodium carbonate → glass
- heating with iron ore and coke → iron → steel

■ We **convert** nitrogen from the air into ammonia for:
fertilisers, for example, ammonium nitrate
household cleaners and brass polish.

■ We convert salt into:
caustic soda – for oven cleaners, drain cleaner and bleach
chlorine – for bleach and PVC plastic.

■ We use phosphoric acid in rust removers.

░░░░ QUESTIONS ░░░░

5 How could you purify rock salt to make table salt?
6 What is the difference between natural and artificial substances?
7 a Find the chemical names for gypsum, quicklime, slaked lime and caustic soda.
  b Write the word equation for converting quicklime into slaked lime.

What's the difference?

If we couldn't manufacture man-made substances, our world would be very different; few metals, no plastics, bricks or glass – no engines or machines.

Some man-made materials do also occur naturally, but not in large enough quantities, so we make more. Here are some examples:

■ Indigo can be **extracted** from a plant, but jeans are dyed with **synthetic** indigo.

■ Citric acid in most lemonade is synthetic, not obtained from lemons. The carbon dioxide fizz comes from chemical processes, not from respiration.

The composition of a pure chemical, whether natural or synthetic, is always the same. It's the impurities in a substance that make the difference.

Surprisingly, natural substances are usually much less pure than synthetic compounds. Lemon juice, for instance, contains more than just citric acid and water.

FIGURE 4: Natural bubbles produced by fermentation? Or gas injected from a cylinder? The carbon dioxide is the same either way.

░░░░ QUESTIONS ░░░░

8 Explain the difference between a synthetic substance and one which is extracted.
9 Name **five** substances from the 'Improving on nature' section that are extracted, besides iron and salt.

Chemical txt msgs

You will find out:
- How symbols and formulae save space, time and effort
- That chemical equations tell you more than you might think
- That the language of chemical symbols is universal

Not-so-simple symbols!

Do you find chemical formulae and equations complicated? Think yourself lucky your teacher isn't John Dalton. In 1806 he thought up the idea of using symbols to show what compounds are made of. He knew that water was made from hydrogen and oxygen, so he joined the symbols together. His drawings also showed the difference between carbon monoxide and carbon dioxide. So far, so good, but just look at his formula for alum!

Short and sweet

Dalton wanted to show which **elements** a **compound** contains – and how many atoms of each. Describing this in words is difficult. Drawing was easier, but his symbols weren't very user-friendly. Only five years later (1811), the letter symbols and **formulae** we use today were introduced.

Writing a **chemical equation** is like sending a text message. It's a quick and simple way to give a lot of information – if you know how to understand it.

Becky needs to describe how methane burns. She knows three ways:

- English: each **molecule** of methane reacts with two molecules of oxygen, to make one molecule of carbon dioxide and two molecules of water

- txt msg: ea molecule of methane reacts W 2 molecules of O_2, 2 mak 1 molecule of CO2 n 2 molecules of H2O

- chemical equation: $CH_4 + 2O_2 \rightarrow CO_2 + 2H_2O$.

Txt msg lingo doesn't help much. It's not designed for scientific words. The equation is much better. It cuts 126 letters and spaces down to only 22.

We change chemical names into formulae and other words into signs:

- + means 'reacts with', or just 'and'

- → means 'go to', or 'turn into'.

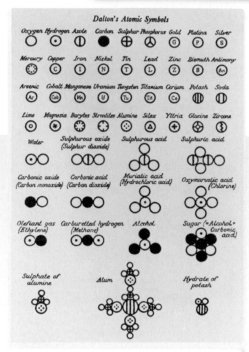

FIGURE 1: Dalton's symbols for atoms and molecules. He also stuck balls together to make models like the molecular models we still use in schools.

FIGURE 2: The methane equation using Dalton's formulae. What errors can you spot?

 Add atoms to balance an equation by writing numbers in front of formulae. Never change the numbers inside a formula.

█ QUESTIONS █

1 What was wrong with Dalton's drawing of a water molecule?
2 What do the modern symbols C, H and O stand for?
3 What do the formulae CH_4 and CO_2 stand for?
4 Write the word equation for burning methane.

...balance   ...chemical equation   ...compound   ...element

Fewer letters, more information

Becky's equation tells you even more than her sentence. Like Dalton's diagrams it also shows what each chemical is made of.

$$CH_4 + 2O_2 \rightarrow CO_2 + 2H_2O$$

There are two types of number in an equation.

- Numbers before a formula show how many molecules of that substance react, or are produced. '$2H_2O$' means 'two water molecules'.

- A number after a symbol shows how many atoms of that element the molecule contains.

Describing the reaction fully:

'A methane molecule contains one carbon and four hydrogen atoms. Each methane molecule reacts with two molecules of oxygen, each containing two oxygen atoms. This produces one molecule of carbon dioxide, containing one carbon and two oxygen atoms. For each carbon dioxide molecule produced, the reaction also produces two molecules of water, each containing two hydrogen and one oxygen atom.'

No wonder chemists use equations. They can write this 60-word description using only 7 letters, 6 numbers and 3 signs! Equations save lots of space.

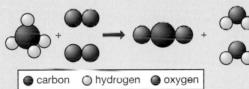

- carbon ○ hydrogen ● oxygen

FIGURE 5. The methane equation shown using models. Note that the numbers of each type of atom are the same on both sides. The equation is balanced.

Which state?

Becky's equation for burning methane doesn't show whether H_2O means water, steam or ice. Similarly, HCl in an equation could mean hydrogen chloride gas or hydrochloric acid (the gas dissolved in water).

We call solid, liquid and gas 'states of matter'. An equation can tell you the state of each substance. It just needs a few more letters, called **state symbols**:

(s) for solid,   (l) for liquid,   (g) for gas,   (aq) for solution

The symbol (aq) stands for 'aqueous' (dissolved in water).

FIGURE 4: Four states of matter. The solid tablet reacts with liquid water, giving carbon dioxide gas and an antacid solution.

Burning methane gas produces steam, so:

$$CH_4(g) + 2O_2(g) \rightarrow CO_2(g) + 2H_2O(g)$$

When solid sodium reacts with liquid water it gives sodium hydroxide solution and hydrogen gas. We write this as:

$$2Na(s) + 2H_2O(l) \rightarrow 2NaOH(aq) + H_2(g)$$

QUESTIONS

5 **a** Is O_2 a symbol or a formula?   **b** What do the two 2's mean in $2O_2$?

6 Write the formula for a molecule containing two hydrogen, one sulphur and four oxygen atoms.

7 How should Becky write the following in a chemical equation?
   a hydrogen chloride gas   **b** hydrochloric acid

Universal speak

Equations don't just pack lots of information into a short space. They use no words, so people can read them in any language.

- We read Pb as 'lead'; the French read 'plombe', the Germans 'blei'.

- The photo shows a periodic table. The words are Russian, including the name МЕНАЕПЕЕВА (Mendeleev), but the symbols are as we know them.

FIGURE 5: A real wall chart!. The heading says 'Periodicheskaya systema elementova'. Guess what that means!

The right balance

Chemical reactions can't create or destroy atoms – only rearrange them. So, equations must show equal numbers of atoms in their reactants and products.

$$CH_4(g) + O_2(g) \rightarrow CO_2(g) + H_2O(g)$$

Correct formulae, but the equation is unbalanced. We **balance** it by writing numbers in front of some formulae, meaning more molecules.

$$CH_4(g) + 2O_2(g) \rightarrow CO_2(g) + 2H_2O(g)$$

Formulae themselves must not be changed.

QUESTIONS

8 Which symbol on the Russian wall chart looks wrong? What should it be?

9 Show why the first equation above is unbalanced.

10 Balance this equation:
   $N_2(g) + H_2(g) \rightarrow NH_3(g)$

...*formula*   ...*molecule*   ...*state symbol*

Life's chemical reactions

You will find out:
- That there are many different types of reactions
- That decomposition, neutralisation, precipitation, dehydration and hydration are very important reactions
- Some reactions are very important to our everyday life

Concrete

Look at the building in figure 1. It's made almost completely of concrete.

It's amazing how many things are made of concrete. Although you may think that concrete is a modern building material, it has been made for many hundreds of years. The Romans knew that limestone and clay, if heated strongly, break down to form new substances, one of which is cement. When a substance breaks down in this way we call it a **decomposition** reaction.

FIGURE 1: A modern building made of concrete.

Losing and gaining water

Some decomposition reactions involve a chemical losing water.

- For example, if we heat some blue crystals called copper sulphate, we notice that they go white.

- A chemical reaction is occurring in which the crystals lose water. This is called a **dehydration** reaction.

- Sugar is a carbohydrate. Heating sugar strongly dehydrates it. Water is given off, leaving black carbon.

So dehydration is a chemist's word meaning 'to lose water'.

- On the other hand, when you add water to cement to form thick grey goo, the mixture gets warm. This is a sure sign that a chemical reaction is taking place!

- The cement doesn't just mix with water, it reacts with it. Lime, CaO, gains water to become hydrated lime, $Ca(OH)_2$.

The process of gaining water is called a **hydration** reaction.

FIGURE 2: When these crystals are heated, water is formed.

QUESTIONS

1. Name **two** substances that make cement.
2. What is the name given to a reaction in which water is formed from a substance being heated?
3. Give an example of a hydration reaction.

EXAM HINTS AND TIPS

Hydration and dehydration are opposite reactions – one is adding water and the other is removing water.

...acid   ...alkali   ...decomposition   ...dehydration

Precipitation reactions

Look at this painting by Vincent van Gogh. Notice how important yellow is.

Artists used to grind up coloured rocks to make a powder which could then be added to a liquid like an oil and mixed – this is how early paints used to be made. However, artists wanted a way to make a really bright yellow but nothing at that time existed. How was it done?

FIGURE 3: Beautiful colours made with chemistry.

FIGURE 4: A bright yellow precipitate forms when two solutions are added together.

It was discovered that reacting together solutions containing lead nitrate and sodium chromate would produce a bright yellow solid. A solid that forms when solutions are added together is called a precipitate, and this type of reaction is called a **precipitation** reaction.

The reaction happening is:

lead nitrate solution	+	sodium chromate solution	→	sodium nitrate solution	+	lead chromate precipitate

Neutralisation reactions

When an **acid** reacts with an **alkali**, a new compound called a salt is formed, together with water. For example, hydrochloric acid and sodium hydroxide solutions react together to form sodium chloride and water:

sodium hydroxide + hydrochloric acid → sodium chloride + water

When the amounts of the acid and alkali react exactly, a neutral solution is formed, (usually). The reaction of an acid with an alkali in this way is called a **neutralisation** reaction.

Fertilisers and fireworks

Potassium nitrate, KNO_3, is a salt. It provides the K, in NPK fertilisers. It also makes up 75% of gunpowder. Its oxygen allows the powder to burn without air.

Fertilisers also contain other salts – mainly ammonium nitrate and ammonium sulphate.

Salts make firework flames coloured – sodium salts give yellow, copper salts blue or green, calcium and lithium salts red flames.

QUESTIONS

4 What is meant by a decomposition reaction?
5 What is meant by a precipitate?
6 Give a name of a precipitate.
7 Give the names of **two** substances that would react in a neutralisation reaction.

LEAD ON THE ROAD

Lead chromate is used today to produce yellow paint for road markings.

Bringing it all together

Some more everyday examples.

Baking clay

When a clay object is moulded and then baked, a complicated chemical reaction occurs, and water is lost from the clay. Losing water is a dehydration reaction, and so the clay has been dehydrated in order to make it harder.

Being stung

If you are stung by a nettle, you may rub the sore area of skin with a dock leaf to ease the pain. A neutralisation reaction takes place. Acid in the nettle reacts with the alkali in the dock leaf.

Furry kettles

When some tap water is heated and boiled in a kettle, a chemical substance breaks down in the water to form calcium carbonate (chalk) – this is a decomposition reaction. The chalk deposits itself on the heater element of the kettle and makes it look as if it has a coating of white fur.

QUESTIONS

8 Give an example of a decomposition reaction.

9 When sugar ($C_{12}H_{22}O_{11}$) is heated, it can be decomposed to form carbon and water. Write a balanced equation to show this reaction.

10 What is the opposite of dehydration?

Neutralisation

You will find out:

● How to neutralise an acid and why neutralisation reactions are important
● What is meant by a 'salt'
● How to make soluble salts from acids and base
● What some important salts are used for

A dose of lime

Acid rain is a big problem. It can enter rivers and lakes, killing plant and animal life there. To allow life to return, the water in a lake needs to be about neutral (pH 7). The acidity of an affected lake can be neutralised by adding lime (calcium hydroxide). But adding too much would make the water **alkaline**. So scientists measure the lake's acidity and work out how much lime is needed.

FIGURE 1: Blowing powdered lime into a lake in Sweden. This one needed 8000 tonnes of lime.

Some everyday neutralisation reactions

Remember the pH scale.

| 1 | 2 | 3 | 4 | 5 | 6 | 7 | 8 | 9 | 10 | 11 | 12 | 13 | 14 |

↑
acidic **neutral** **alkaline**

Any reaction between an **acid** and an **alkali** is called **neutralisation**. It brings the pH closer to **neutral** (but not necessarily exactly pH 7). People use neutralisation in many ways; often without realising it.

■ Tim is a farmer. He spreads lime on his fields to make the soil less acidic.

■ Tim's wife bakes cakes for the farm shop. She uses baking powder containing tartaric acid and sodium hydrogen carbonate. When wet, these neutralise each other, releasing carbon dioxide bubbles. These make the cakes rise.

■ Your stomach produces hydrochloric acid to digest food. Eating too much too quickly produces extra acid. That gives you acid indigestion. To cure it you take an 'antacid' medicine. It neutralises the acid. Your stomach becomes less **acidic** and more comfortable.

■ Toothpaste contains chalk (calcium carbonate). When you brush your teeth, the chalk neutralises acids that cause tooth decay.

■ Tim's spanner is rusty. He treats it with rust remover containing phosphoric acid. The reaction between rust (iron oxide) and any acid is a neutralisation.

FIGURE 2: As the label says, 'Rust Eater removes rust chemically' – by reacting it with an acid.

Watch Out Neutralisation doesn't necessarily make a liquid exactly neutral. It just makes acids less acidic and alkalis less alkaline (closer to pH 7).

QUESTIONS

1 What is the approximate pH value of acid rain?
2 Which **two** types of chemical are needed for neutralisation?
3 Why do antacid tablets often contain calcium carbonate?

EXAM HINTS AND TIPS

Remember:
acid + base → salt + water
Name of salt = metal from the base plus chloride, nitrate, sulphate, etc.

...*acid* ...*acidic* ...*alkali* ...*alkaline*

Basic chemistry

Alkalis and bases both neutralise acids. What's the difference?

- A **base** is any compound that neutralises acids. There are four types:

  - metal oxides, for example, iron oxide, Fe_2O_3

  - metal hydroxides, for example, sodium hydroxide, NaOH

  - metal carbonates, for example, calcium carbonate, $CaCO_3$

  - ammonia, NH_3

- An alkali is a base that dissolves in water, e.g. sodium hydroxide or ammonia.

Alkalis form alkaline solutions. Other bases don't dissolve. They exist only as solids.

Making salts

Acids and bases neutralise each other. Neutralisation reactions always produce water, and a compound called a **salt**. It's worth remembering:

acid + base → salt + water

For example:

sulphuric acid + magnesium oxide → magnesium sulphate + water

$$H_2SO_4(aq) \quad + \quad MgO(s) \quad \rightarrow \quad MgSO_4(aq) \quad + H_2O(l)$$

The name of the salt depends on the acid and base. Can you see how to work them out?

TABLE 1: Acids and bases and the salts they form.

Acid	Base	Name of salt
hydrochloric acid	sodium hydroxide	sodium chloride
hydrochloric acid	calcium carbonate	calcium chloride
sulphuric acid	copper oxide	copper sulphate
sulphuric acid	iron carbonate	iron sulphate
nitric acid	ammonia	ammonium nitrate
phosphoric acid	iron oxide	iron phosphate

FIGURE 3: Iron tablets contain iron sulphate.

Dissolving metals

Acids also react with metals, forming salts and hydrogen, not water. For example:

sulphuric acid + magnesium → magnesium sulphate + hydrogen

$$H_2SO_4(aq) \quad + \quad Mg(s) \quad \rightarrow \quad MgSO_4(aq) \quad + \quad H_2(g)$$

Only metals above hydrogen in the reactivity series can do this.

QUESTIONS

4   Zinc oxide is insoluble. Is it an acid, an alkali, a base or a salt?

5   Which acid and base are used to make ammonium sulphate fertiliser?

6   Name the salt formed when **a)** nitric acid neutralises potassium hydroxide solution, **b)** aluminium metal reacts with hydrochloric acid.

Why do neutralisations produce water?

All acids are hydrogen compounds. This hydrogen combines with oxygen or hydroxide (OH) from a base, forming hydrogen oxide (water). The remainder of the acid and base form the salt.

Copper sulphate:

H_2 (from H_2SO_4) + O (from CuO) → H_2O leaving Cu + SO_4 → $CuSO_4$

Sodium chloride:

HCl + NaOH → NaCl + HOH (=H_2O)

Zinc nitrate:

$2HNO_3$ + ZnO → $Zn(NO_3)_2$ + H_2O

Extra fizz

If the base is a metal carbonate, carbon dioxide gas is also produced. Think of the metal carbonate, MCO_3, as its oxide, MO, with CO_2 added. The oxide reacts as above. The carbon dioxide comes off as bubbles.

Calcium chloride:

$2HCl$ + $CaCO_3$ → $CaCl_2$ + H_2O + CO_2

FIGURE 4: Limescale is calcium carbonate. It can be removed with an acid.

QUESTIONS

7   A rock fizzes when a geologist adds acid. What does this suggest?

8   Work out the balanced equation for neutralising nitric acid, HNO_3, with copper carbonate, $CuCO_3$.

Chemical cross-overs

You will find out:

● That insoluble salts can be made by precipitation

● What a precipitation reaction involves

● Some important uses of insoluble salts

It's a colourful world

Wouldn't life be dull without colour? Nature was always colourful, but man-made colours are fairly new. As young children, your grandparents had only black and white photographs, films and television. Their house was painted cream, green or brown; cars were black. Today, books and newspapers are almost the only black and white things in our everyday lives. We can make almost any object any colour we like. How? By using chemistry.

FIGURE 1: A grey fire engine looks less dramatic than a red one.

Painting with salts

Van Gogh was an artist. He used paints made by mixing oils with coloured powders called **pigments**. These pigments have fancy names, but often contain simple chemical compounds. Some are metal **salts**. For example:

- white lead is lead sulphate

- chrome yellow is lead chromate

- verdigris (a green pigment) is copper acetate

- Egyptian blue is copper silicate.

Unlike the **soluble** salts on the previous page, those used as pigments are **insoluble** salts. They are solids that do not dissolve in water. That makes them suitable for painting things outdoors, including lines on roads.

FIGURE 2: Van Gogh and the road-line painter used the same yellow pigment.

The acid test

Some plants like acidic soil, others prefer it alkaline. Jack the gardener tests the soil's pH. He uses a coloured indicator solution, just like you do in the lab. It's difficult to see the colour in muddy water. So he adds an insoluble salt, barium sulphate.

- The barium sulphate sinks, taking the mud with it.

- The water is left clear enough to see the indicator colour and read the pH.

FIGURE 3: Testing the soil's pH using coloured indicator solution.

■■ QUESTIONS ■■

1 Which insoluble salt did Van Gogh use to paint his 'Sunflowers'?
2 a Copper sulphate gives a blue solution. Why is it not used as a pigment?
   b Which insoluble salt is used as a blue pigment?
3 Why must the salt in a soil test kit be insoluble?

...insoluble   ...ion   ...neutralisation   ...pigment

Making insoluble salts

It's easy to make insoluble salts. You just mix solutions of two soluble salts. Van Gogh could have made his own pigments.

- Mixing solutions of lead nitrate and sodium sulphate gives lead sulphate.

- Copper sulphate and sodium acetate solutions give copper acetate.

The metal and non-metal parts of each salt 'cross over'. For example:

lead nitrate + sodium sulphate

lead sulphate + sodium nitrate

The pairs swap partners. The metal from one salt combines with the non-metal part from the other. The equation is:

$$Pb(NO_3)_2(aq) + Na_2SO_4(aq) \rightarrow PbSO_4(s) + 2NaNO_3(aq)$$

The insoluble salt is labelled '(s)' for solid. Any solid product formed by reacting two solutions is called a **precipitate**. The process is **precipitation**. The solid product sinks and falls to the bottom of the reaction mixture. (Rain, hail or snow falling from the sky are also called 'precipitation'.)

Purifying the precipitate

To get a pure, dry insoluble salt needs a few more steps.

- Filter off the precipitate (for example, lead sulphate).

- Rinse the precipitate with distilled water to wash off the other product (for example, sodium nitrate) which is a soluble salt.

- Dry the precipitate in a warm oven.

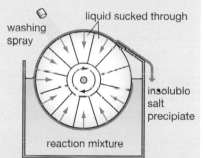

FIGURE 4: Filtering a precipitate in industry. Liquid is sucked through a rotating cloth-covered drum. The insoluble salt is washed by spray, sucked dry and scraped off.

Other uses of insoluble salts

Photographic film and printing paper are coated with insoluble silver bromide, which changes to silver and turns black when exposed to light. Even digital photos are better printed onto photographic paper.

- Mixing silver nitrate, $AgNO_3$, and ammonium bromide, NH_4Br, solutions precipitates silver bromide, $AgBr$.

Antacid medicines and toothpaste contain calcium carbonate. Natural chalk and limestone are too impure.

- Mixing calcium chloride, $CaCl_2$, and sodium carbonate, Na_2CO_3, solutions gives pure calcium carbonate, $CaCO_3$, called 'precipitated chalk'.

QUESTIONS

4 **a** Name **two** soluble salts Van Gogh could have used to make lead chromate.
b Write a word equation for this reaction.

5 Why does rinsing wash away the second product, but not the precipitate?

6 Write a balanced equation for the reaction that gives silver bromide.

How precipitation works

A mixture of two salt solutions contains particles (called **ions**) of two metals and two non-metal groups. If any pair of these ions forms an insoluble salt, they can't stay dissolved. So they form a precipitate.

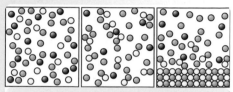

FIGURE 5: Mixture of ions in solution; insoluble salt ions join up; precipitate sinks.

Can neutralisation make insoluble salts?

We make insoluble salts by mixing solutions. So **neutralisation** can work only if the base is soluble (that is, an alkali).

Barium sulphate can be made with barium hydroxide solution and sulphuric acid.

$$Ba(OH)_2(aq) + H_2SO_4(aq) \rightarrow BaSO_4(s) + 2H_2O(l)$$

However, most bases are insoluble solids, so the method can't work.

The base will react with an acid, but if the salt is insoluble it can't dissolve away. The base becomes coated with insoluble salt. The acid can't reach the base any more, so the reaction stops.

 Mixing soluble salts produces a precipitate only if one pair of the two metals and two non-metals is insoluble.

QUESTIONS

7 Name **three** bases that are soluble, and **three** that aren't.

8 Why can barium sulphate be made by neutralisation, but not lead sulphate?

Pass the oxygen

You will find out:

- The importance of oxidation and reduction reactions
- The connection between the reactivity series and redox reactions
- About everyday reactions involving oxidation and reduction

The fastest man on two wheels

It doesn't look much like a motorbike, but it is, because it has two wheels and the rider steers it. British engineer Richard 'Rocketman' Brown rode it at 365 mph (587 km/h). Yes, it's rocket-powered. The rocket motor uses solid fuel. The oxygen that the fuel needs to burn is produced by decomposing hydrogen peroxide, H_2O_2. Richard designed his own rocket, so he needed to understand the chemistry!

FIGURE 1: Is it a missile? Is it a plane? No, it's Superbike – Richard Brown's rocket-powered motorcycle.

A burning need

Fuels can't burn without **oxygen**. They usually get it from the air, but air is only 21% oxygen. A rocket motor can't get all the oxygen it needs from the air. The oxygen has to come from another chemical.

- Richard's rocket bike gets oxygen from hydrogen peroxide, H_2O_2. That's like water, H_2O, with an extra oxygen atom.

- Fireworks get it from potassium nitrate, KNO_3, in the gunpowder.

- Space rockets use liquid oxygen. It's the best, because it's 100% oxygen. The problem is that it must be stored at about -200 °C.

All these substances, and many others, have 'spare' oxygen. They give some to the fuel, so it can burn.

Passing oxygen

Fuels burn by reacting with oxygen.

- The reaction products contain more oxygen than the original fuel. The process of adding oxygen to a chemical is called **oxidation**.

- The fuels in gunpowder are carbon, C, and sulphur, S. They are **oxidised** to carbon dioxide, CO_2, and sulphur dioxide, SO_2.

- The other chemical ends up with less oxygen. It has passed its 'spare' oxygen to the fuel. Removing oxygen from a chemical is called **reduction**. It reduces the amount of oxygen in the substance.

FIGURE 2: Burning gunpowder – oxidation and reduction in action.

EXAM HINTS AND TIPS

Remember!
Reduction reduces the amount of oxygen in a compound.
Oxidation often produces an oxide.

WOW FACTOR!

During a Space Shuttle launch, 1200 kg of liquid oxygen oxidises 200 kg of liquid hydrogen every second.

▫ QUESTIONS ▫

1 Why must liquid oxygen be stored at about -200 °C?
2 Which chemical is reduced (that is, loses oxygen) when gunpowder burns?
3 **a** What does hydrogen peroxide become when it passes oxygen to a fuel?
  b Is hydrogen peroxide oxidised or reduced in this process?

...oxidation ...oxidised ...oxygen ...reactivity

Give and take

Notice that fuels gain oxygen, and the other chemicals lose oxygen. So, both oxidation and reduction take place at the same time. One can't happen without the other.

- The whole process is called a **redox** reaction.
- One reactant gives away oxygen, another takes it in.

Oxidation all around

Many substances react with oxygen in the air around us.

- Fuels burn, providing heat, electricity and transport.
- Unfortunately, things that aren't fuels can also burn, for example, buildings and forests.

Oxidation doesn't only mean combustion. Chemicals can gain oxygen without burning, for example:

- iron and steel rust, by gaining oxygen from air and water
- gloss paint 'dries' by gaining oxygen, not by losing water.

FIGURE 3: Rusty Angel. The colour and texture are produced by natural oxidation.

Oxidation also occurs inside you! The oxygen you breathe in oxidises glucose in your body cells to give you energy.

glucose + oxygen → carbon dioxide + hydrogen oxide (water)

In all these redox reactions, oxygen in the air is **reduced**. The air ends up with less oxygen.

Redox and reactivity

The '**reactivity**' of a metal means how easily it reacts with non-metals, especially oxygen. That is, how easily it is oxidised.

- Gold doesn't react with oxygen, water, or even acids.
- Copper hardly reacts with air. If heated, it forms black copper oxide, CuO, but doesn't burn.
- Iron turns to rust, iron(III) oxide, Fe_2O_3. It burns only if powdered (iron filings).
- Magnesium burns easily, forming magnesium oxide, MgO. It reacts slowly with water.
- Sodium reacts violently with water. Water oxidises sodium easily, while the sodium reduces water to hydrogen.

FIGURE 4: Extremes of reactivity. These gold and silver Roman coins lasted two thousand years buried in wet earth. Sodium lasts only a few seconds in water.

$$2Na(s) + 2H_2O(l) \rightarrow 2NaOH(aq) + H_2(g)$$

sodium + water → sodium hydroxide + hydrogen

QUESTIONS

4 What does 'redox' stand for?

5 Is iron oxidised or reduced when it rusts? Say how you decided.

6 Name the process in living organisms that oxidises glucose

7 Which metal in the reactivity series is oxidised more easily than sodium?

Other uses and problems

The oxygen in redox reactions may come from oxygen gas or a compound.

- Bleach contains sodium chlorate(I), $NaOCl$. It turns dyes colourless by oxidising them (adding oxygen to dye molecules). The bleach loses oxygen, and is reduced to sodium chloride, $NaCl$.
- Hydrogen peroxide, H_2O_2, bleaches hair the same way. Oxidised hair turns 'peroxide blonde'. The peroxide is reduced to water, H_2O.
- Oxygen-rich compounds are used to oxidise other substances when making chemicals. They include nitric acid, HNO_3, potassium manganate(VII), $KMnO_4$, and potassium dichromate, $K_2Cr_2O_7$.
- Metals corrode by gaining oxygen from water as well as air. The water is reduced to hydrogen (see sodium in previous column).
- Wine exposed to air turns to vinegar because ethanol (alcohol), CH_3CH_2OH, is oxidised to ethanoic acid, CH_3COOH.

FIGURE 5: 'Highlighting' the effects of oxidation.

QUESTIONS

8 How do the formulae show that:

  a $NaOCl \rightarrow NaCl$ is reduction?

  b $CH_3CH_2OH \rightarrow CH_3COOH$ is oxidation?

9 Suggest why hydrogen peroxide, not normal bleach, is used on hair.

Making metals

You will find out:

- What ores are and how we extract metals from them
- The importance of carbon in extracting metals
- That the way we extract a metal depends on its reactivity

The fiery furnace

In the orange glow stands a hooded, silvery figure wearing dark glasses. Beside him flows a river of white-hot metal. Into the river he dips a 'cup' on a long pole. No, it's not science fiction. It's everyday science fact. Meet Bob. He takes samples of molten iron as it pours from a blast furnace at about 1500 °C. He's covered from head to toe in protective clothing, coated with aluminium to reflect the heat.

FIGURE 1: Hot as Hell? Taking a sample of molten iron tapped from a blast furnace.

Why was the Bronze Age before the Iron Age?

5000 years ago, people used gold and silver, and knew how to make bronze. They didn't discover how to make iron until 2000 years later. Why? Remember the **reactivity** series.

- Gold and silver are unreactive. They occur 'native', that is, as pure **metals** in rocks, so were discovered first.

- Reactive metals occur as **ores** – rocks and minerals from which we **extract** metals using chemical reactions.

- Bronze is a mixture of copper and tin. These are not very reactive. Turning their ores into metals using fire and charcoal is easy.

- Iron is more reactive. It needs much higher temperatures to turn iron ore into iron.

- Aluminium is more reactive still. There's more aluminium than iron in the Earth, but it's more difficult and expensive to extract it.

FIGURE 2: Mining a mountain of iron ore in Brazil. The red earth is iron oxide, similar to rust.

21st-Century Iron Age

History books say the Iron Age ended 2500 years ago. Really, we're still in it. People like Bob make more iron than all other metals put together – over 500 million tonnes per year worldwide. They extract it by heating iron ore with coke in blast furnaces about 30 m tall. Most iron ends up as steel.

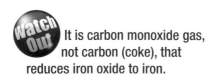

It is carbon monoxide gas, not carbon (coke), that reduces iron oxide to iron.

WOW FACTOR!

Medieval Britain was covered by forest. Much of it was cut down for ship-building and to make charcoal for iron-making.

QUESTIONS

1 Why did the Bronze Age come before the Iron Age?
2 Name **two** metals we can extract from rocks without using any chemical reactions.
3 Which of the six metals above is the most reactive?
4 What is the main use for iron?

...extract ...metal ...ore ...oxidation

Reactivity and reduction

The more reactive a metal, the more strongly it combines with non-metals. So it's more difficult to remove oxygen from the ore in order to extract the metal. That's why aluminium is more difficult to make than iron, but bronze is easier.

Many ores are metal oxides. To extract the metal we must remove the oxygen. This is **reduction**. The process is called **smelting**.

- We reduce metal ores by heating them with carbon. Originally, this was in the form of charcoal. Now we use coke.

- Carbon can only extract metals below aluminium in the reactivity series. Aluminium holds on to oxygen tightly, so the carbon can't take it away.

Inside the fiery furnace

Blast furnaces extract iron from iron oxide. Follow the diagram. A conveyor loads measured amounts of iron ore, coke and limestone into the top. Hot air is blown in near the base. Inside, a series of reactions takes place:

- Coke burns in the air blast, raising the temperature to over 1700 °C.

    carbon + oxygen → carbon monoxide + heat

- Carbon monoxide reduces the iron oxide, and is oxidised to carbon dioxide. (Remember: **oxidation** and reduction always happen together.)

    iron oxide + carbon monoxide → iron + carbon dioxide

- Heat decomposes the limestone (see 'Thermal Decomposition' on page 149).

    calcium carbonate → calcium oxide + carbon dioxide

- Calcium oxide reacts with impurities in the ore, forming liquid slag.

- Molten iron trickles down to the bottom. Later, it is run off ('tapped'), and taken to nearby steel furnaces.

- Liquid slag floats on the molten iron and is tapped off separately.

We extract lead from lead oxide in a similar way.

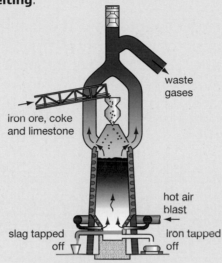

FIGURE 3: Inside a blast furnace. The temperature is hottest near the base, where coke is burning.

FIGURE 4: A large blast furnace. Hot air is blown in through the large pipe in front. Waste gases exit through the sloping 'downcomer' pipe (top centre).

QUESTIONS

5 Why is it called a blast furnace?

6 The furnace is used to remove oxygen from the ore. So why do we add air?

7 What type of reaction converts a metal oxide into the metal?

8 Name a metal (besides iron, copper and lead) that we can extract with carbon.

Smelting reactions

Smelting involves several types of reaction. Some are exothermic, others endothermic.

Oxidation–reduction

- Coke burns (exothermic):

    $$2C(s) + O_2(g) \rightarrow 2CO\ (g)$$

- Carbon monoxide is oxidised and iron(III) oxide is reduced (endothermic):

    $$Fe_2O_3(s) + 3CO(g) \rightarrow 2Fe(s) + 3CO_2(g)$$

Thermal decomposition

- Above 900 °C limestone decomposes (endothermic):

    $$CaCO_3(s) \rightarrow CaO(s) + CO_2(g)$$

Acid–base

- Calcium oxide neutralises silica and other impurities in the ore:

    $$CaO(s) + SiO_2(s) \rightarrow CaSiO_3(l) \text{ [slag]}$$

Reactive metals

Aluminium and the more reactive metals cannot be extracted by smelting. We reduce aluminium oxide, from an ore called bauxite, using electricity. The process is called electrolysis. Metals in groups 1 and 2 of the periodic table, for example sodium and magnesium, are even more reactive. We extract these by electrolysis too.

increasing reactivity ↑	metal	method of extraction
	potassium	electrolysis
	sodium	
	calcium	
	magnesium	
	aluminium	
	zinc	reduction with carbon (smelting)
	iron	
	tin	
	lead	
	copper *	
	silver	mechanical separation
	gold	

* copper ores are mainly sulphides. The smelting process uses no carbon

TABLE 1: The method for extracting a metal depends on its reactivity.

QUESTIONS

9 What is reduced when carbon is oxidised by burning?

10 a Which smelting reactions take in heat?

   b Why doesn't the furnace cool down?

11 Is silica acidic, basic or neutral? How did you decide?

Chemical breakdowns

You will find out:
- How compounds break down into simpler chemicals
- The link between cement, kettles and caves
- The importance of 'cracking' oil

A musical joke

A few months after he died, the composer Beethoven was found sitting on top of his grave, rubbing out notes from sheets of music. 'What are you doing?' 'I'm decomposing!' A dead body decomposes and rots away. A skeleton is left, but where do the flesh and organs go to? And what's it got to do with caves, kettles, cement and oil?

Where did it go?

Decomposition means breaking materials down into simpler substances. Jack the gardener throws garden waste on his compost heap. Complex carbon compounds in dead plants slowly decompose into simple carbon dioxide and water molecules. So most of the dead material 'disappears' into the air. However, without oxygen the story is very different.

Once upon a time ...

This is no fairy story. What happened millions of years ago helps us today. Vast numbers of small sea creatures died and sank to the sea bed.

- Without oxygen, carbon dioxide couldn't form. Instead, the carbon compounds slowly decomposed into a mixture of **hydrocarbons**. They formed **petroleum** (crude oil).

- Under different conditions, skeletons and shells of dead sea creatures formed **limestone** (calcium carbonate).

Notice: hydro<u>carbon</u>s and calcium <u>carbon</u>ate. All living things contain carbon, so dead things do too.

Further breakdown

Petroleum and limestone decompose further when heated strongly. This is called **thermal decomposition**. Both give important everyday products.

- Jack's lawnmower runs on petrol made by decomposing hydrocarbons from petroleum.

- He uses lime to neutralise acid soil, and cement to build a garden wall. Both are made by decomposing limestone.

- Limestone decomposes in blast furnaces when making iron.

FIGURE 1: A dead leaf decomposes, leaving a 'skeleton' – but not made of bone.

FIGURE 2: Even walls may have 'skeletons'! Limestone was decomposed to make both the concrete and the steel reinforcement.

EXAM HINTS AND TIPS

Remember the difference between:
limestone (calcium carbonate), $CaCO_3$
quicklime (calcium oxide), CaO
slaked lime (calcium hydroxide), $Ca(OH)_2$

WOW FACTOR!

More than 10 million tonnes of cement are made in Britain every year, using about 15 million tonnes of limestone.

■ QUESTIONS ■

1. Why does a dead body 'disappear', leaving only the skeleton?
2. Which type of chemical compounds does petroleum contain?
3. Name the process that breaks down limestone into simpler chemicals.

...catalyst ...cracking ...decomposition ...dehydration ...endothermic

Thermal decomposition

Most metal carbonates and hydroxides decompose when heated. Think of them as oxides combined with carbon dioxide or water: for example, $CuCO_3$ as $CuOCO_2$; and $Cu(OH)_2$ as $CuOH_2O$. Heating splits them apart.

$$CuCO_3(s) \rightarrow CuO(s) + CO_2(g)$$

copper carbonate → copper oxide + carbon dioxide

Losing water is called **dehydration**.

$$Cu(OH)_2(s) \rightarrow CuO(s) + H_2O(g)$$

copper hydroxide → copper oxide + water

Thermal decomposition of calcium carbonate (limestone) is important.

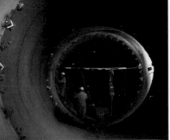

FIGURE 3: Inside a rotary kiln. When in use, limestone and clay get heated as they travel 150 m along this tube while it slowly rotates.

- Heating limestone in lime kilns produces calcium oxide (quicklime) and carbon dioxide.

- Decomposing limestone, while reacting it with clay, makes cement.

- Limestone decomposes in blast furnaces. Calcium oxide and carbon dioxide are both essential in the iron-making process.

Thermal decomposition reactions need heating because they are **endothermic**.

Most quicklime is hydrated to slaked lime (calcium hydroxide) for treating acid soils, purifying sugar and paper-making. **Hydration** is the reverse of dehydration.

$$CaO(s) + H_2O(l) \rightarrow Ca(OH)_2(s)$$

calcium oxide + water → calcium hydroxide

Odd 1 out

Group 1 metals behave differently. Heat doesn't decompose sodium carbonate or sodium hydroxide. Instead, sodium carbonate is made by thermal decomposition.

$$2NaHCO_3(s) \rightarrow Na_2CO_3(s) + CO_2(g) + H_2O(g)$$

sodium hydrogen carbonate → sodium carbonate + carbon dioxide + water

- Sodium carbonate is mainly used in glass making.

- Self-raising flour contains sodium hydrogen carbonate, which decomposes during baking. The bubbles of carbon dioxide and steam make the cake rise.

Kettles and caves

Water in limestone areas contains dissolved calcium hydrogen carbonate. Boiling decomposes it, leaving solid calcium carbonate 'scale' in kettles and boilers.

$$Ca(HCO_3)_2(aq) \rightarrow CaCO_3(s) + CO_2(g) + H_2O(g)$$

calcium hydrogen carbonate → calcium carbonate + carbon dioxide + water

The same reaction very slowly forms stalactites and stalagmites in caves.

QUESTIONS

4 Write the chemical equation for the thermal decomposition of limestone.

5 What is made in the rotary kiln in the figure 3?

6 Why do stalactites and stalagmites take many years to grow?

It's a cracking process, Gromit!

The petroleum product in highest demand is petrol itself (also known as gasoline). Unfortunately, most of the hydrocarbons in crude oil have large molecules that burn too slowly to use in petrol. So, oil refineries break down these large molecules into smaller ones, containing about eight carbon atoms, like octane, C_8H_{18}.

- This process is called '**cracking**'. It's done by heating, so it's another example of thermal decomposition.

- Cracking occurs at lower temperatures if a **catalyst** is used. This is 'cat cracking'.

- Cracking gives a mixture of two types of hydrocarbon:

  alkanes needed for petrol

  alkenes (for example, ethene, C_2H_4) used to make plastics.

Cracking is therefore an important process. You will learn more about it, and both types of hydrocarbon, later in your course.

FIGURE 4: Oil is cracked by heating with a catalyst in these columns at an oil refinery.

QUESTIONS

7 Why do the hydrocarbons in petrol need to burn quickly?

8 Suggest why the process is called cracking.

Cookery is chemistry

You will find out:

● That cooking causes chemical reactions in food which change its appearance, texture and taste

● That food additives have advantages and disadvantages

Food junkie

You're watching a television cookery programme. The chef produces a hypodermic syringe and injects a chip! It's an unusual piece of kitchen equipment. But how else can he get tomato sauce <u>in</u> his chips rather than on them? Don't try it with raw potato, though. It's the cooking that makes it possible. Frying leaves the potato soft in the middle, but harder on the outside, so the sauce doesn't leak out.

FIGURE 1: The chips' crispy golden surface forms by reacting with hot oil.

Cookery – art and science

Humans have cooked food ever since we discovered fire in prehistoric times. Cookery was an art. New ideas developed by trial and error – literally 'suck it and see'.

Most recipes still develop this way, but we now apply scientific principles. It's not called 'Domestic Science' or 'Food Technology' for nothing.

■ Knowing about types of foods (for example, sugars and fats) helps us stay healthy. We know which foods are good for us, and which are bad.

■ Cooking causes chemical reactions. The ingredients react, forming new substances. These look, feel and taste different. For example:

    a lump of dough becomes a loaf of bread

    chewy, pink meat becomes golden brown and tender

    transparent, runny egg turns white and solid.

Reaction rates increase with temperature. Water boils at a higher temperature in a pressure cooker, so foods cook faster. Frying is hotter and faster still.

FIGURE 2: Bread dough rises but won't turn brown until heated in an oven.

Cooking processes also make a big difference. Boiled, baked and fried potatoes are similar on the inside, but not on the outside. Foods react differently with hot water, air and fat.

Food additives colour, sweeten and preserve foods. They can also cause problems.

QUESTIONS

1   Why do cooked foods taste different from raw foods?
2   What makes chips golden and crispy on the surface?
3   Why does food cook faster in a pressure cooker?

EXAM HINTS AND TIPS

Food cooks faster at higher temperatures because reaction rates increase. Different reactions occur, so the food looks and tastes different.

...carbohydrate ...dehydration ...food additive

Edible foams

Bread and cakes are foams – bubbles of carbon dioxide trapped in a solid. In bread, they're produced by fermenting yeast. In cakes, baking powder produces the gas by two reactions:

- **neutralisation** of tartaric acid and sodium hydrogen carbonate
- **thermal decomposition** of sodium hydrogen carbonate.

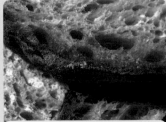

FIGURE 3: Bubbles in bread. During baking, carbon dioxide bubbles expand while the dough solidifies. Dehydration turns the crust brown.

Why is toast brown?

When you heat bread, water evaporates. But toast isn't just dried bread. It also turns brown. It's been chemically changed.

- Bread is mainly starch, a **carbohydrate** – a compound of carbon, hydrogen and oxygen, with twice as many hydrogen atoms as oxygen.
- Starch molecules contain lots of H atoms and OH groups. Heating drives off some H and OH to form water. This is another thermal decomposition.
- It's also a **dehydration** reaction, because the elements of water are lost. This produces complex brown compounds. The more dehydration, the darker brown it turns.
- Driving off all the hydrogen and oxygen leaves only black carbon – burnt toast!

Similar dehydration reactions decompose other foods. So meat also goes brown when cooked at high temperatures.

I can't believe it's not natural

Is butter a natural product? Not really. Cows produce milk, but machines turn milk into butter. Similarly, plants produce olive oil and sunflower oil. Machines turn these into margarine.

We think of butter as 'natural', but margarine as 'artificial' because:

- we make butter by just separating out the fat from milk
- margarine needs chemical reactions. Liquid vegetable oils react with hydrogen to form solid fats.

The solid fats in butter and margarine are the same types of chemical, whether natural or artificial. They react in the same way, so margarine can be used instead of butter in most cookery recipes.

FIGURE 4: Mmm! Dehydrated starch and hydrogenated vegetable oils. Delicious!

QUESTIONS

4 **a** What causes the neutralisation reaction of baking powder to start?
   b What causes the thermal decomposition to start?
5 Is each of these a carbohydrate?
   a) glucose, $C_6H_{12}O_6$ **b)** alcohol, C_2H_5OH
6 How is sunflower oil converted into margarine?

Cooking by numbers

Processed foods contain additives – chemicals used as:

- sweeteners – replacing sugar in low-calorie foods
- preservatives – increasing storage life
- stabilisers – stopping mixtures separating
- colourings, flavourings, and many others.

Additives approved for use in Europe are given E-numbers. These must be shown on the food's ingredients list.

Many additives are 'nature-identical' – man-made, but chemically identical to natural substances. For example:

- E170 – calcium carbonate, added to flour
- E252 – potassium nitrate, preservative in bacon and ham
- E300 – vitamin C, added to many foods.

Health issues   (H)

- Artificial additives in 'junk foods' are linked to hyperactivity.
- Too much salt is linked to heart disease.
- Over-cooked chips, crisps and barbecued food contain 'unsafe' levels of acrylamide.

However, proving that these substances actually cause health problems is difficult, since most people seem unaffected by them.

QUESTIONS

7 Why are additives given E-numbers?
8 Suggest why colourings are often added to cooked foods.
9 Caramel is a colouring and flavouring made by heating sugar. Why is it brown?

Catch that gas!

You will find out:

- How to collect samples of gases by various methods
- How to identify some common gases
- The importance of hazard labels on chemical bottles

First catch your pig

They say that you can use every part of a pig except its squeal. Meat, lard, pigskin, sausage skins ... but few people would think of using pigs as chemical apparatus. However, guess how chemists collected and stored gases before they had cheap glass tubes and flasks. That's right, in bits of pig! A pig's bladder is like a balloon. You can fill it and then squeeze the gas out again when needed.

FIGURE 1: Don't try this at home! The methods shown on this page are much easier.

Bubble, bubble, not much trouble

A simple way to collect a gas is to bubble it into a test tube of water in a trough. Bubbles rise to the surface, so this method is called collecting **over water**.

- Stopper a tube full of water. Open it upside down under water.

- Let the first few bubbles escape from the delivery tube. Then put the test tube over the end.

- Stopper the tube of gas before removing from the water.

Note: This method can't be used if the gas dissolves in water, like ammonia, or if the gas needs to be dry.

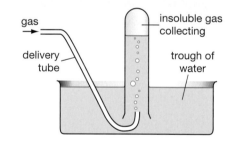

FIGURE 2: The delivery tube is under water, but the gas collects over water.

Using density

To keep a gas dry, deliver it straight into a dry test tube.

- If the gas is denser ('heavier') than air, collect it by **downward delivery**. Push the delivery tube to the bottom of the test tube. The gas sinks, pushing the air out of the top.

- If it's less dense ('lighter than air') use **upward delivery** into an upside-down test tube. The gas rises, pushing the air out of the bottom.

In all three methods, to collect more gas use a gas jar instead of a test tube.

QUESTIONS

1 When collecting over water, why should you let the first few bubbles escape?

2 Where should the end of the delivery tube be for upward delivery? Why?

3 Why can you collect hydrogen over water, or by upward delivery?

4 Is fluorine less dense or more dense than air? (Hint: look at Figure 3.)

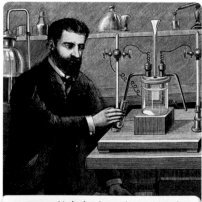

FIGURE 3: Nobel prize-winner Henri Moissan collecting fluorine by downward delivery.

Which method?

Kris is a laboratory technician. He prepares gases for science lessons. He decides how to collect a gas by asking himself these questions.

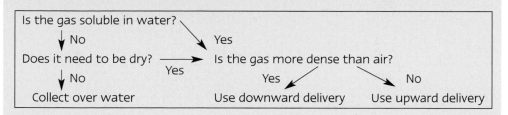

FIGURE 4: What do the hazard labels tell you about phosphorus?

What's that gas?

Most gases are colourless, but simple tests will tell Kris which is which.

- Ammonia smells like nappies (urine). It turns damp universal indicator paper blue.

- Carbon dioxide turns limewater milky when bubbled through it.

- Chlorine smells of swimming baths or bleach. It turns damp universal indicator red, then colourless.

- Hydrogen burns with a 'pop' when ignited.

- Oxygen makes a glowing splint catch fire again (reignite).

Some laboratories use gases regularly. They are stored in gas cylinders. A cylinder's colour shows which gas is inside, for example:

black = carbon dioxide; red = hydrogen; yellow = chlorine.

Beware!

Gases can be more dangerous than solids or liquids because they escape and spread more easily. Gas cylinders and chemical bottles carry **hazard labels** to show the type of hazard. For example:

- hydrogen and ethanol are **flammable**

- chlorine and lead nitrate are **toxic** (poisonous)

- ammonia and sulphuric acid are **corrosive**

- **harmful** chemicals (for example, copper sulphate) are less dangerous than toxic ones, but could make you sick if swallowed

- **irritant** substances (for example, calcium chloride) aren't corrosive, but may redden or blister your skin.

Hazard labels show why the substance may be dangerous if not handled correctly. Kris looks at the labels to decide what precautions he needs to take.

Bladders updated

The advantage of pig's bladders is that they are flexible. They expand as more gas goes in, and you can squeeze gas out again. The modern equivalent is a gas syringe.

- Start with the syringe empty. Unlike upward or downward delivery there's no air to displace.

- Pass gas into the nozzle. The piston moves along the scale, showing the volume collected.

- Seal the nozzle with a rubber cap.

- Push the piston to remove gas when required.

Gas syringes are very convenient. They can be used whatever the solubility or density of the gas. Unfortunately, they're fragile and cost over £20 each, because they're precision-made. The gap between the piston and barrel must be gas-tight, but allow free movement.

FIGURE 5: Gas syringes are precision made.

QUESTIONS

5 Ammonia gas is very soluble in water and less dense than air. How should Kris collect ammonia?

6 Describe how to show that a test tube of gas is oxygen.

7 What does 'corrosive' mean? How does the hazard symbol show this?

QUESTIONS

8 Why must you clamp a gas syringe only gently?

9 Why is it a good idea to tie the piston onto the barrel with string?

Unit summary

Concept map

Atoms are made up of even smaller particles. Negative electrons orbit a positive nucleus, containing protons and neutrons. The number of protons equals the number of electrons.

The Periodic Table lists elements in order of atomic number. Metals are on the left; non-metals on the right. The table is divided into rows (periods) and columns (groups).

Each element has a symbol. Elements combine to form compounds. Each compound has a formula.

Patterns in properties

Alkali metals (Group 1) include sodium and potassium. They react violently with water and non-metal elements. Reactivity <u>increases</u> down the group.

Halogens (Group 7) include chlorine, bromine and iodine. Boiling point increases, colour darkens and reactivity <u>decreases</u> down the group.

Transition metals include iron, copper, silver and gold. Iron rusts, but gold is totally unaffected by air or water.

Noble gases (Group 0) include helium and neon. They are useful because they are almost totally unreactive.

Chemical equations show which substances react and what they form.

Some metals give coloured flames. Iron and copper compounds form coloured precipitates with sodium hydroxide. Chlorine displaces bromine and iodine from their solutions.

Everything is made up of chemicals – some natural, mostly man-made. We change existing materials into those that we want by using chemical reactions.

Making changes

Reactions can be exothermic (give out heat) or endothermic (take heat in). Temperature change is measured with a thermometer, or by data-logging.

We collect a gas:
- over water – if it is insoluble
- by downward delivery – if it is denser than air
- by upward delivery – if it is less dense.

Balanced equations show the same number of atoms of each element in the products as in the reactants.

Thermal decomposition of carbonates and hydrogen carbonates releases carbon dioxide.

In redox reactions chemicals swap oxygen. Gaining oxygen is oxidation. Losing it is reduction. We extract metals from ores by reduction. Carbon (coke) removes oxygen from the metal oxide.

Metal oxides, hydroxides and carbonates are bases. Acids and bases neutralise each other, forming soluble salts. Acids also form soluble salts by reacting with metals.

Unit quiz

1. In the Periodic Table, what do we call **a)** a horizontal row and **b)** a vertical column?

2. In which group of the Periodic Table are the following families of elements found:
   a) alkali metals **b)** halogens **c)** noble gases?

3. Describe the appearance, at room temperature, of:
   a) chlorine **b)** bromine **c)** iodine.

4. What is the chemical symbol for:
   a) sulphur **b)** sodium **c)** iron?

5. What is the chemical formula for:
   a) water
   b) calcium carbonate
   c) sulphuric acid?

6. Write both a word and balanced symbol equation for the reaction when magnesium burns in air.

7. The number of protons in the nucleus of an atom is called which of the following?

   atomic number   **atomic mass**
   atomic structure

8. Which metal's salts give a blue-green flame test and blue precipitate with sodium hydroxide?

   calcium   **copper**   **potassium**

9. Suggest **one** example of **a)** a very fast reaction and **b)** a very slow reaction.

10. Hydrogen chloride gas is very soluble in water and denser than air. How should you collect a sample?

11. When an acid is added to an alkali, the mixture gets hot. Which **two** words describe this reaction?

    exothermic   endothermic
    decomposition   neutralisation
    precipitation

12. What is the meaning of the term 'oxidation'?

13. Is the mass of a rusty nail higher or lower than the original nail? Explain your answer.

14. Which element is heated with iron oxide to produce iron metal?

15. Which soluble salt is formed when copper oxide reacts with dilute sulphuric acid?

16. What type of reaction is used to prepare insoluble salts?

17. Which **two** compounds are produced by the thermal decomposition of limestone (calcium carbonate)?

18. What type of reaction gives roasted, toasted and fried foods their golden brown colour?

19. Citric acid is a nature identical food additive. What does 'nature identical' mean?

20. What produces the bubbles in bread and cakes?

Literacy activity

Dmitri Mendeleev was a Russian chemistry professor, best known for his Periodic Table. In 1869, he arranged the 63 known elements in rows and columns, in order of atomic mass. He studied the reactions of each element, and put those with similar reactions next to each other, leaving gaps where no known element fitted the pattern. Mendeleev predicted that chemists would discover new elements to fit these gaps. He was even able to predict their properties. Three were discovered within 20 years, and his predictions proved to be accurate. His table did not include the noble gases. None were known at that time, so there were no obvious gaps in his pattern of reactions.

QUESTIONS

1. Explain why the noble gases were unknown in Mendeleev's time.
2. Explain how Mendeleev was able to predict the properties of yet-to-be-discovered elements.
3. Several scientists had tried to work out patterns of elements before Mendeleev. Suggest why others were not convinced that the patterns were correct.

Exam practice

1 Which of these statements about these non-metals elements is correct?
- **A** Iodine is a brown liquid found in Group 7 of the periodic table.
- **B** Neon is an unreactive solid found in group 0 of the periodic table.
- **C** Chlorine is a pale green gas found in Group 7 of the periodic table.
- **D** Argon is a useful gas and reacts with oxygen to make argon oxide. [1]

2 Choose the **incorrect** answer. Copper is ...
- **A** A useful metal as it is so reactive
- **B** A good conductor of electricity and used for electrical wiring.
- **C** A good conductor of heat and used in saucepan bases.
- **D** Easy to bend and does not corrode easily. [1]

3 A salt solution is coloured green. Some sodium hydroxide solution is added to the solution and a green precipitate forms. What metal is present in the solution?
- **A** Copper   **B** Iron
- **C** Sodium   **D** Zinc [1]

4 Which of the following is a non-metal?
- **A** Ca   **B** Zn   **C** S   **D** Al [1]

5 What is the correct formula for sodium hydroxide?
- **A** NAOH   **B** $Na(OH)_2$ **C** Na_2OH **D** NaOH [1]

6 Elements with similar properties appear in the same ...
- **A** Group   **B** Horizontal row
- **C** Table   **D** Period [1]

7 Which of these statements about atoms is correct?
- **A** Atoms are neutral because they contain the same number of neutrons as protons.
- **B** Atoms contain the same number of protons, neutrons and electrons.
- **C** Atoms have a positive charge because the protons are positively charged.
- **D** Protons and neutrons are found in the nucleus of an atom while negative electrons surround it. [1]

Select the correct answers for questions 8 and 9.

8 The elements of Group 1 ...
- **A** are all reactive non-metals.
- **B** get more reactive as the atomic number increases.
- **C** all react with water making oxygen gas.
- **D** get less reactive as the atomic number increases. [1]

9 Iodine ...
- **A** is less reactive than fluorine.
- **B** has a lower boiling point than bromine.
- **C** is more reactive than chlorine.
- **D** is more reactive than bromine. [1]

10 Which equation is correctly balanced?
- **A** $NaOH + HCl \longrightarrow NaOH + 2H_2O$
- **B** $Ca(OH)_2 + 2H_2SO_4 \longrightarrow CaSO_4 + H_2O$
- **C** $C_2H_6O + 3O_2 \longrightarrow 2CO_2 + 3H_2O$
- **D** $C_3H_8 + 10 O_2 \longrightarrow 3CO_2 + 4H_2O$ [1]

11 The correct word equation is....
- **A** copper oxide + hydrochloric acid $\longrightarrow$ copper sulphate + hydrogen
- **B** sodium hydroxide + hydrochloric acid $\longrightarrow$ sodium hydrochloride + water
- **C** sodium hydroxide + sulphuric acid $\longrightarrow$ sodium sulphate + water
- **D** calcium carbonate + sulphuric acid $\longrightarrow$ calcium sulphate + water [1]

12 Which statement about the metals and their ores is correct?
- **A** Magnesium can be found uncombined in the Earth's crust.
- **B** Sodium can be extracted from its ores by heating with carbon.
- **C** When carbon is heated with lead oxide the lead is oxidised.
- **D** many metals are extracted from their ores by reduction of oxides [1]

13 Which statement about sodium hydrogen carbonate is incorrect?
- **A** It is common salt.
- **B** It reacts with acids to release carbon dioxide.
- **C** It is used in baking powder.
- **D** It undergoes thermal decomposition when heated. [1]

14 The correct word equation is:
- **A** calcium carbonate ➔ calcium hydroxide + carbon dioxide
- **B** sodium hydrogen carbonate ➔ sodium carbonate + water + carbon dioxide
- **C** calcium carbonate + hydrochloric acid ➔ calcium chloride + water
- **D** magnesium carbonate ➔ magnesium + carbon dioxide [1]

15 Two gases, A and B, are tested to identify them. The table below shows the results.

	Effect on damp blue litmus	Effect on damp red litmus	Effect on limewater	Effect on glowing splint	Effect on lighted splint
A	blue	red	remains clear	Relights it	Burns more brightly
B	blue	blue	Remains clear	Does not relight	Splint goes out

Which statement is correct?
- **A** A is hydrogen and B is ammonia
- **B** A is hydrogen and B is chlorine
- **C** A is oxygen and B is ammonia
- **D** A is oxygen and B is chlorine [1]

(Total 15 marks)

Worked example

Use the following data on the properties of gases to choose the correct statement from the key.
- **A** Ammonia can be collected over water
- **B** Chlorine can be collected by upward delivery
- **C** Hydrogen can be collected by downward delivery
- **D** Oxygen can be collected over water

hydrogen	less dense	very low
oxygen	similar	low
ammonia	less dense	very high
chlorine	denser	fairly

Ammonia is very soluble in water so it could not be collected over water, as it would dissolve in it instead of being collected. **A is incorrect**. As ammonia is less dense than air you would normally collect it by upward delivery or by using a gas syringe.

Chlorine is denser than air so it cannot be collected by upward delivery. It would fall out of the gas jar as you were collecting it. **B is incorrect**. It is also soluble in water, so could not collect it over water. You would normally collect chlorine by downward delivery. As the dense chlorine fills the gas jar from the bottom it displaces the lighter air upwards. A gas syringe could also be used.

Hydrogen is less dense than air. It if was collected by downward delivery the hydrogen would enter the gas jar and promptly leave it again as it is less dense than the air. **C is incorrect.** It could be collected over water as it is not very soluble in water. If it is important that a dry gas is obtained, then you can collect it by upward delivery. It could also be collected in a gas syringe.

Oxygen is not very soluble in water so collecting it over water is a good method by which to collect it. **D is correct.**

How to get an A
When doing multi-choice questions of this sort it is very important to read all of the data provided before you start answering the question. Start to build up an idea about what the answer might be before you look at them, and then go through each answer in turn. If you think one answer is right, then make sure that every other answer is wrong.

DISCOVER THE EARTH!

The Earth provides us with fuels – substances that, when burnt, provide energy. We need this energy in order to live.

Burning some fuels produces gases that harm our planet. The amounts of these gases must be controlled, otherwise we could damage the Earth.

The Earth is an amazing place. It provides us with all of the natural resources that we need in order to live. However, many of these resources will run out at some point, and for the sake of future generations, we must, therefore, find other ways to use what the Earth provides.

The air and seawater are both useful resources for providing chemicals. We use many of these chemicals everyday and our lives would certainly be different without them.

The sea can also provide us with energy through the power of waves. Energy of this type is called renewable energy as it is continuously being made by the wind. This type of energy production is important for sustainable development, which involves using as many renewable sources of energy as possible.

CONTENTS

Air

You will find out:

- That air is an important substance
- That air is a mixture of other gases
- How air can be separated so that the substances that make it up can be used

Let there be life!

When a baby is born, it takes its first breath of **air** to begin life.

Air is a mixture of gases. One of the gases in air is called **oxygen** – this is a gas that we all need in order to live.

FIGURE 1: A newly-born baby needs air in order to live.

The air we breathe

When we are looking for life on other planets, oxygen gas on a planet is an exciting sign that life may exist.

- The air that we breathe is a colourless gas which is not a pure substance – it is a mixture of more than one gas.

- Air is a mixture of gases like oxygen gas and **nitrogen** gas as well as rarer gases like argon.

- Normal air also contains gases like **carbon dioxide** and water vapour – but the amounts of these gases is small and tends to change a lot.

The woman in the picture has been involved in a serious accident and is in hospital. The mask over her face is connected to a supply of pure oxygen gas which keeps her alive.

There are many uses of the gases that make up the air, but we need to separate them first before we can use each gas.

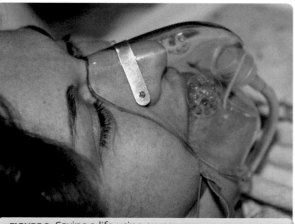

FIGURE 2: Saving a life using oxygen gas.

WOW FACTOR!

Nitrogen is used to make hundreds of compounds – chemicals we eat, the houses we live in, the clothes we wear, the cars we drive …

QUESTIONS

1 What important gas found in air do we need in order to live?
2 Name **three** gases found in the air.
3 Give a use for oxygen gas.

EXAM HINTS AND TIPS

Oxygen and nitrogen gases are made up of molecules that contain 2 atoms bonded together. This is why the chemical formulae of these two gases have a 2 in it, like O_2.

…air …argon …carbon dioxide …compound …element

What's in air?

Many years ago, it was thought that air was a single substance. Today we know that air is made of many gases. Some of these gases are chemical **elements** and others are **compounds**.

The pie chart in figure 3 shows the names and amounts of the gases making up the air.

As the pie chart shows, about 80% of the air is nitrogen, and most of the remaining gas is oxygen. So the gas that supports life on Earth (oxygen) only makes up about 20%, or a fifth, of the air that we breathe. **Argon** is the third most common gas in the air – about 0.9% of the air is made of argon.

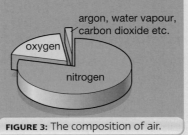

FIGURE 3: The composition of air.

Uses for the gases?

When air is separated, the individual gases that make up air can then be used for special things.

- Oxygen gas (chemical formula: O_2) is used in hospitals to help patients breathe and feel better. Oxygen is also of great use when making steel from iron. Figure 4 shows some liquid oxygen, which has a temperature of −183 °C and has a light blue colour.

- Nitrogen gas (chemical formula: N_2) is used in the form of liquid nitrogen to keep some food cold.

- Argon (chemical formula: Ar) is used to fill light bulbs.

- Carbon dioxide gas (chemical formula: CO_2) is used to fill up fire extinguishers. When carbon dioxide is a solid, it is called dry ice and can be used to keep ice creams cold.

FIGURE 4: Liquid oxygen is very cold!

FIGURE 5: A fractionating tower that separates the gases in liquid air.

How is air separated?

Air is a mixture of different gases – nitrogen gas, oxygen gas and other gases that are in smaller amounts.

To separate air into the gases that make it up, the air is cooled so that all gases are turned into a liquid.

The process of **fractional distillation** is then used to separate the air since the liquids all have different boiling points.

Name of gas	Boiling point (°C)
nitrogen	−196
oxygen	−183
argon	−186

Figure 5 shows a typical **fractionating column** which is where the liquids are sorted out into pure gases.

QUESTIONS

4 Give a use for nitrogen gas.

5 What is the formula for carbon dioxide gas?

6 Give a use for carbon dioxide gas.

7 What is the name of the third most common gas in the air?

QUESTIONS

8 What is the boiling point of nitrogen?

9 When air is liquefied and allowed to separate, which gas appears at the highest point in the column?

10 What is the name of the technique used to separate air into its separate gases?

...fractional distillation   ...fractionating column   ...nitrogen   ...oxygen

Sea and salt

You will find out:

● That seawater is a very important substance
● That salt is a compound of two important elements
● That salt can be turned into important substances using electricity

It's winter and it's cold, very cold

Sometimes, when it is winter, it gets very cold. Water is normally a liquid when it rains, but when it is very cold, water freezes to make solid water, or ice. Ice on the ground can be dangerous to walk on,
and driving a car on ice can be very dangerous.

To make ice turn back into water when it is cold, trucks grit the roads with **salt** – this melts the ice and makes it safer to drive.

FIGURE 1: When water turns to ice, the gritter trucks sprinkle salt on the roads to melt the ice.

'Add enough salt to taste'

You have probably seen table salt being added to food to make it taste nicer.

Salt that is added to food is a chemical compound of two elements – sodium and chlorine. The chemical name of salt is **sodium chloride** and it has the chemical formula NaCl.

Where does salt come from?

Salt is a substance that dissolves in water. Seawater contains a lot of salt, and other substances that are dissolved too.

In the Dead Sea, there is a lot of salt dissolved in the water. It is very easy to float in the Dead Sea because there is so much salt dissolved in the water. The Dead Sea is so called because nothing can live in the water when so much salt is dissolved in it.

FIGURE 2: Adding salt to food can make it taste good.

WOW FACTOR!

There is about 350 000 cubic miles of salt found in the ground – all of this was once dissolved in water.

▪ QUESTIONS ▪

1 Give **two** uses for salt.
2 Where is salt found in the earth?
3 Why do people float in the Dead Sea?
4 Name **two** elements that make table salt.

EXAM HINTS AND TIPS

The word 'soluble' is used to describe a substance that dissolves in a liquid, like water.

...*anode*   ...*cathode*   ...*chlorine*   ...*electrolysis*   ...*hydrogen*

Uses of salt products

The county of Cheshire is built on salt beds that were laid down by ancient oceans. When water is pumped into the salt beds, the salt dissolves and salt solution (or brine) is formed.

Some very important chemicals like **chlorine**, **hydrogen** and **sodium hydroxide** can be made from this.

As table 1 shows, the chemical substances that we make from salt are very useful. The everyday uses listed are only a few of the many hundreds of uses of these special chemicals.

Name of substance made from salt	Chemical formula	Everyday uses
hydrogen gas	H_2	As a fuel
chlorine gas	Cl_2	Water treatment, antiseptics, in plastics like PVC
sodium hydroxide	NaOH	An alkali, bleach, aspirin, soaps

TABLE 1: Everyday uses for hydrogen, chlorine and sodium hydroxide.

All these items are made from chlorine (which comes from seawater).

FIGURE 3: Just a few of the everyday uses of chlorine: bleach used in cleaning; destroying pests with pesticide; objects made from polyvinylchloride.

Testing for hydrogen, chlorine and sodium hydroxide

These three important substances can be tested in the laboratory by carrying out the following procedures.

- Hydrogen: If a lighted splint is placed into a test tube that contains hydrogen, a squeaky pop is produced.

- Chlorine: If a piece of moist universal indicator paper is placed into a test tube of chlorine, the indicator paper goes red and then is bleached (it goes white).

- Sodium hydroxide: Sodium hydroxide is a strong alkali, so if universal indicator is added to the solution, it should go purple or dark blue.

QUESTIONS

5   Give **three** uses for sodium hydroxide.
6   What is the formula for sodium hydroxide?
7   What does the '2' mean in the formula: H_2?
8   How would **a** hydrogen and **b** chlorine gases be tested in the laboratory?

Electrolysis of brine

Brine is a solution of salt, or sodium chloride.

When a concentrated solution of brine has electricity passed through it, the sodium chloride (and the water) breaks down – the process of breaking down a compound using electrical energy is called **electrolysis**.

FIGURE 4: Electrolysis of brine. Chlorine forms in the left-hand tube and hydrogen in the right-hand tube.

Note the following points about the electrolysis of salt.

- Electrolysis involves placing electrodes into a solution of salt.

- The electrodes are connected to an electrical power supply. When the power is turned on, an electrical current flows through the circuit.

- On the surface of each electrode, new chemical substances are formed.

Name of electrode	Charge on electrode	Chemical formed on electrode
cathode	negative	hydrogen gas and sodium hydroxide
anode	positive	chlorine gas

TABLE 2: Chemicals formed by electrolysis of salt.

QUESTIONS

9   What is the name of the method by which brine is separated into other substances?
10 At which electrode would chlorine be formed during the experiment?
11 What charge does a cathode electrode have?

Green energy

You will find out:
- That rubbish could be used to provide fuels
- That oils from plants may make fuels
- That plant oils could act as replacements for fuels like petrol

Fuel from rubbish

When some rubbish is buried in the ground, it breaks down to make a gas called methane. This gas normally escapes into the atmosphere, but it could be trapped and burnt. If we did this, we could make electricity from rubbish!

FIGURE 1: Fuel from rubbish. Is this possible?

Powering tractors

The tractor in figure 2 uses an oil that is made from rapeseed. This flower is often grown in fields around the UK and is often recognised as fields filled with yellow flowers.

The rapeseed is removed from the plant and then crushed to make oil; this oil burns to make a **fuel**.

- Fuels that are made from plants (like rapeseed oil, sunflower oil and wood) are called **biofuels**.

They can either be burnt on their own, or could be mixed with other 'normal' fuels like petrol and diesel to make fuels that are described as green fuels. These fuels are better for the environment.

Why are biofuels better than fossil fuels?

- Fossil fuels like those we get from crude oil as well as coal, will eventually run out. When there is none left, that is it. This type of fuel is called a **non-renewable** fuel (once it's used up, it's gone, there is no more left).

- Biofuels can be burnt too, but once they are used up, more plants can be grown to make more fuel. These types of fuels are called **renewable** fuels.

- Fuels made from plant oils are 'greenhouse neutral' because although they produce carbon dioxide when they burn, the plants absorb carbon dioxide from the air when they grow. So the carbon dioxide levels in the air stay the same.

FIGURE 2: Can a tractor run on plant fuel?

QUESTIONS

1. What is the name of the gas that is produced from rotting rubbish?
2. What are biofuels?
3. Why are biofuels better for the environment?
4. What is a renewable fuel?

EXAM HINTS AND TIPS

Remember! Fuels that can be made from plants are called renewable fuels since they will never run out.

...biodegradable ...biodiesel ...biofuel ...crude oil ...energy

Why do we need to look at new fuels?

Fuels are used in many of the activities in everyday life. Petrol and diesel are used to power cars and lorries, fuel oil is used to power ships, and kerosene is a fuel for aircraft. All of these fuels come from **crude oil**, but we know that within 50 years there will be very little crude oil left. We must therefore look around for alternative fuels.

Crude oil, known as black gold, has driven the economies of many countries for more than a century. Over the next several decades, green gold, or plant oils, may become just as important.

Can sugar help?

Sugar beet can be used to make **ethanol** by a process called fermentation. In this process, sugar is added to yeast and a chemical reaction takes place in which ethanol and carbon dioxide are formed. The ethanol made can be used as a biofuel to power car engines, and so will reduce the demand for petrol. However, large areas of fertile land will be needed to grow the sugar beet, and this may be a problem.

Are oils from plants the answer?

When plant oil is used as a fuel, it burns in the same way that petrol and diesel do. Heat **energy** produced is used to power the vehicle. However, plant oils in their pure form are not often used as fuels; they are normally mixed with traditional fuels like diesel to make 'greener' fuels.

When plant oil burns, it produces gases such as carbon dioxide and water vapour. In a limited supply of oxygen, carbon monoxide (chemical formula: CO) is formed. This is a toxic gas. Also, some soot may form when it burns.

One issue with powering vehicles with pure plant oils is that the engines would have to be modified so that this new fuel could be used. This may prove to be expensive.

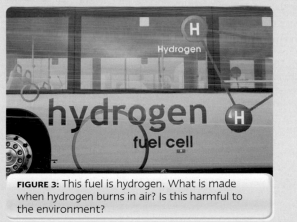

FIGURE 3: This fuel is hydrogen. What is made when hydrogen burns in air? Is this harmful to the environment?

QUESTIONS

5 Give the names of **four** fuels made from crude oil.

6 Name a toxic gas that is produced when a fuel that contains carbon burns in air.

7 Give one disadvantage of using pure plant oil as a fuel.

Biodiesel – a fuel of the future?

Biodiesel is the name of a clean-burning alternative fuel produced from renewable resources. Biodiesel contains no petroleum, but it can be mixed at any level with petroleum diesel to create a biodiesel blend. It can be used in (diesel) engines with little or no modifications. Biodiesel is simple to use, **biodegradable**, non-toxic, and essentially free of sulphur and aromatics.

FIGURE 4: Biodiesel like this is made from plant oils!

Biodiesel is made through a chemical process called **transesterification**. In this process, glycerine is separated from fat or vegetable oil. The process leaves behind two products, methyl esters (the chemical name for biodiesel) and glycerine (a valuable byproduct used in soaps and other products).

Biodiesel is better for the environment because it is made from renewable resources and has lower emissions compared to petroleum diesel. It is less toxic than table salt and biodegrades as fast as sugar. Since it is made from renewable resources such as soybeans, its use decreases our dependence on crude oil.

QUESTIONS

8 What is meant by the term 'transesterification'?

9 Give an advantage of using biodiesel.

10 What is the chemical name for biodiesel?

The black stuff

You will find out:
- That crude oil is a very important substance found in the Earth
- How crude oil can be separated into other very useful substances
- What crude oil is made up of in terms of chemical compounds

Filling up the car

We like to drive cars. We need to drive cars so that we can travel to work, do the shopping, see our friends, and soon.

A car is able to work because it uses petrol (or sometimes diesel) as its fuel. Without petrol, driving a car would not be possible.

FIGURE 1: Petrol for your car.

Where it all comes from

Petrol, like many other fuels, comes from a substance called **crude oil**.

Crude oil is sometimes called black gold because of its colour and because it is very precious. It was formed many millions of years ago when plankton in the sea was squashed.

Crude oil is found in the ground in certain parts of the world. We drill in the ground and hopefully, crude oil is found.

Crude oil is black, gooey and has a nasty smell – it does not look very special at all.

We heat crude oil up in a process known as **fractional distillation** and the crude oil mixture is then separated to make useful substance such as:

- liquid petroleum gases – used in some cars and as a fuel in gas burners
- petrol – used in cars
- naphtha – used to make other very useful chemicals
- kerosene – used in aircraft
- diesel oil – lorries and some cars use this
- fuel oil – ships use this
- bitumen – tar and roof surfacing.

FIGURE 2: Drilling for oil.

QUESTIONS

1 Describe what crude oil looks like.
2 What process is used to separate crude oil into the things that make it up?
3 Give a use for liquid petroleum gas.

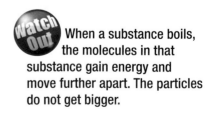

Watch Out When a substance boils, the molecules in that substance gain energy and move further apart. The particles do not get bigger.

...boiling point   ...crude oil   ...fractional distillation   ...fractionating column

Distilling crude oil

Crude oil is very useful to modern society. Nearly all transport that is used today needs chemicals from crude oil.

Figure 3 shows an oil refinery. Notice how complicated it all is. The large, tall tower is where crude oil is separated and it is called the **fractionating column**.

FIGURE 3: An oil refinery.

When we look at a fractionating column more closely, we see some interesting things about it.

As we go up the column ... (H)

- The **boiling points** of the **molecules** decrease. Liquid petroleum gases are produced at the top of the column since their boiling point is lowest. Bitumen (asphalt) forms at the bottom of the column since its boiling point is highest.

- As we go up the column, the size of the molecules in the crude oil decreases – smaller molecules have lower boiling points, larger molecules have higher boiling points.

- The substances become runnier or less viscous. For example, bitumen is gooier (has a higher **viscosity**) than petrol since bitumen is found at the base of the fractionating column.

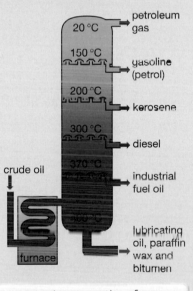

FIGURE 4: A cross-section of a fractionating column.

- The ease of ignition of the fractions increases. This means that substances are easier to set alight moving up the column. So, petrol is easier to ignite than diesel for example since petrol forms higher up the fractionating column.

QUESTIONS

4 Give the names of **three** forms of transport that need substances from crude oil for power.

5 What happens to the boiling point of the oil fraction when we go up the column?

6 What happens to the size of the molecules when we go up the column?

7 What is the meaning of the word 'viscous'?

EXAM HINTS AND TIPS

A fraction of crude oil is a part of it. Substances within a fraction have similar boiling points.

Getting small ... (H)

Sometimes we need to look at things at the molecular level to gain a better understanding.

- Crude oil is a complicated mixture of substances called **hydrocarbons**. These are compounds containing hydrogen and carbon only.

- As hydrocarbon molecules get bigger, their boiling points increase.

- When we boil a substance, we provide the molecules with more energy. When they have enough energy, they are able to move away from each other.

- Larger molecules are more difficult to separate from each other because the forces that act between the molecules are larger.

- The forces that exist between molecules are called **intermolecular forces**.

QUESTIONS

8 What is a hydrocarbon?

9 When a substance is heated, the molecules in the substance are provided with more ....

10 What is another name for the forces that act between molecules?

...hydrocarbon   ...intermolecular forces   ...molecule   ...viscosity

Burning to give energy

You will find out:
- The meaning of the term 'fuel'
- What happens when a fuel burns
- Why a poisonous substance can sometimes be formed when a fuel burns

Living life in luxury

Figure 1 is of a Bentley car – it is a powerful and beautiful car that many people would like to own. It is powered by petrol, the same **fuel** that powers many other cars.

In a car engine, petrol is a fuel. This means that it burns to produce heat **energy** – this heat is then used to make the car move.

FIGURE 1: A luxury car like this one needs petrol as a fuel.

What's a good fuel, what's a bad fuel?

There are many fuels. They are substances that react with the oxygen gas
in the air. As they do so, they burn to produce heat energy that can then be used. Some fuels are good and others are not as good.

Look at figure 2, it shows lots of used car tyres. Millions of car tyres are just thrown away every year. Most used tyres are placed in refuse tips and buried. This is a problem since rubber does not break down or biodegrade, and so the tyres will be there for a long time. Why not burn tyres and use the heat energy for doing something useful?

When rubber burns, it produces lots of black smoke, therefore creating a lot of **pollution**, as well as producing lots of the toxic gas called **carbon monoxide**.

- So, one important thing about a good fuel is that when it burns, it shouldn't produce too much soot.

Wood could be a good fuel, but one problem with wood is that it leaves lots of ash. This then needs to be cleared out of wherever it is burning. What happens to the ash? Normally, it is thrown away and forgotten about.

- So another important feature of a good fuel is for it to leave little residue when it burns.

FIGURE 2: Could car tyres like these be burnt to provide heat energy?

QUESTIONS

1. Give a name of a toxic gas produced when some substances are burnt.
2. When substances burn, they are joining with ………from the air.
3. When substances burn, they produce heat …………..

WOW FACTOR!

Substances, like petrol, will not burn in space because there is no oxygen in space.

…carbon monoxide …complete combustion …energy …fuel

How are our homes heated?

Many houses in the world, including the UK, are heated using natural gas which is called **methane**. It is a **hydrocarbon** with the chemical formula CH_4.

The methane reacts with oxygen (or burns) in a boiler found in the home. Figure 3 is a photograph of a typical boiler found in a UK house.

When methane burns, it joins with oxygen to produce heat energy, and this heat is then used to heat water, which then goes to radiators and keeps us warm.

However, a boiler must be checked every year to make sure that it works properly and, above all, is safe. Sometimes, the amount of oxygen (in the air) entering the boiler is not enough, and this means that the methane will not burn properly. This is when carbon monoxide gas will form.

It is important to have a gas boiler checked to make sure that carbon monoxide levels are small and not a risk to health.

It is interesting to know that carbon monoxide sensors can now be bought from shops. A picture of one is shown below.

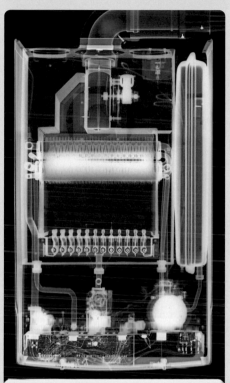

FIGURE 3: Methane burns in this boiler to produce heat energy that keeps people in the house warm.

FIGURE 4: A carbon monoxide sensor will tell you when carbon monoxide is in the air.

When carbon monoxide is present in the air, the spot on the sensor will go black. This device saves many lives every year!

Carbon monoxide is an invisible, odourless and tasteless gas – you don't know it is there, but if breathed in, it can kill.

Carbon monoxide kills by binding to the haemoglobin in the blood. This means that the blood is not able to carry round as much oxygen, and this may result in death.

EXAM HINTS AND TIPS

Carbon monoxide has the chemical formula CO. Mono- means one oxygen; di- means two oxygens. Carbon dioxide is CO_2.

Incomplete combustion!

When a hydrocarbon, like methane, burns in a limited supply of oxygen gas, carbon monoxide is produced. It is poisonous. This type of combustion is called **incomplete combustion**.

Normally, when a fuel burns, lots of oxygen is present and carbon dioxide and water vapour are formed, for example:

methane + oxygen →
carbon dioxide + water vapour

$$CH_4 + 2O_2 \rightarrow CO_2 + 2H_2O$$

This is known as **complete combustion**.

When the oxygen supply is limited, the following happens:

methane + oxygen →
carbon monoxide + water vapour

$$2CH_4 + 3O_2 \rightarrow 2CO + 4H_2O$$

This is known as incomplete combustion.

QUESTIONS

7 When carbon monoxide is formed when a substance burns, we call this type of reaction .... combustion.

8 What are the names of the substances formed when methane burns in lots of oxygen?

9 What is the name of the type of combustion in question 8?

QUESTIONS

4 What is the name of the gas that is used as a fuel in most UK homes?

5 Why must a gas boiler be serviced regularly?

6 How may a leak of carbon monoxide be detected?

...hydrocarbon   ...incomplete combustion   ...methane   ...oxygen   ...pollution

The air we breathe

You will find out:
- That our planet is under threat from certain gases in the atmosphere
- Where some of the air pollutants come from
- How our health may be affected due to some of the pollutants

Paying for air

It is now possible to buy air to breathe. We already buy millions of bottles of water every year, but are people really buying air too?

People are worried about the quality of the air that we breathe. This is because the air sometimes contains other gases that are supposed to be bad for us.

FIGURE 1: This machine produces air with added oxygen.

What is air?

We all take the **air** for granted. We can't see it, taste it or smell it but it is there and we need it in order to survive.

Air is made up of several gases that occur in different amounts. Table 1 shows the proportions of each gas that a dry sample of air contains.

We can monitor the amounts of various pollutants within the air very carefully. The data can be collected by a sensor and the information sent to a computer. The data is then analysed by scientists to see what is happening.

Name of gas	Chemical formula of gas	Approximate percentage of gas in the air
nitrogen	N_2	79
oxygen	O_2	20
argon	Ar	0.9
carbon dioxide and other gases	CO_2	0.1

TABLE 1: The composition of dry air.

Whose fault is it?

Industries and transport all release many tonnes of pollutants into the air every year. Many of these gases harm our planet, and it is only now that we are beginning to realise the damage that some of these gases cause.

Gases like sulphur dioxide, nitrogen oxides and **chlorofluorocarbons (CFCs)** are all air pollutants.

The human race has progressed enormously and our lives are a lot more comfortable today than they used to be a century ago. The price to pay for this is **pollution**. As industries increase and as we use more forms of transport, more pollution is added to the air. This is the price we pay for progress. Do you think that this is right?

◼ QUESTIONS ◼

1 Name three elements that are present in dry air.
2 Approximately what proportion of the air is nitrogen and oxygen gas?
3 What is the chemical formula for nitrogen gas?
4 What does the abbreviation CFC stand for?

WOW FACTOR!

The record acid rain fall recorded occurred in California, USA. The rain had a pH of 2.1 – this is similar to the pH of car battery acid!

...*acid rain* ...*air* ...*asthma* ...*chlorofluorocarbons (CFCs)*

Acidic gases

When fossil fuels, like coal, are burnt carbon dioxide forms and heat energy too. However, in many fossil fuels there is a small amount of the element sulphur. This burns too and a new gas called **sulphur dioxide** forms.

Sulphur dioxide (chemical formula: SO_2) is a smelly and poisonous gas, but it also dissolves in rainwater to form an acid.

This acid lowers the pH of (makes more acidic) rivers and lakes and can kill aquatic life, such as fish. It can also kill trees since the pH of the soil becomes acidic.

FIGURE 2: This is what acid rain can do.

How is the Internet useful?

The internet has proven very important for allowing many different people to share their experimental data with the world. It is now possible to research up-to-date data about **acid rain** or air pollution and use it in your own work. However, it is important to realise that other people's data should be checked to see whether it is biased, and whether it is based on real, rather than made-up or altered data.

QUESTIONS

5 Write the word equation to show how sulphur dioxide is formed when some fossil fuels are burnt.

6 What are the main sources of air pollutants?

7 Name a gas which could form acid rain.

Asthma and pollution (H)

Figure 3 shows how the number of people with the condition called **asthma** has varied with time. Notice how the number of people affected has increased over the years. Why is this?

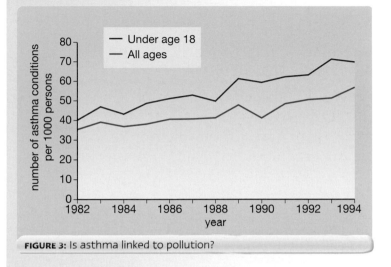

FIGURE 3: Is asthma linked to pollution?

Figure 4 shows how some pollutants within the air have changed with time.

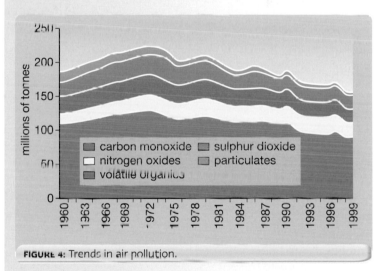

FIGURE 4: Trends in air pollution.

Do you think that these two graphs show that there is link between air pollution and asthma?

QUESTIONS

8 What does the first graph indicate about the sensitivity of certain age groups to asthma?

9 What has happened to the total amount of pollutants with time, according to the second graph?

10 Approximately how many people of all ages had asthma in 1994 per 1000 people?

Evolution of the air

You will find out:

- That volcanoes played an important role in making the atmosphere on Earth
- That the composition of the atmosphere is very different today from millions of years ago

Volcanoes

Volcanoes can be very dangerous to life on Earth. Many people have been killed by them.

However, volcanoes have played a very important role in making the Earth as we see it today. The **air**, for example, was originally made up of gases that came from volcanoes!

'Modern' Air

The sea-level composition of air is given below.

Gas	Formula	Composition (%)
nitrogen	N_2	78.084
oxygen	O_2	20.9476
argon	Ar	0.934
carbon dioxide	CO_2	0.0314
neon	Ne	0.001 818
helium	He	0.000 524
methane	CH_4	0.0002
krypton	Kr	0.000 114
hydrogen	H_2	0.000 05
xenon	Xe	0.000 0087

TABLE 1: The composition of air.

FIGURE 1: Volcanoes – can they really be useful?

Air has not always been the same as shown in the table. It has been changing over many millions of years. The composition of the air about 1000 million years ago was very different from that of today's air.

How did the atmosphere begin?

The Earth formed 4600 million years ago. We believe that the very first **atmosphere** may have been made of helium and hydrogen. These were the most common gases after the **Big Bang** which was the explosion that built the universe.

These two gases are light and would have escaped from the Earth's gravity, so would not have lasted for a long time before escaping into space.

The very first atmosphere may have been made of helium and hydrogen

WOW FACTOR!

Argon belongs to a group of elements in the periodic table that used to be called the rare gases. However, argon is the third most common gas in the air. It is not rare at all!

QUESTIONS

1. What is the name and formula for the third most common gas in the air?
2. What are the names of the two gases that were believed to make up Earth's first atmosphere?
3. How many substances in table 1 are compounds?
4. What is the meaning of the '2' in the formula for oxygen, O_2?

...air   ...atmosphere   ...Big Bang   ...carbon dioxide

How has the composition of air evolved?

Look at figure 2. It shows how the levels of methane (CH_4), nitrogen (N_2), oxygen (O_2) and carbon dioxide (CO_2) are thought to have changed with time.

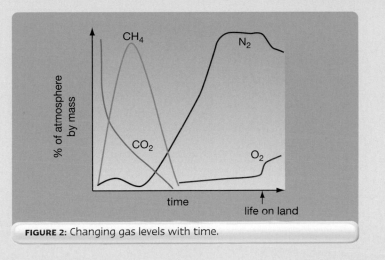

FIGURE 2: Changing gas levels with time.

The graph can be explained by the following important stages in the Earth's history.

- Levels of **carbon dioxide** were very high when the Earth first formed. We believe that this was due to volcanoes making lots of carbon dioxide gas.

- Water vapour is also produced from volcanoes. However, as the Earth started to cool, this vapour would have **condensed** to form liquid water. This liquid water would have made up the very early oceans and seas.

- Carbon dioxide would have **dissolved** in these seas so the levels of this gas would have started to decrease.

- Life appears very late in Earth's history. Early plants would have been able to photosynthesise and this would have further reduced the levels of carbon dioxide in the air, but this would have also meant that oxygen levels start to increase.

- Ammonia, also from volcanoes, would have reacted with oxygen gas forming nitrogen, so nitrogen levels start to increase. Bacterial action was also able to turn ammonia into nitrogen gas.

Venus and the greenhouse effect

The swirling clouds around Venus look peaceful, but they are definitely not.

FIGURE 3: Venus, a planet that could have an atmosphere like Earth millions of years ago.

The planet receives heat from the Sun, but, because of its thick cloud cover, the heat is trapped under the cloud, unable to escape back into space as it does on Earth. This is similar to how a greenhouse works on Earth. Temperatures can reach up to 600 °C. This is why Venus is the hottest planet in the Solar System, even though it is not the closest planet to the Sun.

The cloud that covers Venus is not like the cloud that we have in our skies. It is full of deadly sulphuric acid droplets, not water droplets as on Earth. Nearly Venus' entire atmosphere is made up of carbon dioxide, a poisonous, suffocating gas which would kill any living creature if it was breathed in.

It is thought that Earth's early atmosphere, which had high levels of carbon dioxide, may have been very similar to that on Venus.

> **QUESTIONS**
>
> 8 Suggest how a gardener's greenhouse keeps flowers warmer than surrounding air.
>
> 9 Why would breathing in carbon dioxide be considered to be very dangerous?
>
> 10 Why is there concern about the increasing levels of carbon dioxide gas on Earth?

> **QUESTIONS**
>
> 5 Give **two** causes for the decreasing levels of carbon dioxide gas with time.
>
> 6 From where did the nitrogen gas in today's air originate?
>
> 7 Why is photosynthesis important in maintaining the composition of the atmosphere?

...condensed ...dissolved ...volcano

Global warming

You will find out:

- That our planet is under threat from changes in our atmosphere
- That certain gases that humans produce could be responsible for changes
- What is meant by global warming

Melting icebergs

You may be aware that massive lumps of ice called icebergs can be found on our planet. Figure 1 shows some icebergs that are found in the Arctic.

Icebergs are enormous and contain a lot of fresh water in the form of ice. It is a real worry when we realise that some of these icebergs are melting because of global warming.

FIGURE 1: A beautiful collection of icebergs in the Arctic.

The planet is getting hotter!

It may not seem an obvious thing to say, but our planet is becoming warmer. Scientists have been measuring the **temperature** of our planet over many years and have found that it is slowly becoming warmer. This is called **global warming**.

FIGURE 2: Islands like the Maldives may become a thing of the past.

The theory of global warming started off as one person's idea, and then lots of scientists agreed with this idea. It is now a widely accepted theory and most people believe it.

As our planet has become steadily warmer over the last century, what could be the Earth's temperature in another century?

Scientists believe that the following things may happen if the Earth's temperature continues to increase.

- Ice that is found on land will melt and this will increase the sea level. This means that small, flat islands like the Maldives may be flooded forever.

- The world's **weather** may change. It may become stormier, hotter in summer, and also very cold in winter. Weather may become more extreme.

- If the weather changes, it may mean that we all have to get used to very different ways of life in future. Countries that are warm at the moment may become very hot. Other countries may become very cold.

EXAM HINTS AND TIPS

Remember! 'The evidence suggests that the increased levels of carbon dioxide are contributing to global warming' is not the same statement as 'The evidence proves that increased levels …'. We can only make definite conclusions when we have all of the evidence.

WOW FACTOR!

578 000 million tonnes of carbon dioxide were present in the air in 1700, and this increased to about 766 000 million tonnes in 1999, and continues to increase at the rate of about 6100 million tonnes per year!

QUESTIONS

1 How do we know that the Earth is becoming warmer?
2 What is the name given to the idea that the planet is becoming warmer?
3 What may happen if sea water levels increase?

…carbon dioxide   …fossil fuel   …global warming   …photosynthesis

What can be done to combat global warming? (H)

We know that our planet is becoming warmer and this means that serious things may happen to the Earth. If we assume that the increasing temperature is due to humans producing more and more **carbon dioxide**, we must, as a precaution, do something to slow down the rate at which carbon dioxide is produced.

We could reduce the amount of **fossil fuels** that we burn. Most fossil fuels come from crude oil and they all contain carbon. When they burn, they make lots of carbon dioxide.

What happens to carbon dioxide in the air?

Although levels of carbon dioxide are increasing, it is important to realise that carbon dioxide can be removed from our atmosphere too.

- Carbon dioxide is quite soluble in water, so it is likely to dissolve in rain water as well as sea water. This will decrease levels of carbon dioxide in the air.

- Once carbon dioxide is dissolved in water, it reacts to form an acid called carbonic acid. This acid can react with minerals like calcium which is dissolved in water to form calcium carbonate, which then sinks to the bottom of the sea. Calcium carbonate rocks are then formed.

FIGURE 3: Rocks like this act as carbon 'sinks', since they have absorbed carbon dioxide from the air.

- Carbon dioxide can be absorbed by plants through **photosynthesis**. More carbon dioxide could be absorbed by growing more plants, by **reforestation** for example. This carbon may end up in the form of fossil fuels, although this may take many years to form.

QUESTIONS

4   Give **one** source of the carbon dioxide that enters the air.

5   Give **three** ways in which carbon dioxide is removed from the air.

6   The amount of carbon dioxide in the air is steadily increasing every year. What does this suggest about the rate at which carbon dioxide is being added to the air and the rate at which it is being removed?

A need for caution

Let us consider what we know about global warming.

- Scientists have taken many measurements of the Earth's average temperature over many years and have shown that it is increasing.

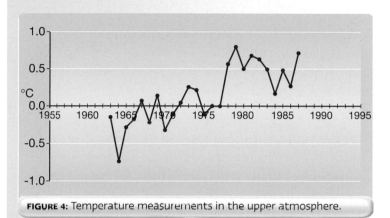

FIGURE 4: Temperature measurements in the upper atmosphere.

- Scientists have measured the average levels of carbon dioxide gas in the air and have shown that it, too, is increasing.

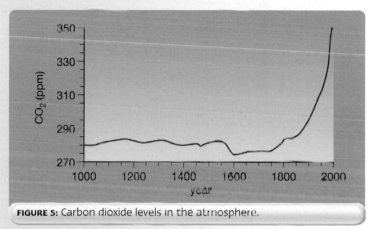

FIGURE 5: Carbon dioxide levels in the atmosphere.

So the average temperature is increasing as are the levels of carbon dioxide in the air. Are they linked? In other words, are the increasing levels of carbon dioxide in the air solely responsible for the increasing global temperatures? This is an important question, and the answer could be very complicated.

QUESTIONS

7   Look carefully at figure 4. What evidence is there that the graph is not a measure of average global temperature?

8   In figure 5, suggest why the levels of carbon dioxide have rapidly increased during the 20th century.

The future

You will find out:
- That throwing away rubbish is a real problem
- What is meant by recycling
- About alternative fuels to the fuels we use today

Bottles!

Most bottles that are used are made of glass. Glass needs a lot of energy to be made – making glass also makes a lot of pollution. We could throw away glass bottles when we have finished with them and put them into a rubbish dump like the one in figure 1.

Rubbish dumps don't look very nice – they also smell. Also, most rubbish would still be there in 100 years – it does not break down naturally, or biodegrade. We need to look at another way of dealing with our rubbish which is better for the environment.

FIGURE 1: A waste dump – the place where most of our rubbish ends up.

A waste time-bomb

When Hannah eats food that she likes, she normally throws away the packaging (wrappers, boxes, bottles) without thinking about it. She puts it in a bin and then expects someone else to take it away – she then forgets about it.

There are lots of people like Hannah living in the UK – many, many millions of people! Everybody throws away rubbish and most of this gets put in a hole in the ground.

The future – some important questions to think about

- Do you think that we can keep on filling up **waste** dumps with rubbish?
- If we can't see rubbish when it is in the ground, does it really matter?
- If you think that we cannot carry on as we are, what can we do about it?

Making rubbish useful

One thing that we can do is to turn rubbish into useful things – this is called **recycling**.

Instead of things made of paper, metal or glass being thrown away, they can be placed into special banks, for example, bottle banks. The bottles are broken up and then reheated to melt them – then new bottles can be made.

> **EXAM HINTS AND TIPS**
>
> If something biodegrades it means that it breaks down in the earth.

FIGURE 2: Bottles like these can be used again, and again.

> **WOW FACTOR!**
>
> Drinkable water is a precious resource. We could heat sea water to make pure water, but this is environmentally damaging since it requires fuels to be burnt to provide the energy to evaporate the water. However, the Sun in hot countries could be used to remove water.

> **QUESTIONS**
>
> 1 Why are rubbish dumps thought to be a bad thing?
> 2 What does recycling mean?
> 3 Name a substance that can be recycled.

...energy   ...fuel   ...hydrogen   ...pollution

Glass, paper and metal

Melting glass to make new bottles, shredding old paper to make new paper, and melting metal things and making new ones is all expensive. However, making metals, glass and paper from raw materials is a lot more expensive.

Figure 3 shows glass being made – look at the **energy** involved in making it – everything is really hot and therefore very expensive.

FIGURE 3: Huge amounts of energy are needed to make glass.

What about our cars?

We need to be able to travel from one place to another – we like to own cars in order to have complete freedom to do what we want, when we want.

A worrying fact – the amount of crude oil in the Earth is running out; in 50 years' time, there will be very little left.

Petrol, diesel, some gases and fuel oil are all used to power cars, lorries, aircraft and ships – but all of these fuels are running out. We need to find another, new **fuel**.

Hydrogen

One example of a fuel of the future is **hydrogen** gas. This gas burns in air to make water and heat energy – this is not polluting in any way!

hydrogen gas + oxygen gas → water

or in symbols:

$2H_2(g) + O_2(g) → 2H_2O(l)$

Hydrogen can be made from water using the Sun – light from the Sun is turned into electricity and this can then break down water to make hydrogen.

What are the advantages and disadvantages of hydrogen?

- Hydrogen burns cleanly and only produces water when it burns. No **pollution** is therefore formed.

- There is lots of water about. Could we find an environmentally friendly way of removing hydrogen from water?

- However, hydrogen is a highly flammable gas. This could make it dangerous to use when filling the car up, for example.

QUESTIONS

4   Why is it less expensive to recycle paper, than to make it from the wood from trees?

5   What is formed when hydrogen burns in oxygen?

6   Give an advantage of using hydrogen as a fuel.

The hydrogen economy

Hydrogen may be the fuel of the future. Scientists all over the world are trying to find a cheap way of making hydrogen, which also does not damage the planet.

There is lots of water on Earth – over 70% of the planet is covered with water.

We know electricity breaks down water to make hydrogen, but where is the electricity going to come from?

The Sun's energy could be used to make electricity, using a **solar cell** – this could then make hydrogen.

Alternatively, it may be possible to make special chemicals called enzymes that are able to turn water into hydrogen.

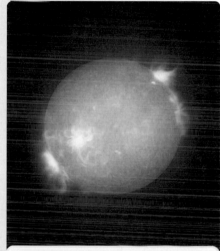

FIGURE 4: Will the Sun provide the energy to make the next fuel – hydrogen?

We will need to look at geothermal energy (energy from volcanic areas of the Earth), wind energy, tidal energy, nuclear fusion and nuclear fission too – all of these forms of power will be required.

QUESTIONS

7   Approximately how much of the Earth is covered with water?

8   Give one way that hydrogen could be made from water.

9   If water is turned into hydrogen, what is this chemical change called?

How big is your environmental footprint?

SELF-CHECK ACTIVITY

CONTEXT

Richard is a TV Producer living and working in Newcastle. His company does a lot of work for TV broadcasters and companies wanting advertising and promotional materials.

Richard's work takes him all over the country on a regular basis, as well as abroad. With the growth in low-cost airlines and more routes opening up within the UK, he often flies to Manchester, London or Plymouth. He could drive or go by train, but flying is usually quicker, even allowing for the journey to and from the airport.

However, flying has a much worse impact on the environment. Aircraft exhausts release a variety of pollutants into the air, including carbon dioxide, nitrous oxides and sulphur dioxide. A return trip from Newcastle to Plymouth will produce 0.12 tonnes of carbon dioxide per passenger.

At work, Richard was talking to Lesley, a colleague, about pollution from traffic. She said she now restricts herself to one return air journey per year, as her contribution to protecting the environment.

"I couldn't do that," said Richard. "Clients expect me to get to meetings at short notice. If we lose business, the company will have to lose staff."

"But if we carry on dumping gases in the atmosphere the damage we do will be catastrophic," replied Lesley. "There's no point in getting a good job so you can afford a better lifestyle if you've ruined the environment. Why not try video conferencing instead?"

"Well," said Richard, "We're taking our children to Disney World this year. We'll have to fly to do that. Anyway, we recycle our newspapers," he called after her as she left.

CHALLENGE

STEP 1

Read the text and think about the issues involved. Make notes to support each of the following statements:

- Richard and his family enjoy a high standard of living.
- His company is helping to create wealth and jobs.
- Humans sometimes have a negative impact on the environment.

STEP 2

Richard feels that the only way he could be more environmentally friendly is by enjoying life less or the company not being as active and successful. Do you agree?

STEP 3

Lesley feels that people don't always try hard enough to find alternatives to activities that damage the environment. Do you agree?

Maximise your grade

These sentences show what you need to include in your work to achieve each grade. Use them to improve your work and be more successful.

Grade	Answer includes...
F	Give an example of an activity which damages the environment.
	Give examples of activities which damage the environment.
	Suggest a way in which human activity can be modified to ease the impact on the environment.
	Suggest more than one way in which human activity can be modified to ease the impact on the environment.
C	Explain how commercial activities may have a negative impact on the environment.
	Start to explain how it may be possible to balance economic development, standards of living and caring for the environment.
A	Explain how it may be possible to balance economic development, standards of living and caring for the environment.
	As above, but with particular clarity and detail.

Getting smart

You will find out:

- That there are some amazing materials called smart materials
- What smart materials can do
- Some uses in everyday life for smart materials

Car airbags

When a car is involved in an accident, people in the car are protected against a serious injury by lots of modern technology. Airbags are an example of just this type of protection.

How does an airbag know when to go off?

There is a special sensor that can tell if the car has been hit, and this then sends electricity to the bag, setting it off. The substance in the sensor that can tell when to do this is called a **smart material**.

FIGURE 1: Could an airbag have helped the driver of this car survive?

Clever substances

We could take an ordinary piece of wire and bend it to make a shape, we could then leave it and look at it again later – it will be the same.

Most substances are like the wire – we can change them by bending, heating, hitting, etc., and they will be changed for good. However, there are very special substances called **shape memory alloys** that can 'remember' their starting shape!

How is it done?

- Sophie changes the shape of a metal object and makes it look interesting. She then cools it down to a certain temperature.

- She then messes up the shape so that it looks very different.

- She then gives the metal object to James. He then increases the temperature of the metal by warming it up. The original shape comes back! The substance has remembered!

CARBON FIBRE

Another smart material is **carbon fibre**. It is used to make car bodies, including those of some Formula 1 cars.

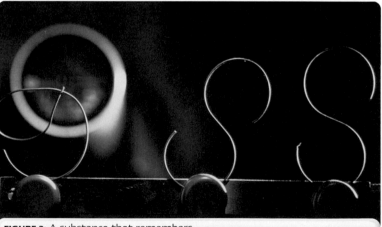

FIGURE 2: A substance that remembers.

▪▪ QUESTIONS ▪▪

1. Give a use for a smart material that is found in a car.
2. What are substances called that can remember their shape?

...carbon fibres ...Lycra® ...shape memory alloy

Smart fluids

We are used to living with substances that do not have unusual properties. For example, when we heat some oil, it becomes a little thinner or less **viscous** – but that is all.

A smart material will often change dramatically when it is heated. It may change shape or size with the addition of a little bit of heat, or change from a liquid to a solid almost instantly when near a magnet.

Clever mobile phones

Figure 3 shows a phone disassembling itself! It is made of a polymer, or plastic, that shrinks in size when it is placed in hot water – the phone then falls apart. When a phone has reached the end of its life, it can therefore fall apart on its own. The pieces can then be collected and recycled.

FIGURE 3: A mobile phone that takes itself apart.

Sport materials

When we play sport, we like to wear the right kit. An ice hockey player or a snowboarder needs to wear a lot of equipment mainly for protection and to keep warm.

Thinsulate™ Thermal Insulation

When we play sport in cold conditions, we need to keep warm. Otherwise our muscles do not work as well.

- One material that keeps us warm in this way is called **Thinsulate™** Thermal Insulation.
- It is a smart material.
- The fibres in Thinsulate™ materials are very thin so that they can trap air inside the material. This means that they do not allow much of the heat from a body to escape, so the body stays warmer.
- Thinsulate™ materials are lighter than normal materials, as the fibres are thinner, so weight for weight, it can keep us a lot warmer than other materials.

FIGURE 4: Look at the different materials needed to kit out this snow boarder.

▨▨▨▨ **QUESTIONS** ▨▨▨▨

3   What is the meaning of the term 'viscous'?

4   What is a smart liquid?

5   Why is Thinsulate™ special?

Stretchy stuff

Another really important fabric is called **Lycra**®. It is a smart material because it can 'remember' its original shape.

If we take a piece of Lycra® and stretch it, we can then remove the stretch force and the Lycra® turns back to its original length – exactly. This can happen if Lycra® is stretched up to 6 times its original length!

Lycra® is therefore added to clothes to make them more comfortable, since Lycra® can easily stretch and return to its original shape.

Lycra® is often blended with other fabrics like cotton, wool, silk and linen. It is lighter in weight than rubber thread, and unlike rubber thread, it does not break down when it comes into contact with body oils, perspiration, lotions or detergents on the skin.

FIGURE 5: Made from Lycra®!

Watch Out Are smart materials really smart? Are they actually clever? What do you think?

▨▨▨▨ **QUESTIONS** ▨▨▨▨

6   Why is Lycra® a smart material?

7   If a piece of Lycra® is 10 cm, to what length does it stretch if its length is increased by 600%?

8   Give some other special properties of Lycra®.

The nano world

You will find out:

● What nanotechnology is all about

● How nanotechnology is used

● Some future uses for this useful technology

Molecular robots

It may be possible in future to make ill people feel better by injecting microscopic robots into them – these robots contain the drugs that the person needs. The robots then release the drug slowly into the body on their own.

The robot may also be able tell whether the person needs to have less or more of a drug by measuring the amounts of certain chemicals in their blood.

FIGURE 1: Robots like this may be able to give us medicines on their own.

Seeing with atoms

Figure 2 shows a Japanese word – it means 'atom' and amazingly is written with atoms! Each Japanese letter is very small, so small that a million of them could fit across a human hair.

We can now make molecules (or groups of atoms) that can do very special things. This new and exciting technology is called **nanotechnology**.

Nanotechnologies are already being used today in making computer chips, CDs and mobile phones. In these objects, there are very small invisible molecules that are made to do useful things.

Invisible surgery

When we have an operation, we may have a scar that may not look very nice. In the future, it may be possible to inject in a nanobot (a **microscopic robot**) through a needle into a person. The nanobot could then do the surgery on the body but on a microscopic scale – it could repair individual cells.

FIGURE 2: Invisible writing – too small to be seen.

QUESTIONS

1 Give **two** uses of nanotechnology in our lives today.
2 What is a nanobot?
3 Why are nanobots useful?

...bucky ball ...microscopic robot ...nanocluster ...nanoparticle

A beautiful molecule

The molecule in Figure 3 looks like a football. It is made up of 60 carbon atoms joined together to make up a molecule called buckminsterfullerene or just a **bucky ball**.

We can call this structure a **nanocluster** – it is a group (or cluster) of atoms on the nano scale.

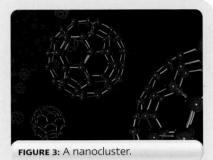

FIGURE 3: A nanocluster.

When a metal atom is placed into this molecule of C60, the substance formed can have **superconductivity** properties. This means that it can conduct electricity with very low electrical resistance.

We can make lots of other clusters that look like bucky balls form a bucky tube, or **nanotube**.

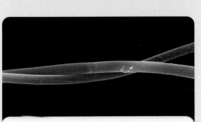

FIGURE 4: Nanotubes – they could have many uses.

Nanotubes could be useful for making new materials that are stronger and lighter than steel. They could also be used to make electronic parts for new computer systems, and molecular capsules for giving people drugs.

Computers of the future may have their electronic 'brains' made from machines on the nano scale. We could not see these brains because they would be so small, and yet they may be millions of times faster than present-day computers.

FIGURE 5: Computers of the future may have processors made from nanoclusters.

Protection from the sun

Nanoparticles are tiny particles with special properties; they are very useful.

FIGURE 6: Protecting the skin with nanoparticles.

- Nanoparticles of titanium dioxide have been added to some suntan lotions and cosmetics. These tiny particles are transparent on the skin and can absorb and reflect harmful ultraviolet rays.

- Titanium dioxide clusters can also be added to glass to make self-cleaning windows. These are windows that repel water and use sunlight to break down dirt, so that rain washes it away and the glass is left clean.

QUESTIONS

4   What is a nanocluster?

5   Give an example of a nanocluster.

6   Give a property of a nanocluster.

Nanotechnology – (H) some concerns

The future applications of nanotechnologies are difficult to predict. The use of small sensors and powerful computers could lead to greater personal security and safety, but the same technologies could also be used to spy on people and this may raise concerns.

There are many benefits that could be obtained from nanotechnology. However, there are also concerns that this new technology may be open to abuse.

Who decides which areas of nanotechnology should be developed? Who should control the use of nanotechnologies? Who should benefit from the new uses of nanotechnology?

What about the role of the media? They will often tell a story that may present a biased view of the truth. Is the media likely to sensationalise nanotechnology as a good or as an evil?

QUESTIONS

7   How may nanotechnology be used to protect our personal safety?

8   Give a problem that may result from misuse of nanotechnology.

9   The media's opinion on a new scientific issue is important. Why is this?

Designing materials

You will find out:

- About some special plastics (or polymers)
- Some uses for some special materials like that used to make bullet-proof vests
- About chemicals added to substances to change their properties

Materials that protect

Figure 1 shows a bullet-proof vest. People wear these in danger zones where there is a risk of being shot.

They are made of a special material called **Kevlar**® which is made specially for the purpose of protecting people from bullets. It is made of many layers of woven fabric and is five times stronger than steel at the same weight.

FIGURE 1: Protection from bullets.

Slippery stuff

When some people are older, their hips can sometimes start to wear out and it becomes difficult to move around. This is because the bones that need to move start to show signs of wear; this can be very painful.

We can design a substance that helps with this problem.

Figure 2 shows an artificial hip – it is made of titanium and a special **plastic** called **Teflon**®. Teflon® is a slippery plastic that other substances just slide off!

Tough stuff

The man in Figure 3 is surfing using a surfboard made of another special plastic called **polyurethane**. It is tough and light and is not likely to break when he is surfing even on a rough sea.

Polyurethane is another example of a plastic that we have designed to make our lives more enjoyable.

FIGURE 3: Surfing using a designer material called polyurethane.

FIGURE 2: Teflon is used to make hip joints – it is a designer material.

WOW FACTOR!

Teflon® and the glue used to make 'Post-its' were both discovered by chance. They were recognised as novel materials, but no uses were known for these substances until many years after they were discovered.

▌ QUESTIONS ▐

1 What makes Teflon® special?
2 What is the inside of a surfboard made of?
3 Give an example of a very strong material used to make bullet-proof vests.

...breathable fabric ...composite ...GORE-TEX® ...Kevlar® ...plastic

High-impact stuff

One new type of **plastic**, or polymer, is a sort of **composite** rather like glass-strengthened plastic or fibreglass. It has fibres, in which the polymer molecules are lined up alongside each other, and these are then placed into another plastic called polythene. This substance has properties that make it suitable as protective shields and for making delicate electronic components. It can also be used to protect people playing sports like cricket and American football.

Kevlar® too can be used as a high-impact material. It can therefore be used to prevent people from being hurt in a collision.

FIGURE 4: Protection using a designer polymer.

Fabrics that can breathe

GORE-TEX® fabric is a well known **waterproof** and **breathable fabric** originally developed over 30 years ago. How it works is a secret, but it is known to consist of a microporous Teflon membrane, laminated or bonded, to a variety of high performance fabrics.

- Notice in the diagram how water is repelled by the surface layer so the person wearing the article keeps dry.

- Any heat that the person produces is allowed to pass through the layers of fabric.

- Any strong winds would not be able to enter the fabric.

- So GORE-TEX® garments act to keep the wearer cool and dry, and protect them from strong winds.

GORE-TEX® garments are therefore made up of four main layers of fabric, all of the fabrics having their own unique properties. The combination of these four fabrics together makes a special, breathable material.

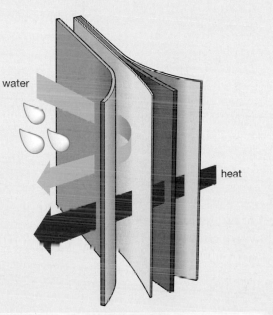

water

heat

FIGURE 5: How GORE-TEX® fabric works.

EXAM HINTS AND TIPS

Remember! A polymer is a long chain molecule made up of millions of atoms joined together.

QUESTIONS

4 Give a use for fibreglass.
5 What is meant by the term 'microporous'?
6 Explain why GORE-TEX® garments are described as breathable.

Designer stuff – the future

Polymers are really important in our lives – we can engineer or make them so that the properties of the final product are exactly what we want.

Polymers that conduct electricity

Polymers can now be made that conduct electricity – it may soon be possible to make printed circuit boards metal-free. Smart cards and security labelling (presently metal-based) could soon be plastic-based, cheaper, and more disposable.

Polymers that make light

When a special polymer is sandwiched between a piece of glass and a metal surface (connected to an electrical source), light can be produced – this is very exciting. Polymers of this type are called **light-emitting polymers**.

Display devices – like those that can be used in mobile phones, computer screens and TV sets – could use this technology.

FIGURE 6: A polymer flat screen – very thin, light and can produce pictures!

QUESTIONS

7 Give a use for a polymer that conducts electricity.
8 Give a use for a light-emitting polymer.

Alcohol from sugar

You will find out:

- That we can make a fuel called alcohol from sugar
- About the dangers of too much alcohol
- What is meant by fermentation

Watch out, alcohol about!

Many drinks can be bought that contain **alcohol** – some have a lot of alcohol in them, like whisky or gin (known as spirits), whereas others have a lower amount, for example, wine, cider and 'alcopops'. But it is important to remember that all of these drinks contain alcohol.

FIGURE 1: All of these drinks have alcohol in them.

Alcohol-free drinks

It is possible to reduce the amount of alcohol in a drink by using **fractional distillation**. In this process, a mixture of alcohol and water is heated up, and the alcohol boils first since it has a lower boiling point. This process is continued until most of the alcohol is removed. The taste of the drink is unaffected but the alcohol is removed.

Alcohol abuse

Alcohol, like any other drug, can be used in the wrong way. Many people are sensible when they drink – they know how much is enough and they do not drive after drinking.

However, some people drink too much alcohol – this can be a real problem.

- Drinking alcohol may give you a hangover, but this eventually disappears. Drinking too much alcohol can cause serious illnesses like cancer and problems with the liver – sometimes these **diseases** can result in death.
- Many people who turn up in hospital have had **accidents** due to drinking lots of alcohol.

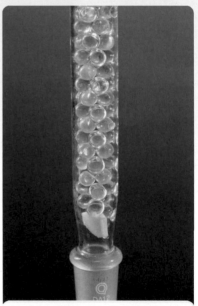

FIGURE 2: A fractionating column used to separate alcohol and water.

> Some people drink too much alcohol – this can be a real problem

QUESTIONS

1. What is meant by an alcohol-free drink?
2. Give **two** problems, other than being drunk, that may result from drinking too much alcohol.

...accident ...alcohol ...beer ...biofuel ...disease ...ethanol

From sugar to alcohol

Grapevines produce grapes that are used to make wine.

Sugars are found naturally in most fruit, as well as in sugar beet and cane sugar. When these sugars are dissolved in water, and yeast is added, an important reaction called **fermentation** occurs. During fermentation, the sugar is changed to alcohol.

Alcohol burns very cleanly to produce heat energy. It can therefore be used as a fuel, and since it is made from plants, like sugar cane, it is called a **biofuel**.

The alcohol made from fermentation is called **ethanol**. It can be added to petrol or used as a replacement for petrol since it burns to produce heat energy.

Once the sugar cane has been used to make ethanol, it can then be grown again to make more – so ethanol is a renewable fuel.

Beer and wine

Beer and **wine** are drinks that contain ethanol. These drinks are both made by taking natural sugars and starches and allowing fermentation to take place – ethanol is then formed.

When making wine, grapes are compressed and then the juice is fermented. In beer manufacture, grain is mashed and the starch allowed to ferment in the presence of hops to add flavour.

FIGURE 3: Grapes are used to make wine.

FIGURE 4: Sugar cane like this can be used to make alcohol – a fuel.

EXAM HINTS AND TIPS

Remember! The chemical formula for sugar is $C_6H_{12}O_6$ and for ethanol is C_2H_5OH.

What's the chemistry of fermentation?

In fermentation, the sugars are changed, via a chemical reaction, into a new substance called ethanol and carbon dioxide gas.

This reaction can be shown using both word and symbol equations:

$$\text{sugar solution} \xrightarrow{\text{yeast}} \text{alcohol} + \text{carbon dioxide gas}$$

$$C_6H_{12}O_6 \rightarrow 2C_2H_5OH + 2CO_2$$

The alcohol formed can be removed by fractional distillation of the mixture.

Uses of ethanol

Ethanol is used as a fuel and also as a **solvent**. A solvent is a liquid that dissolves other chemicals. Figure 5 shows large tanks of ethanol waiting to be used as a solvent.

FIGURE 5: Ethanol ready to behave as a solvent.

QUESTIONS

3 What chemical change takes place in fermentation?

4 From where does the sugar come from to make alcohol?

5 Give a reason why it is a better idea for alcohol to be made from plants rather then from crude oil.

QUESTIONS

6 Which gas is produced in fermentation?

7 What is a solvent?

8 What is the technique used to remove alcohol from a solution of ethanol in water?

Emulsions

You will find out:
- What is meant by emulsions
- How emulsions are made
- Some everyday uses for emulsions

The colourful world of paints

Emulsions are everywhere in our lives. They are special mixtures that are used in foods as well as for making paints.

But what is meant by an emulsion? What type of substance is an emulsion? How are emulsions made?

FIGURE 1: These paints are emulsion based.

What is an emulsion?

We all know that oil and water do not mix. When oil is added to water, the oil floats on the water. However, when they are shaken together, the liquids form small droplets that mix together to make an emulsion.

If an emulsion is left, it will separate back into the oily and water liquids. This can be prevented by adding an **emulsifier** that stops the layers separating out.

Figure 3 shows an emulsion. It is made of oily droplets **suspended** in water.

Milk is an emulsion. The fatty droplets in milk are spread out in water. Butter, on the other hand, is an emulsion in which water particles are spread out in vegetable oils.

FIGURE 2: Why must French dressing be shaken before it can be used?

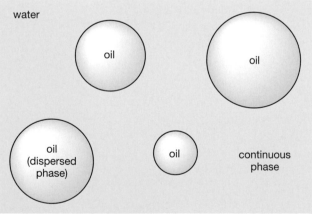

FIGURE 3: A water-based emulsion.

QUESTIONS

1 Give **three** examples of emulsions used in everyday life.
2 What would happen if an emulsion were left alone?
3 What is the name of the type of substance added to an emulsion to stop the process in question 2 from taking place?

...*aqueous* ...*droplet size* ...*emulsifier* ...*emulsion* ...*hydrophilic* ...*hydrophobic*

How do emulsions work?

Emulsions are made up of more than one **immiscible** liquid mixed together. There could be droplets of oil suspended in a water-based (or **aqueous**) liquid (like in milk), or an aqueous liquid suspended in an oily liquid (like in butter). The different **phases** (liquids) in an emulsion are normally called the continuous phase (the supporting liquid) and the disperse phase (the suspended liquid).

When you shake an emulsion very hard, you make the **droplet size** smaller. The droplets formed by shaking are normally very small, and are just visible to the naked eye. Using a proper emulsion mixer, it is possible to achieve a droplet size of 100 to 1000 **nanometres** (1 000 000 nanometres = 1 mm). This is very small and these droplets cannot be seen.

FIGURE 4: Milk is an emulsion. But do you know why milk is white?

The small droplets in an emulsion scatter light passing through it. The result is that the emulsion appears to be either an **opaque** grey or white. This effect is similar to a bowl of salt - each individual grain is transparent (just like an emulsion droplet), but a collection of grains appears white since all light is scattered.

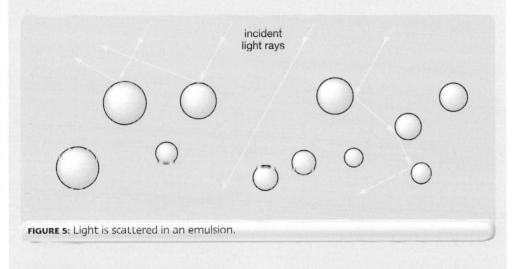

incident light rays

FIGURE 5: Light is scattered in an emulsion.

FRENCH DRESSING

When vinegar is added to olive oil, French dressing is made. It is made up of two immiscible liquids that need shaking together before the dressing can be used.

EXAM HINTS AND TIPS

Liquids that do not mix together are called immiscible liquids. Those that do mix together are called miscible liquids.

QUESTIONS

4 Explain why milk appears as a white liquid.

5 How large, in millimetres (mm), is 1000 nanometres?

6 Is the continuous phase in butter the aqueous or fatty phase?

What is mayonnaise?

Mayonnaise is a thick, creamy sauce or dressing that is made of oil, egg yolks, lemon juice or vinegar, and seasonings.

FIGURE 6: Mayonnaise is an example of an emulsion.

Mayonnaise is an emulsion. Oil and water is the classic example of an emulsion. Emulsifying is done by slowly adding one ingredient to another while simultaneously mixing rapidly. This disperses and suspends tiny droplets of one liquid through another.

However, the two liquids would quickly separate again if an emulsifier were not added. Emulsifiers are substances that are added to the emulsion to prevent them from separating. Emulsifiers have a 'water loving' (**hydrophilic**) part and an 'oil loving' (**hydrophobic**) part. This means that they are attracted to both the aqueous and oily layers, and therefore help 'bond' the liquids together, and also keep them mixed together. Eggs and gelatine are among the foods that contain substances called emulsifiers. In mayonnaise, the emulsifier is egg yolk, which contains lecithin, which is a fat emulsifier.

QUESTIONS

7 What is the name of the chemical substance in egg yolk that acts as an emulsifier in mayonnaise?

8 Gelatine is sometimes added to yoghurts. Suggest why this is done.

9 What is the meaning of the terms 'hydrophobic' and 'hydrophilic'?

...immiscible ...nanometre ...opaque ...phase ...suspended

Additives

You will find out:
- What food additives are and why they are used in certain foods
- About important issues regarding some additives
- About smart packaging for foods

Colours in sweets

When we look at sweets and food in shops, we realise what a colourful world it is. Food looks a lot tastier when it is brightly coloured and looking fresh. We are more likely to buy it if it looks nice.

People are now more aware that some additives may have side effects that may not be pleasant. However, most people can consume additives without any risk to health at all.

Additives – what are they?

There are many potentially harmful or toxic chemicals present in the **food** we eat, whether they are found naturally or as **additives** that are added for a particular reason. But these chemicals are not necessarily harmful in small amounts. Normally, the effects they have depend upon the amount that we consume.

The various types of additive include: antioxidants, colours, emulsifiers, stabilisers, gelling agents and thickeners, flavourings, preservatives, and sweeteners.

FIGURE 1: How are sweets made to look as colourful as this?

Intelligent packaging

When we buy food, we expect it to last for a certain amount of time without going off. Sometimes **oxygen** and **water vapour** from the air will find their way through packaging, and the food will then go bad.

How do we prevent food going bad?

Small packets of **iron powder** can be used to react with any oxygen gas that may get through the packaging:

 iron + oxygen gas → iron oxide

It can be used to prolong the life of some packaged meat.

Packets of **silica gel** can be used to absorb water in packets of biscuits and therefore help to stop them going off.

FIGURE 2: This cream cake has lots of additives in it to make eating it an even nicer experience!

FIGURE 3: Silica gel can help preserve biscuits.

:: QUESTIONS ::

1. Give **five** examples of types of additive.
2. Name **two** substances that can cause food to go off.
3. Explain how silica gel can help preserve biscuits.

...additive ...food ...iron powder ...oxygen

Are additives safe?

Additives are chemicals that make food tastier, longer lasting and more colourful. Without additives, many foods would look so off-putting that you might not want to eat them.

Many of the chemicals occur naturally and others are man-made. However, important testing takes place on both natural and man-made additives to make sure that they are safe.

How safe is safe?

This is a really important question. A scientist can never say whether anything is 100% safe. Why is this?

When **testing** to see whether a chemical is safe or not, it is important that thorough tests are carried out. A large group of people (or animals) is selected and a chemical is then given to them. The health of the group is monitored.

If there are 1000 people in the group, how few people need to be affected by the chemical before we can say that the chemical is safe? What happens if one person in 1000 is affected? Is this safe? What about if one million people are tested and one person is affected? Does this mean that the chemical is safe? It certainly is not 100% safe, but will it ever be?

There will always be a **risk** of something happening, no matter how small that risk. Although the measurement of risk is difficult, we must decide whether the benefits of an activity, like eating food additives, outweigh the risks.

The most important thing is to make sure that we are informed. To find out the truth behind the risks in life we should seek the correct information. However, we must always realise that, in the end, there will be no such thing as total safety.

 The term 'organic' is used to describe food that has a smaller amount of additives. It does not mean that food is completely additive-free.

> **WOW FACTOR!**
>
> Aloe Vera, the special ingredient added to many shampoos, is 99.8% water. The remainder comes from various sugars.

> **QUESTIONS**
>
> 4 Many people believe that 'all chemicals are bad for us'. Is this statement true? Give an example of a piece of evidence which strengthens your answer.
>
> 5 A scientist may say that an additive is safe in that 1 in 1 000 000 people will show a reaction to the chemical. Does this mean that the chemical is safe or not? Explain your answer.
>
> 6 In a scientific test, it is shown that 3 people in 45 000 developed a minor skin rash when exposed to a certain chemical substance. What number of people needs to be in a group for us to be confident of 1 person developing a rash?

The perfect shampoo – does it exist? (H)

Wander down an aisle in any chemist shop and you will see a non-ending selection of **shampoos**. How do you choose which one is right for you? What makes one better than the next? Most people look at the cost. Does this tell you anything? And fragrance is a close second. If it smells wonderful, then it must work! Lastly, the amount of bubbles that it produces ... does this make for a good shampoo?

FIGURE 4: Do the special ingredients added to some shampoos make any difference?

Some manufacturers add 'special ingredients' and often blind the customer with science, hoping that the customer will eventually weaken and buy. Typical 'special ingredients' added are: ylang-ylang, heliogenol, Aloe Vera and nutri ceramide.

How do we test the claims of shampoo manufacturers that these special ingredients make the shampoo better?

> **QUESTIONS**
>
> 7 Suggest a way in which the claims about beauty products, like shampoos, containing special ingredients could be tested.
>
> 8 Why do many advertisements for beauty products use scientific language when describing their special ingredients?

Unit summary

Concept map

Carbon dioxide levels have increased in the air, raising the temperature of the planet's atmosphere. This is called global warming.

Biofuels can be made from living organisms such as plants and bacterial action on sewage.

Seawater and the air can be separated to produce useful chemicals.

Fuels

Fuels produce heat energy and gases, such as carbon dioxide, when burnt.

Ethanol and hydrogen are two fuels that can be made. In the future, they could be used instead of fuels obtained from crude oil.

Crude oil contains compounds called hydrocarbons. These can be separated by a process called fractional distillation.

Hydrocarbons are separated from crude oil in fractions such as petrol and diesel.

Each fraction has different properties. For example the size of the molecules is larger in higher boiling point fractions.

Wood, metals and plastics are particularly important materials as they can be used to make a variety of useful things.

Materials

Materials are everywhere.

Smart materials are extremely 'clever' as they can change, for example when the temperature changes. They have a variety of interesting uses.

Extreme sports enthusiasts use a variety of smart materials such as Goretex®, Thinsulate™ and carbon fibres.

Goretex® is a breathable fibre that keeps the heat in, so we stay warm, but allows water to escape.

Kevlar® is a tough polymer that is used to make a variety of important items, such as bullet-proof vests.

Teflon® is a slippery polymer that also has numerous uses.

Molecules can also be made to do clever things. This is called nanotechnology.

Unit quiz

1. What is the name of the gas which is mainly responsible for global warming? Where does this gas come from?

2. What is the name given to compounds present in crude oil that contain hydrogen and carbon only?

3. List **four** properties of a good fuel.

4. Some people have predicted what the temperature of the Earth's atmosphere will be in around 50 years' time. Explain why there are uncertainties in the figures given.

5. What is meant by a 'biofuel'?

6. Suggest **one** example of an alternative fuel to petrol.

7. List the names of **three** fractions obtained from crude oil.

8. How does the size of the molecules in a particular fraction vary on moving **up** the fractionating column?

9. What is meant by the term 'fermentation'?

10. What is meant by 'incomplete combustion' of a fuel?

11. Explain why incomplete combustion is a concern to human health.

12. Indicate how a gas boiler in a house can be dangerous if it is not serviced regularly.

13. What is the name of the process by which liquid air is separated into its constituent gases?

14. What are the names of the **three** most common gases in air?

15. How is seawater used to make chlorine gas? List **three** other useful substances that are made from seawater.

16. What is the chemical formula for **a)** hydrogen gas and **b)** sodium chloride?

17. A substance obtained from crude oil has the formula C_4H_{10}. What is its name?

18. Suggest **one** reason why it is better to recycle glass objects than to make glass from the raw materials within the Earth.

Literacy activity

Siberia's rapid thaw causes alarm

The world's largest frozen peat bog is melting and could speed the rate of global warming. A huge expanse of western Siberia is thawing for the first time since its formation, 11 000 years ago. The area, which is the size of France and Germany combined, could release billions of tonnes of greenhouse gases into the atmosphere. This could potentially act as a tipping point, causing global warming to snowball, scientists fear.

Western Siberia has warmed faster than almost anywhere on the planet, with average temperatures increasing by about 3 °C in the last 40 years. The warming is believed to be due to a combination of man-made climate change, a cyclical atmospheric phenomenon known as the Arctic oscillation and feedbacks caused by melting ice. The 11 000-year-old bogs contain billions of tonnes of methane, most of which has been trapped in permafrost and deeper ice-like structures called clathrates.

QUESTIONS

1. What is the name of the gas trapped in the ice that could cause global warming?

2. What is the name of the gas that is produced by burning fossil fuels which also adds to global warming?

3. Suggest a way in which global warming may be slowed down.

Exam practice

1 Which statement about global warming is correct?
- **A** Burning of fossils fuels is known to be causing global warming
- **B** Predictions about the amount of global warming are made by computer models and so they must be correct.
- **C** Combustion of hydrocarbon fuels produces carbon dioxide which may lead to global warming.
- **D** The precautionary principle says that it is only thought that burning fossil fuels causes global warming, so you don't really need to reduce the burning of fossil fuels. [1]

2 Which statement about recycling is **incorrect**?
- **A** It is relatively easy to recycle glass, metal and paper.
- **B** It is quite difficult to recycle plastics because it is difficult to separate the different types.
- **C** Desalination of water is a cheap way of obtaining pure water.
- **D** Many more councils are introducing composting schemes to make sure organic waste is not placed into landfill sites. [1]

3 Which statement about bio-fuels is true?
- **A** Bio-fuels cannot be produced in Britain.
- **B** Bio-fuels do not produce carbon dioxide when they burn.
- **C** Bio-fuels cannot be used as an alternative to petrol in cars.
- **D** One source of a bio-fuel is ethanol which can be obtained from fermentation of sugars. [1]

4 Which statement is true? During the fractional distillation of crude oil ...
- **A** the crude oil is heated to make it condense before it enters the fractionating column.
- **B** large molecules, such as those in the bitumen fraction, have the lowest boiling point.
- **C** small molecules such as propane and butane go right to the top of the column.
- **D** each fraction obtained contains molecules of one sort only. [1]

5 Choose the correct use for the fraction obtained by fractional distillation.
- **A** Fuel oil is burnt in power stations to provide energy for electricity production.
- **B** Naphtha is condensed and sold as bottled gases for camping.
- **C** Refinery gases are not very useful and are just burnt at the refinery to dispose of them.
- **D** Bitumen is used as fuel for airplanes. [1]

6 Choose the **incorrect** statement about the combustion of hydrocarbon fuels.
- **A** It may produce toxic carbon monoxide unless enough oxygen is available.
- **B** Complete combustion produces carbon and carbon monoxide.
- **C** It produces carbon dioxide and water vapour, provided sufficient oxygen is present.
- **D** It can produce gases which cause respiratory diseases such as asthma. [1]

7 Carbon monoxide is toxic because...
- **A** it reduces the ability of our lungs to draw in air.
- **B** it improves the ability of haemoglobin in our blood to carry oxygen.
- **C** it decreases the amount of oxygen that our blood can carry.
- **D** it causes asthma. [1]

8 During the fractional distillation of air...
- **A** Only the nitrogen in the air is turned to a liquid and this is how it is separated.
- **B** The air is first liquefied by cooling it and compressing it.
- **C** The air is first liquefied by heating it and compressing it
- **D** The different gases in air are separated because they have different melting points. [1]

9 Which list best represents the substances obtained from seawater by electrolysis?
- **A** Sodium hydroxide, chlorine, hydrogen.
- **B** Sodium hydroxide, oxygen, chlorine, hydrogen.
- **C** Sodium hydroxide, oxygen, chlorine.
- **D** Sodium hydroxide, oxygen, hydrogen, chlorine. [1]

10 Which statement about smart materials is true?
- **A** Scientists have created new materials and have only found a use for them later.
- **B** Goretex™ is a useful material for outdoor clothing because it absorbs only very small amounts of water and has very good insulation properties.
- **C** Thinsulate™ is a very useful material for outdoor clothing because of its breathability.
- **D** Teflon is very useful for making cycling shorts as it is very stretchy and its shape returns after it has been stretched. [1]

11 How big are nanoparticles?
  A about 1 million times smaller than a metre.
  B about 1 million times smaller than a centimetre.
  C about 1 million times larger than a metre.
  D about 1 million times larger than a centimetre. [1]

12 What is meant when we say a substance is hydrophobic?
  A It is a substance that is attracted to water.
  B It is a substance that releases water when heated.
  C It is a substance that is not attracted to water.
  D It is a substance that contains water within its structure. [1]

(Total 12 marks)

Worked example

Use the data in this table to select the correct answer form the key below.
  A Fraction A is more viscous and more volatile than fraction B.
  B The molecules in Fraction D have the lowest boiling points.
  C Fraction A is more viscous but less volatile than fraction C.
  D Fraction C is lighter in colour than fraction D but darker than fraction B.

Fraction	Average number of carbons in each molecule
A	3
B	12
C	20
D	120

To answer this question you need to know the following:
Fractions from the top of the fractionating column
  a have the smallest molecules, with the least number of carbon atoms
  b are the most volatile, (this means they easily turn to gasses).
  c are the least viscous, (this means they pour extremely easily)
  d are the most flammable (this means they ignite easily).
  e have the lowest boiling points.
  f make the best fuels.
  g are much lighter in colour. As you go down the column, the colour becomes darker.

Fraction A is from the top of the fractionating column as it has a small number of carbon atoms. It will be **less viscous** and more volatile than fraction B. **A is incorrect.**

The molecules in B are very large and would be found at the bottom of the fractionating column where the boiling points of the molecules are very high. **B is incorrect.**

Fraction A contains the least viscous molecules and the most volatile molecules. **Answer C is wrong on both counts.**

Fraction C contains smaller molecules than fraction D, so it will be lighter in colour than D. The molecules in Fraction B are smaller than those in Fraction C, so these molecules will be lighter in colour. **Answer D is therefore correct.**

How to get an A

In this sort of multi-choice question, make sure that each part of the statement is correct. Do not stop looking when you have spotted just one part that is correct. It would be a good idea to sketch the fractionating column out and add all of the information that you know to the sketch. This will help you keep a clear head when you start reading the statements. This is also a very useful way of revising; try turning the information you have to learn into a series of diagrams. This helps you to really understand the work and some people are bettered visual learners than others – you might be one of them!

DISCOVER SPRITES, JETS AND ELVES!

We all know that there can be lots going on underneath a thundercloud, but did you know that there are all sorts of strange things going on above as well? Some of them are shown here, but it is a complex and still emerging area of science.

Blue jets shoot up from thunder clouds to heights of 40 km. They last for about a quarter of a second.

In 2002, giant jets were seen for the first time shooting all the way from the cloud tops to the ionosphere. They looked like sprites at the top.

High in the atmosphere faint red discs can sometimes be seen. These are called elves and last for less than one millisecond.

Sprites are red and occur between 35–90 km high. They last for a few milliseconds. They usually coincide with large lightning strikes on the ground.

CONTENTS

Charges, currents and circuits

You will find out:
- What we mean by electric current
- About the basic properties of electrical circuits
- About series and parallel circuits
- About solar cells providing current

Living without circuits? ... Never

We use electrical devices in almost every area of our lives, from the simple filament lamp, to the TV and computer, to the mobile phone. All these devices have components inside them which are connected together to form circuits. But what is actually going on in these circuits?

FIGURE 1: Cells connect together to form batteries...

...we can think of cells and batteries as pumps.

Cells and batteries

Most **circuits** contain a power supply such as a **cell** or a **battery**. It is these which make **charges** in the circuit flow.

We can think of cells and batteries as being pumps. Several cells can be connected together to form a battery.

Electric **current** is moving charges. In most circuits, the charges are carried by tiny particles called the **electrons**. This is where the name 'electricity' comes from.

Circuits are the pathways along which the charges flow.

Circuit diagrams

Unless you are a skilled artist, drawing an accurate picture of a circuit would be very difficult and take a very long time. To get around this problem, we use simple circuit diagrams. Each of the **components** in a circuit has an easy-to-draw symbol. These are connected together to form an electrical circuit.

An example of a real circuit and its circuit diagram is shown in figure 2.

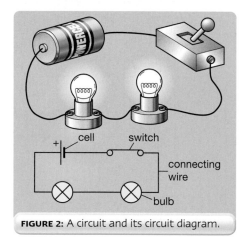

FIGURE 2: A circuit and its circuit diagram.

Circuit symbols

Here are some of the symbols you will need to know:

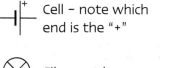
Cell – note which end is the "+"

Battery – if the battery is made from lots of cells, we don't draw them all

Filament lamp

Switch

QUESTIONS

1 What is an electrical circuit?
2 What is an electric current?
3 Explain the difference between a cell and a battery.
4 Draw the symbol for **a)** a cell and **b)** a battery.

WANT TO KNOW MORE?

Go to this web page to find out how batteries work:

http://science.howstuffworks.com/battery1.htm

...battery ...cell ...charge ...circuit ...component ...conventional current ...current

Series and parallel circuits

There are two main types of circuit. These are called **series** circuits and **parallel** circuits.

In a series circuit, there are no junctions and the current can only follow one route.

In parallel circuits, there are junctions and currents can follow different paths.

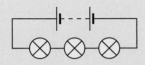

FIGURE 3: A simple series circuit.

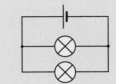

FIGURE 4: A simple parallel circuit.

EXAM HINTS AND TIPS

Remember! A battery is several cells connected together so that a larger current can be provided in the circuit.

Switches and circuits

Look carefully at the parallel circuit in figure 5. If we start with all the switches closed and then open and close them again one at a time we will see two lamps glow continuously and one go on and off.

Compare this with a series circuit with several switches. If any of the switches are opened, all the lamps go out.

In a parallel circuit, it is possible to turn part of it on or off. In series circuits, switches turn the whole circuit on or off.

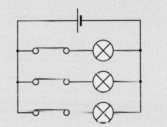

FIGURE 5: A parallel circuit with three switches and three bulbs.

Conventional current and electron flow

Early scientists investigating electricity made a decision that electric current was due to the movement of **positive** charges. These positive charges moved away from the positive terminal of the cell and towards the negative terminal of the cell. This is known as the **conventional current** direction. In metal wires, it is negatively charged electrons that move and not the positive charges. The direction of **electron flow** is in the opposite direction to the conventional current direction.

Solar cells

FIGURE 6: Solar cells are a sensible choice for an orbiting satellite.

A chemical cell changes chemical energy into electrical energy. A **solar cell** can also be used to move charges in an electrical circuit. A solar cell is an electronic device that changes light into electrical energy. This type of cell produces a direct current. Solar cells can be used for low current devices like a pocket calculator. They are also very useful in remote and hot regions of the world. Solar cells have been used to power the onboard equipment on artificial satellites.

QUESTIONS

7 Why do electrons flow from the negative terminal of a battery to its positive terminal?

8 Suggest why it may be sensible to use solar cells instead of chemical cells onboard a satellite orbiting the Earth.

QUESTIONS

5 Draw a circuit with a cell and two lamps in series. Draw labelled arrows to show which way the conventional current is flowing, and which way the electrons are flowing.

6 In a circuit with three lamps **a)** in series and **b)** in parallel, what happens if one lamp fails? Explain your answer fully.

...*electron* ...*electron flow* ...*parallel* ...*series* ...*solar cell*

Current

You will find out:

- How current is related to the flow of charge
- How current is measured
- About the coulomb
- About the Amp-hour

Currents in nature

The photograph shows one of the most dramatic effects of **charges** on the move. The current during the flash is often in excess of 10 000 A. The air around the flash becomes so hot that it expands at a rate which is faster than the speed of sound. The sonic boom created by this is what we call thunder.

Currents in circuits are much, much smaller than this, but it is important to be able to measure them and control their size.

FIGURE 1: A flash of lightning.

Measuring current

- A **current** is a flow of charge.
- If the current in a **circuit** is small then this means the amount of charge which flows through a **component** each second is small.
- If the current in the circuit is large then this means the amount of charge flowing through the component each second is larger.
- The size of a current is a measure of the rate at which charge is flowing.

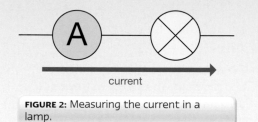

current

FIGURE 2: Measuring the current in a lamp.

We measure the current in a component using an **ammeter**. We connect the ammeter in series with the component. Current is measured in **amperes** or amps (A), or sometimes milliamps (mA)

Cells, batteries and solar cells are sources of direct current (d.c). The direction of the direct current remains the same around a circuit.

Alternators are also sources of current but their current is called alternating current (a.c). The direction of alternating current changes (see page 205).

FIGURE 3: An ammeter used to measure current.

■ QUESTIONS ■

1   Draw a circuit with a cell lighting a lamp, include a switch, and an ammeter to measure the current in the lamp.
2   Draw a circuit that has a battery, two lamps in parallel with each other and an ammeter measuring the current in each lamp.

...ammeter ...ampere ...Amp-hour ...battery ...capacity ...charge

Determining charge

Remember that electrical current is defined as the rate of flow of charge. That is:

current = charge/time

We know that current is measured in amperes, but what is the unit for charge? Electrical charge is measured in **coulombs** (C). A charge of 1 C flows past a given point in a circuit when a current of 1A exists for a time of 1 s.

Currents in series and parallel circuits

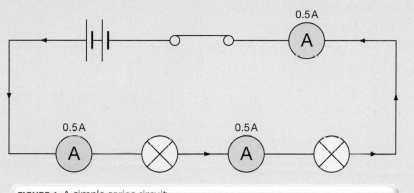

FIGURE 4: A simple series circuit.

The current in a **series** circuit is the **same** everywhere.

The currents in a **parallel** circuit may be of **different** sizes.

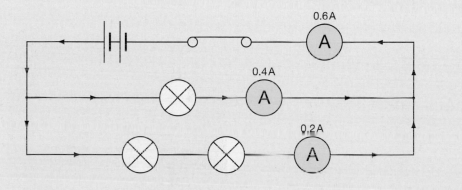

FIGURE 5: A simple two-branch parallel circuit.

WOW FACTOR!

When a current of 1A flows, it means that 6,250,000,000,000,000,000 electrons are passing every point in the wire each second!

QUESTIONS

3   Explain in your own words why the current in a series circuit is the same everywhere.

4   Suggest in your own words why the currents in different parts of a parallel circuit may not be the same.

WANT TO KNOW MORE?

Find out about André Marie Ampère at www-groups.dcs.st-and.ac.uk/~history/Mathematicians/Ampere.html

How long will my battery last?

FIGURE 6: A leisure battery used in a caravan.

The label on this **battery** tells us its **capacity**. It is a 85 **Amp-hour** battery. This means that, in theory, if this battery was connected to a circuit and the current was 1 A, the battery would last 85 hours, but if the current was 4 A it would only last approximately 21 hours.

Amp-hours = current x time

QUESTIONS

5   Calculate the time for which a 60 Amp-hour battery could produce a current of 0.5 A.

6   Calculate the current that could be drawn from a 60 Amp-hour battery if used for 15 hours.

7   Find out why these figures are only approximate and depend upon the size of the current required.

Voltage

You will find out:
- How to measure voltage
- How voltage is produced using magnets and coils
- The factors affecting the size of the voltage

Creating electricity

A current-carrying wire is surrounded by a magnetic field. Hence electric current or moving charges create magnetism. The magnetic field can be made stronger by twisting the wire into a coil of several turns and wrapping it round a chunk of soft iron. Early scientists like Michael Faraday wondered how electricity itself could be produced using magnetism. Without Faraday's pioneering work, we would not have mains electricity!

FIGURE 1: Michael Faraday showed how magnetism could be used to produce current and voltage

What is voltage?

When electrical charges travel through a cell, they gain electrical energy. When the same charges travel through components like resistors and filament lamps, they transfer their electrical energy into other forms (heat, light etc). The voltage, also known as **potential difference** (**p.d.**), across a component tells us how much electrical energy is transferred by each coulomb of charge.

The **voltage** across a component is defined as the amount of energy transferred from electrical to other forms by a charge of one coulomb. Energy is measured in joules (J). Hence a voltage of 3 V across a lamp means that 3 J of electrical energy is transferred into heat and light by every coulomb of charge passing through the lamp.

Sometimes, the term potential difference is used instead of voltage.

FIGURE 2: A voltmeter is used to measure voltage.

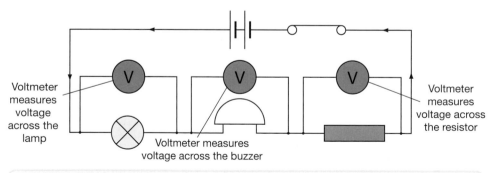

Voltmeter measures voltage across the lamp

Voltmeter measures voltage across the buzzer

Voltmeter measures voltage across the resistor

FIGURE 3: *Measuring the voltage across different components.*

We measure voltage across a component using a **voltmeter**. The voltmeter is always placed across the component. We measure voltage in **volts** (V) or millivolts (mV).

QUESTIONS

1 What instrument is used to measure voltage?
2 Do charges gain or lose electrical energy in a cell?
3 What is the energy transfer for charges travelling through a lamp?
4 A voltage of 6 V means '6 joules of energy transferred by a charge of 1 coulomb'. Is this correct?

...dynamo ...electromagnetic induction ...induced voltage

Electromagnetic induction

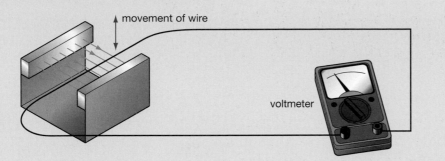

FIGURE 4: Inducing a voltage by moving a wire in a magnetic field.

A voltmeter is connected across the ends of a copper wire. The copper wire is quickly moved through the magnetic field of a strong **magnet**. What happens to the reading on the voltmeter? The voltmeter shows a deflection every time the wire cuts the magnetic field. The voltmeter shows the **induced voltage** across the ends of the copper wire. Producing a voltage in this manner is referred to as **electromagnetic induction**.

Where does the electrical energy come from? Some of the kinetic energy of the moving copper wire is converted into electrical energy.

The direction of the induced voltage depends on the direction in which the copper wire cuts the magnetic field. An alternating voltage may be produced in the wire when it is repeatedly moved up and down through the magnetic field of the magnet.

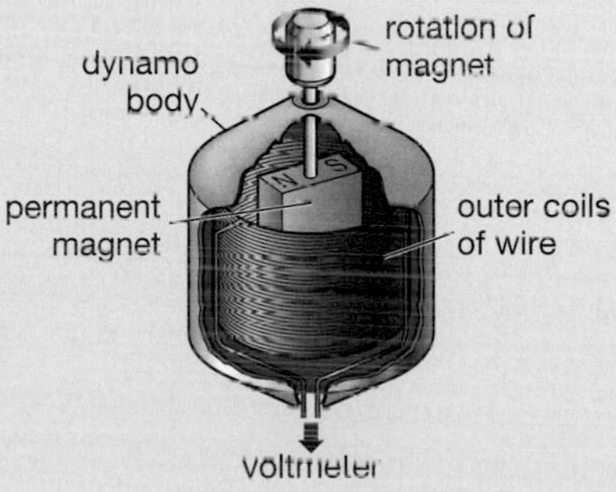

A voltage may also be induced in a coil by moving a magnet towards or away from the coil.

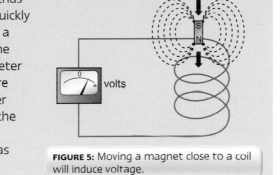

FIGURE 5: Moving a magnet close to a coil will induce voltage.

FIGURE 6: A bicycle dynamo works on the principle of electromagnetic induction.

The voltmeter will not show an induced voltage when the magnet is stationary. There is only a voltage when either the magnet or the coil is moved. For an induced voltage, the magnetic field must cut the circuit.

In a bicycle **dynamo**, a magnet rotates near a coil of wire. The magnetic field of the rotating magnet repeatedly cuts the coil and this induces a voltage across the ends of the coil. The induced voltage helps to produce an induced current in the bicycle lamp.

Factors affecting the induced voltage and current

When a magnet is moved towards a coil, how can we increase the size of the induced voltage or current?

The induced voltage or current may be increased by:

- Increasing the speed of the magnet
- Using a magnet with a stronger magnetic field
- Increasing the number of turns on the coil.

For a bicycle dynamo, the bicycle lamp can be made brighter by pedalling faster. This makes the magnet rotate faster and therefore a greater current is induced in the dynamo coil.

QUESTIONS

5. How can you induce a voltage across the ends of a wire using a magnet?
6. How can you induce an alternating voltage using a magnet and a coil?
7. What is the induced voltage across the ends of a coil when a strong magnet is stationary within its core?
8. Explain how current is induced in the coil in a bicycle dynamo.

QUESTIONS

9. How can you produce a greater induced current with a loop of wire and a magnet?
10. Explain why pedalling faster makes a bicycle dynamo produce a larger current.

At home with electricity

You will find out:
- How electricity is created and transmitted to our homes
- The difference between direct and alternating currents
- About devices producing alternating and direct currents

When the lights go out

Bad weather is miserable enough on its own but when you lose your electricity supply as well, then things can be very unpleasant and even dangerous. Normally, of course, our supply works well and we take it for granted. But how is our electricity generated at a power station?

FIGURE 1: Bad weather can cause power cuts.

Generating electricity

Electricity is generated in **power stations**. You will find out more about power stations in other sections, but here is a description of how a coal-fired power station works:

- coal is burned to release heat
- the heat is used to warm water
- the water turns to steam
- the steam rushes past a turbine causing it to spin
- the turbine is connected to a generator so that spins as well (generators work on the principle of electromagnetic induction)
- the spinning causes an electric current to be produced.

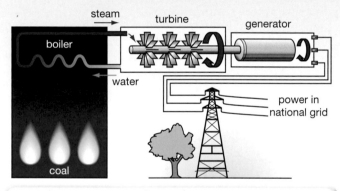

FIGURE 2: How a power station works.

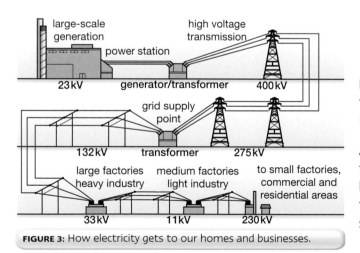

FIGURE 3: How electricity gets to our homes and businesses.

From the power station the electricity is transported to homes, hospitals, factories, etc., through the National Grid.

As you can see, the **voltage** is changed quite often in the system. The high voltages are used because they help to transmit electrical power more efficiently, but they have to be made lower before they can be used safely in the home.

QUESTIONS

1. What is the purpose of the coal in a power station?
2. What is the steam used for in a power station?
3. Why is electricity transmitted at such high voltages?
4. Why do the voltages have to be reduced again before we can use it?

 Direct current always travels in one direction.

...alternating current (a.c.) ...direct current (d.c.) ...electricity ...Hertz (Hz)

Let's be clear about current

Let's start with a nice familiar battery.

FIGURE 4: Batteries generate a current.

- Every battery has a + and a − marked on it somewhere.
- The current that is supplied by a battery is called **direct current** or **d.c**.
- The current might not always have the same value, but its direction is always the same.

Mains electricity is different.

- The current from the mains is an **alternating current** or **a.c**.
- The direction of the current changes all the time.
- The current changes direction 50 times per second.
- We say that the mains has a frequency of 50 **Hertz (Hz)**.

Why bother with a.c.?

- Less energy is lost if you transmit at high voltage.
- It is necessary to change the size of the voltages to transmit over long distances.
- It is difficult to change the size of direct voltages.
- It is easy to change the size of alternating voltages using transformers.

WANT TO KNOW MORE?

For more about the competition between the a.c. and d.c. systems see http://en.wikipedia.org/wiki/War_of_Currents.

QUESTIONS

5   What is a direct current?

6   What is an alternating current?

Picturing the current

The picture shows a cathode ray **oscilloscope**. It shows how a voltage varies with time.

FIGURE 5: A cathode ray oscilloscope.

When no voltage is applied, you get a horizontal line across the middle of the screen. This is 0 V.

When a battery is connected the horizontal line moves up or down depending on which way the battery is connected.

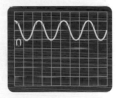

If you connect an alternating supply, you will usually see a wave-form like this ...

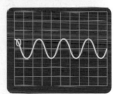

For an alternating voltage, there must be signal above and below the 0 V line. This picture shows a varying direct voltage.

In the UK, the mains voltage is said to be 230 V, but as you can see the voltage changes all the time.

QUESTIONS

7   Copy the sentence, choosing the correct options. The UK mains supply is alternating / direct current at 230 / 50 volts and a frequency of 230 / 50 volts / amps / Hertz.

8   Sketch what alternating voltage and direct voltage look like on an oscilloscope screen.

Resistance

You will find out:
- What resistance means and its unit, the ohm (Ω)
- How to calculate resistance
- How resistance affects the current in a circuit

Resistance is important

When you are watching the TV, playing a game on the computer or simply listening to your favourite CD, you are likely to want to adjust the volume of the sound.

Getting the right settings for any of the above is quite straightforward. But have you ever wondered what is happening in the circuits of these devices when you make your changes? Almost certainly you will be altering the sizes of the currents in the different circuits by altering their resistance.

FIGURE 1: How is the volume turned up?

What is electrical resistance?

- All **components** in **circuits** behave as if they are obstacles which **charges** have to flow through.
- If it is easy for charges to flow through a component, we say it has a **low resistance**.
- If it is difficult for charges to flow through a component, we say it has a **high resistance**.

We can use resistance to control the size of a **current** in a circuit. The photograph opposite shows some **resistors** of different values.

FIGURE 2: Resistors of various values.

We measure resistance in **ohms** (Ω). A 100 Ω resistor is a much greater obstacle to the flow of charge than a 10 Ω resistor.

Variable resistors have values which can be altered so that the current in a circuit can be adjusted. This is exactly what you do when you adjust the volume on your CD player.

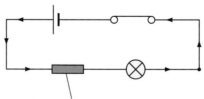

Connecting this fixed resistor into the circuit reduces the current in the lamp

FIGURE 3: A simple circuit with a fixed resistor.

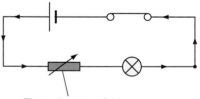

The resistance of this variable resistor can be adjusted so that the lamp becomes brighter or dimmer

FIGURE 4: A simple circuit with a variable resistor included.

QUESTIONS

1. The graphite in your pencil does not conduct current very well. Does it have a high or a low resistance?
2. As the resistance of a circuit increases suggest what happens to the current?
3. Give **two** examples of where you use a variable resistor in the home.

...ampere ...charge ...circuit ...component ...current ...high resistance

Determining resistance

To determine the resistance (R) of a component, we need to know the voltage (V) across the it and the current (I) it carries. The circuit below shows how we can use a voltmeter and an ammeter to determine the quantities needed for determining the resistance of the wire.

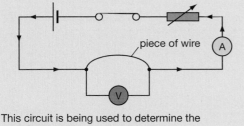

This circuit is being used to determine the resistance of a piece of wire

FIGURE 5: A circuit used to determine resistance.

The resistance is calculated using the equation:

resistance = voltage/current

or
$$R = \frac{V}{I}$$

The resistance will be in **ohms** (Ω), while the current is in **amperes** (A) and the voltage is in **volts** (V).

In general, the relationship between voltage, current and resistance is:

voltage = current × resistance

Example: Calculate the resistance of the resistor in the circuit.

resistance = voltage/current
$$R = \frac{V}{I} = \frac{24}{2}$$
$$R = 12 \ \Omega$$

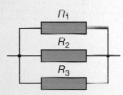

WANT TO KNOW MORE?

Find out about Georg Ohm at
http://inventors.about.com/library/inventors/blohm.htm

QUESTIONS

4 Calculate the resistance of a fixed resistor with a current of 0.1 A when the voltage across it is 10 V.

5 A variable resistor is connected to a 5.0 V battery. The smallest current it gives is 0.01 A and the largest current it gives is 0.2 A. Calculate the range of the resistance values available from this variable resistor.

Resistors in series and parallel

When resistors are connected in either series or parallel combinations, the total resistance can be determined by using the following rules:

Resistors in series

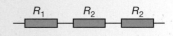

Three resistors of resistance values R_1, and R_2 and R_3 are connected in series. What is the total resistance (R_T) of all three resistors in this combination? The total resistance is given by:

$$R_T = R_1 + R_2 + R_3$$

Example: Three resistors of values 3 Ω, 4 Ω and 5 Ω are connected in series. Their total resistance is:

$$R_T = 3 + 4 + 5 = 12 \ \Omega$$

Resistors in parallel

Three resistors of resistance values R_1, R_2 and R_3 are connected in parallel. What is the total resistance (R_T) of all three resistors in this combination? The total resistance is given by:

$$\frac{1}{R_T} = \frac{1}{R_1} + \frac{1}{R_2} + \frac{1}{R_3}$$

Example: Three resistors of values 3 Ω, 4 Ω and 5 Ω are connected in parallel. Their total resistance is determined as follows:

$$\frac{1}{R_T} = \frac{1}{3} + \frac{1}{4} + \frac{1}{5}$$
$$R_T = 1.28 \ \Omega$$

QUESTIONS

6 Calculate the resistance of three 3 Ω resistors connected **a)** in series and **b)** in parallel.

7 What is the maximum resistance you could make with ten 10 Ω resistors? Draw a diagram to show how they should be connected.

8 What is the minimum resistance you could make with ten 10 Ω resistors? Draw a diagram to show how they should be connected.

More about resistance

You will find out:

- About the heating effect of a current
- How to interpret current-voltage graphs for resistors
- How the resistance of a lamp changes with current
- The shape of the current-voltage graph for a lamp

Spotting changes in resistance

These spotlights produce a very intense bright light. They also become very hot. This increase in temperature has a dramatic effect on their resistance. If we look carefully at how altering the voltages across the lights affect the currents through them, we will be able to see any changes in resistance. The best way to do this is to construct a current – voltage (*I–V*) graph.

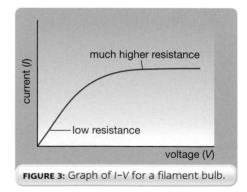

FIGURE 1: Huge spotlights become very hot!

Current, voltage and resistance

The fixed resistor

When the switch is closed in the circuit on the right, we can measure the **voltage** across the fixed **resistor** and the **current** through it.

If we then alter the value of the variable resistor, another pair of readings can be taken. If this process is repeated for five or six readings over a wide range of currents and voltages, we can draw an *I–V* graph from these results.

The steepness of this graph tells us about the **resistance** of the fixed resistor.

- If the graph is steep, this tells us that the resistor has a small resistance.
- If the graph is not steep, this tells us that it has a high resistance.
- The graph is a straight line. This tells us that the value of the resistor does not change during the experiment. (Remember, resistance is always calculated using:

$$\text{resistance} = \frac{\text{voltage}}{\text{current}} .)$$

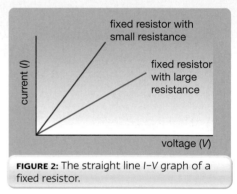

FIGURE 2: The straight line *I–V* graph of a fixed resistor.

The filament lamp

Figure 3 shows the *I–V* graph for a **filament** lamp. It is very different from that for a fixed resistor.

The graph is curved showing that the resistance changes as the current in the lamp changes.

- When the current in the lamp is high, the resistance is high.
- When the current in the lamp is small, the resistance is much less.
- The change in resistance is caused by the heating effect of the current.

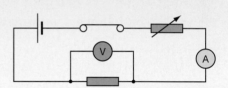

FIGURE 3: Graph of *I–V* for a filament bulb.

▮▮ QUESTIONS ▮▮

1   Draw an *I–V* graph for a fixed resistor. How do we know from this graph that the resistance of the fixed resistor has not changed?

2   Draw an *I–V* graph for a filament lamp. How do we know from this graph that the resistance of the lamp has changed? What caused this change?

What causes the change in resistance when a lamp is switched on?

FIGURE 4: Resistance in a light bulb.

The resistance of a filament lamp changes as its **temperature** changes. The hotter the filament gets, the more its **atoms** vibrate and that means more resistance, because it's harder for the **electrons** to flow between the atoms.

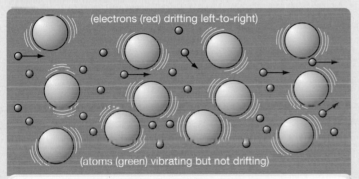

(electrons (red) drifting left-to-right)

(atoms (green) vibrating but not drifting)

FIGURE 5: Electrons collide more frequently with the atoms at higher temperatures.

QUESTIONS

3 Draw an *I–V* graph for a filament lamp. Add the following labels to your graph: lamp bright, lamp dim, high resistance, low resistance.

4 Explain in your own words what happens to the resistance of a filament bulb when it is turned off and its temperature decreases.

Thomas Edison, the inventor of the light bulb?

The usual answer to 'who invented the light bulb' is 'Thomas Edison'. However, this is not quite true – actually he did not invent it. In 1879, he developed an experimental idea that was already 50 years old into something that worked properly and people could use in their homes. His lamps used a filament made

FIGURE 6: Thomas Alva Edison, 1847–1931. His most famous quote is 'Genius is one per cent inspiration and 99 per cent perspiration'.

from carbonised sewing thread. Today we use filaments made of tungsten, which melts at 3410 °C. This means we can run the lamps much hotter, and therefore brighter.

FIGURE 7: A modern display lighting rig.

Figure 8 shows the *I–V* graph for a diode. A **diode** is a component which behaves almost like a one-way street. When current travels through it in one direction it can do so easily, that is, it has a low resistance. But if current tries to travel in the opposite direction, the diode has a very high resistance. Diodes are, therefore, often used in circuits where it is important that current travels in one direction.

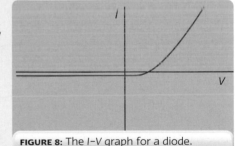

FIGURE 8: The *I–V* graph for a diode.

QUESTIONS

5 Read about Thomas Edison on page 218. Where was the first place to be fitted with an electric lighting system? Try and find out more about his work.

6 What is a diode and what does it do?

7 Why is it important when recharging a battery that the current only flows in one direction?

...resistance   ...resistor   ...temperature   ...voltage

Sensing light and heat

You will find out:
- About light-dependent resistors (LDRs)
- About thermistors
- The shapes of the current-voltage graphs for these components
- How LDRs are used to control the shutter of a camera

Sensing-circuits

Our world is surrounded by surveillance devices in order to keep us safe. Even in our homes, we have electrical circuits that can sense small changes in light or temperature. Burglar alarms and many other sensing-circuits contain thermistors and light-dependent resistors.

Thermistors and light-dependent resistors

Figure 1 shows a typical **thermistor** together with its electrical symbol.

- Thermistors are resistors whose **resistance** is very sensitive to **temperature** changes.
- In the most common thermistors their resistance decreases as their temperature increases; these are known as negative temperature coefficient (NTC) thermistors.
- Thermistors are often used in temperature-sensitive **circuits**.

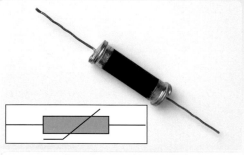

FIGURE 1: A thermistor and its symbol.

FIGURE 2: Controls for central heating.

This central heating controller senses the temperature using a thermistor. When the room gets cold, the resistance of the thermistor increases so the **current** in it falls. This sends a signal to the controller to switch the room heating on.

Figure 3 shows a typical **light-dependent resistor** (LDR) together with its electrical symbol.

If the brightness of the light falling upon an LDR increases, its resistance decreases. LDRs are often used in light-sensitive circuits such as burglar alarms or in **digital cameras** to automatically control how much light is allowed in. The amount of light entering the camera is controlled by the shutter.

Street lights use LDRs to detect when it is dark and the lights need to be switched on, and when it is light and they need to be switched off.

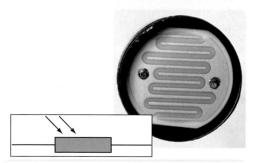

FIGURE 3: A light-dependent resistor and its symbol.

FIGURE 4: LDRs help street lights to come on at night.

:: QUESTIONS ::

1. Draw the symbol for a light-dependent resistor (LDR).
2. Copy the sentence, choosing the correct options: When light falls on an LDR connected to a cell, the resistance rises / falls, and more/less current flows.
3. Draw the symbol for a thermistor.
4. Give one use for **a)** a thermistor and **b)** an LDR.

...*circuit* ...*current* ...*electron* ...*energy* ...*light-dependent resistor*

How do they do it?

In a piece of wire there are lots of free **electrons** that can carry charge when a voltage is applied across it. As a result, pieces of wire are good conductors and usually have a low resistance.

In some materials, called **semiconductors**, there are far fewer electrons available to carry charge. As a result, the resistance of a piece of semiconductor may be much higher than that of a piece of wire. It is, however, possible to free more electrons in a semiconductor by giving them **energy**. In thermistors, the energy is provided as heat. Warming them releases more charge carriers, so their resistance decreases.

In an LDR, the energy is provided as light. In dark conditions, there are only a few charge carriers available in an LDR but in bright conditions more are 'freed' and so the resistance of the LDR decreases.

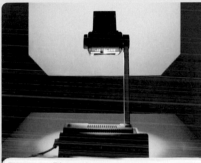

FIGURE 5: Thermistors protect projector lamps.

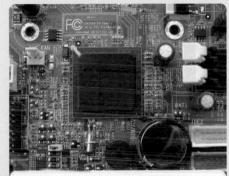

FIGURE 6: Thermistors in a computer.

Thermistors are used to protect powerful projector lamps from high current surges when they are first switched on. Remember that a cold bulb has a low resistance, so a large current exists when you switch it on. A cold thermistor has a high resistance so it limits the current. Then as the projector bulb warms up, the thermistor does too so the resistance falls and the current is allowed to increase in a controlled manner.

Computers use thermistors to sense the temperature of the central processor, which can be damaged if it gets too hot.

 There are two types of thermistors available. This page outlines the 'negative temperature coefficient' type, where the resistance falls as the temperature increases. You can also get 'positive temperature coefficient' thermistors, where the resistance increases as the temperature increases, but you do not need to worry about this second type at this stage.

QUESTIONS

5 What are the charge carriers in a metal wire?

6 How can you release more charge carriers in **a)** a thermistor and in **b)** an LDR?

7 Describe in detail **one** use for a thermistor.

WANT TO KNOW MORE?

Find out more about how to use LDRs at www.doctronics.co.uk /ldr_sensors.htm.

More about thermistors

FIGURE 7: This security light reacts to body heat – but only at night-time. It has an LDR to tell it when night falls.

The current-voltage (I–V) graph for a thermistor is curved – but the opposite way to the light bulb.

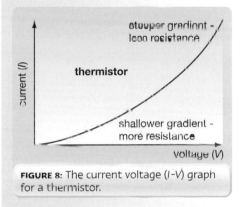

FIGURE 8: The current voltage (I–V) graph for a thermistor.

This is because as the current in the thermistor *increases*, the thermistor becomes hotter and the resistance *decreases*.

QUESTIONS

8 Sketch the I–V graph for a thermistor.

9 Explain why the graph has that shape.

10 Explain why the I–V graph for a lamp is curved the other way.

11 Try to find a circuit or a device which might use both a thermistor and an LDR.

...*resistance*   ...*semiconductor*   ...*temperature*   ...*thermistor*

Batteries and cells

You will find out:

- What batteries and cells actually are
- About the properties of dry cells and rechargable cells
- About some of the environmental problems caused by batteries

The world's first battery

In 1794 Alessandro Volta demonstrated the first battery, though it was then called a 'voltaic pile'. It was made of a stack of silver and zinc discs separated by discs of paper soaked in salt water. You could argue that this was one of the most important inventions ever.

FIGURE 1: Volta's original pile.

What is a battery?

Volta experimented with different metals such as copper, tin and brass, silver and zinc. He also tried different liquids, some of which, like sulphuric acid, were not nice to work with. He found that many different materials could be used to produce an electric current.

You can make a really simple **battery** from a fruit like a lemon and two strips of metal. You need some way to see that it works, so a voltmeter is needed as well.

Basically a battery must have:

- two different conductors – the **electrodes**
- a conducting liquid – the **electrolyte**
- for the battery to produce a current the electrodes must be connected to a complete circuit of some sort.

Battery or a cell?

The word battery was used before Volta built his, but it was used to describe a set of electrically charged plates.

Strictly speaking, a single pair of electrodes in an electrolyte should be called a **cell**, and two or more cells connected together in the same box is called a battery.

A small torch battery is not really a battery, it is a single cell.

A car battery is made of six cells connected together so it really is a battery.

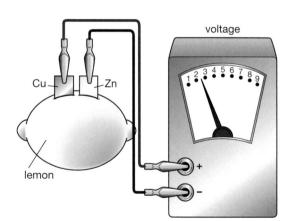

FIGURE 2: Using a lemon to make a battery.

Every year the UK generates over 20 000 tonnes of waste household batteries

---

║ QUESTIONS ║

1 What are the components you must have to make a cell?
2 What do you need to do with a cell or battery to draw current from it?
3 What are the electrodes in Volta's battery?
4 What is the electrolyte in Volta's battery?

...battery   ...cadmium   ...cell   ...electrode   ...electrolyte   ...electron

Real batteries

Inside a cell, a chemical reaction causes **electrons** to collect at one of the electrodes. This becomes the **negative** electrode. As a result there is a shortage of electrons on the other electrode, the **positive** electrode. If the battery is connected into a circuit, electrons can flow and do some useful work such as causing a lamp to glow.

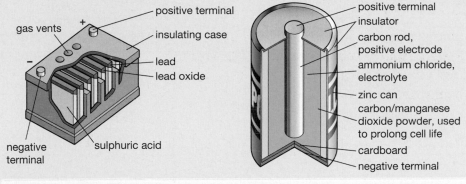

FIGURE 3: The inside of car and torch batteries.

Volta's pile is a 'wet' battery as the electrolyte is simply a liquid. A car battery is also 'wet', but a torch battery is a 'dry' cell.

In a dry-cell, the liquid electrolyte is made into a paste; electrons can still flow through the material but the battery is safer.

Some important types of cell and battery are:

Non-rechargeable batteries

Zinc–carbon batteries – Most AA, C and D dry-cell batteries are this type. The electrodes are made of zinc and carbon, and the electrolyte is an acidic paste.

Alkaline batteries – These are the more expensive, longer-life batteries. The electrodes are zinc and manganese dioxide, with an alkaline electrolyte.

Rechargeable batteries are designed so that the chemical reactions are reversible. A battery charger applies a current in the reverse direction returning the battery to (nearly) its original state.

Lead–acid batteries – This is the car battery. The electrodes are made of lead and lead dioxide with an acidic electrolyte.

Nickel–cadmium batteries – These are often used instead of zinc–carbon or alkaline batteries. The electrodes are nickel hydroxide and cadmium and the electrolyte is potassium hydroxide.

Nickel–metal hydride batteries – These are increasingly replacing nickel–cadmium batteries as they last longer and cope with being only partially charged much better. The electrodes are nickel hydroxide and an alloy which can be made using different elements. The electrolyte is potassium hydroxide.

QUESTIONS

5 Name a wet rechargeable battery.

6 Name a dry non-rechargeable battery.

7 Name a dry rechargeable battery.

8 Why do you think a 'dry' battery is considered safer than a 'wet' one?

Dispose carefully

It is estimated that every year the UK generates over 20 000 tonnes of waste household batteries and only about 5% are recycled. The situation is better for vehicle batteries with about 90% of the 100 000+ tonnes of these being recycled. Batteries that aren't recycled take up space in landfill sites and many of the materials used in batteries are dangerous. Three of the metals used are toxic and all can have various health effects.

Cadmium accumulates in body tissues. It can cause kidney problems, can affect bones and may cause a range of cancers.

Some button cell batteries contain **mercury**. Mercury can cause miscarriages and damage to babies.

Lead can cause damage to the nervous system including the brain. Children are particularly at risk.

FIGURE 4: Only about 5% of waste household batteries are recycled.

QUESTIONS

9 Why might nickel–metal hydride batteries be preferred to nickel–cadmium batteries?

10 Solar cells provide an alternative to batteries. Find out:

   a How a solar cell works.

   b The advantages and disadvantages of solar cells compared to batteries or a mains supply.

...lead   ...mercury   ...negative   ...positive   ...rechargeable

Making the 20th century

You will find out:
- How electricity has provided many things to make our lives easier
- How the development of telephones has changed our world
- How a telephone receiver works

Where there's muck ...

People had environmental worries at the end of the 19th century, such as whether their streets were going to become clogged with horse manure. Soon motor vehicles largely replaced horses so the manure went away. Other big changes since that time have been brought about by electricity.

People power

If you lived in an ordinary home in a British city these are some of the changes you would have noticed as a result of **electricity**.

- 1881 – electric street lights began to replace gas lights.
- 1915 – you might have had electricity supplied to your house, though in 1920 only 10% of homes in Britain had an electricity supply.
- 1920–1930 – more electrical **appliances** became available but they were very expensive. The first neon signs were put up, changing the look of city centres forever.
- 1922 – radio broadcasts began. Many people used crystal sets, which need no electrical supply, or battery powered radios, but larger mains-powered radios became increasingly available.
- 1936 – the year of the first TV broadcast by the BBC. The television most in use in Britain cost about £90 (equivalent to £3300 today).

FIGURE 1: The age before electricity.

Over the next 40 years, more and more people were connected to the **mains** supply and were able to afford electrical appliances. These became relatively cheaper and better.

The next big change in the types of appliances people owned came in the 1980s, when video recorders and home computers started to become widespread.

Appliance	First made	Price during 1920s	Equivalent price today	Actual cost of a similar appliance today
Kettle	1891	£1.20	£48	£25
Vacuum cleaner	1908	£16.00	£640	£50
Electric fire	1892	£1.10	£44	£10
Electric iron	1882	£0.80	£32	£9

QUESTIONS

1. Which electrical appliance in the table has dropped in price the most since it was first sold?
2. Some electrical appliances are very similar to the non-electrical appliances they replaced. Give **one** example of an appliance like this.
3. Some electrical appliances were completely new, there was no non-electrical version. Give **one** example of an appliance like this.
4. Which is the most important electrical appliance in your home? Why is it so important?

FIGURE 2: Vacuum cleaners became common appliances.

...*appliance* ...*communication* ...*electricity*

'Mr. Watson – come here – I want to see you.'

This was the first **telephone** message, it was spoken by Alexander Graham Bell to his assistant, Thomas Watson, who was in the next room. The date was 10 March 1876.

Before the telephone, **communication** was generally slow:

- a letter could take weeks to arrive, and then you had to wait for the answer
- the telegraph was quick (if you lived somewhere near a telegraph office) but very expensive
- going to speak to the person directly was possible if they lived near you.

The need for a more rapid communication system was clear and several inventors came close to a suitable system before Bell.

FIGURE 3: Alexander Graham Bell – telephone inventor.

- The telephone was invented independently by Elisha Gray, who filed notice of his patent application on the same day (14 February 1876) as Bell, but a few hours later.
- In 1877, the first telephone line was installed between Boston and Somerville in Massachusetts in the USA. That same year, the first telephones arrived in Britain.
- By 1880 there were over 47 000 telephones in the USA.
- Many people had telephones long before they had mains electricity. A telephone only needs a small amount of electrical **power** and that is supplied by the telephone company.
- In 1884 the first public telephones became available in Britain.
- In 1973 the first cell phone call was made by Martin Cooper of Motorola.
- There are nearly 3 billion (3 000 000 000) phones (fixed and mobile) in the world today.

FIGURE 4: Red telephone boxes – very rare these days.

WOW FACTOR!

Cwm Brefi, a small village in Wales, was first connected to mains electricity in 2003.

QUESTIONS

5 Why does your home phone still work when there is a power cut?

6 In the early days of phones you had to ask an operator to connect you to the person you wanted to talk to. What are **two** disadvantages of this arrangement?

7 There is an argument for getting rid of public telephones as so many people have mobiles. What do you think?

Keep on talking

Communicating at a distance has been important in the development of human societies. Here are a few selected highlights.

- By about 900 BC, a postal service existed in China for official messages.
- In 776 BC, in Greece, there was the first recorded use of homing pigeons.

FIGURE 5: Which way home?

- By about 100 BC, men on foot or horseback carried messages in Egypt and China and messenger relay stations existed. Fire beacons were also used to send messages.
- In AD 37, there is a record of the use of mirrors to send messages by the Roman Emperor Tiberius.
- In AD 1831, Joseph Henry invented the electric telegraph.
- In AD 1835, Samuel Morse invented the Morse code.
- In AD 1843, Samuel Morse set up the first long-distance electric telegraph line.
- In AD 1902, Guglielmo Marconi transmitted radio signals across the Atlantic Ocean.

QUESTIONS

8 There was a long gap without any major new advances. When was the gap? Why do you think it was there?

9 One of the first successes of radio communication was in catching the murderer Dr H. H. Crippen. Do you think that instantaneous communication has helped to make the world safer or not?

SOUTHALL & WEST LONDON COLLEGE

Making the 21ˢᵗ century

You will find out:
- Some of the history of computers
- How the reducing size of electric circuits has let computers improve
- Some of the progress and setbacks for 'floating' trains (Maglev)
- What superconductivity is

Trains might fly

They already have, but not very far. This picture shows the Maglev train in China. The train is suspended above its guide rail and moved along by electromagnets. Maglev trains were talked about throughout the 20th century but only in 2003 did this high speed line start operating. Computers also, have a long history, but (unlike Maglev trains) they can now be found almost everywhere.

FIGURE 1: The first commercial Maglev train.

A bit of computing history

A **computer** is a machine that:

- can accept data (the input)
- can store data
- can process data
- can produce a result of the processing (the output).

Here are a few important dates in computer history.

- In 1834, Charles Babbage designed an 'analytical engine' that would do some of the things that our modern computers do. At the time, technology was not good enough to build it successfully. This 'first computer' didn't run on **electricity**.

- The development of electrically powered computers began during the Second World War.

- The first programmable computer 'Colossus', was designed to break the codes used by the Germans.

- The first commercially successful computer, the Univac, accurately predicted the results of the presidential election in 1952. A Univac cost over $1 million even then.

- In 1969, a small network of computers was created in America, the first step on the way to the Internet.

- The first successful computer intended for home use was the MITS Altair 8800 produced in 1975.

- Software produced in 1975 for the MITS Altair 8800 was the first product of Microsoft, the company which eventually produced the 'Windows' operating system.

Since 1975 computers have got faster and much easier to use. Computers are now present in many homes and there are nearly 1 billion (1000 million) Internet users in the world.

▐ QUESTIONS ▐

1 What **four** things happen to data in a computer?
2 Computers like the 'Univac' filled whole rooms. Suggest **two** ways in which a home computer would have to be different to a 'Univac'.
3 A three letter word is represented in code by XJB.
   a How many different letters could the X represent?
   b How many different possibilities are there for each of the other letters?
   c How many possibilities are there for what the three letters could be? (Hint: multiply the possibilities for each letter together)
   d A computer can do millions of tasks per second. Why was a computer so helpful in breaking codes?

FIGURE 2: Part of a reconstruction of Babbage's analytical engine in the Science Museum.

...computer ...electricity ...integrated circuit (IC) ...magnetic levitation

Size matters

The smaller the better – at least for electric circuits in computers.

Computers store their data as 0s and 1s. These are represented by separate switches being 'on' or 'off'. It is changes in how these switches are made which have allowed the development of a computer that you can hold in your hand which would outperform a room-sized computer of the 1950s or 1960s like the Univac.

FIGURE 3: Univac filled up a whole room!

Colossus and Univac used thermionic **valves** (vacuum tubes) and so did all computers until the late 1960s.

- A valve is a component which will only allow electrons to flow in one direction.
- A computer needs thousands of valves and they take up a lot of space
- Valves take time to 'warm up', produce a lot of heat and go wrong very frequently

The invention and development of the **transistor** allowed computers to move forward. The first transistor was made in 1947.

- Transistors can do the same job as valves, but are much smaller.
- They do not need to warm up so the switching happens much faster.
- They do not use as much power and do not produce as much heat.

Computers no longer use separate components like transistors, instead **integrated circuits** (IC) built on microchips are used.

- An integrated circuit can hold the equivalent of millions of separate transistors.
- As well as saving space, the components being so close together reduces any time delay in communicating between components.

WOW FACTOR!

A real computer 'bug', a moth, was caught in a computer in 1951 by software pioneer, Grace Hopper.

WANT TO KNOW MORE?

For how a valve works see http://en.wikipedia.org/wiki/Thermionic_valve

Magnetic levitation (H)

Magnetic levitation history:

- 1934 – German scientist, Hermann Kemper, awarded the first patent for a Maglev train
- 1960s–1980s – development work carried out in USA, Germany and Japan
- 1984 – Maglev built from Birmingham railway station to its airport
- 1995 – Birmingham Maglev closes
- 2000–2003 – Germany abandons plans for two Maglev routes
- 2003 – Shanghai Maglev opens for business (built by a German company)

Another discovery from the early 20th century may help Maglev trains become economic in the 21st century – **superconductivity**.

- This is where a material can be made to have no resistance to an electric current.
- To make a superconductor, materials have to be kept at very low temperatures.
- Research into producing superconductivity at higher temperatures continues.
- The Japanese Maglev design saves energy by using superconducting magnets.

QUESTIONS

4 Give **two** reasons why computers are faster today than in the 1960s.

5 'Pocket PCs' are becoming more popular, but are not really replacing laptops for most users. What are some of the factors which limit how small a computer can be?

6 A thermionic valve (vacuum tube) is quite a simple device. Find out what parts it has and how it works.

QUESTIONS

7 How would making electromagnets from superconducting materials save energy?

8 Find out about some of the other uses of superconductors.

The Wizard of Menlo Park

SELF-CHECK ACTIVITY

CONTEXT

Most people live in houses with a mains electricity supply and are used to running numerous appliances from it. One of the first uses of mains electricity was lighting, and the person who made this happen was Thomas Alva Edison, an American born in 1847.

In 1882, Edison's company built a power station in Pearl Street, an area of downtown Manhattan, New York, and supplied local houses with electricity. This wasn't the first house lighting (gas lighting had been in use for years) and it wasn't the first electric lighting (arc lighting had been used to illuminate large events), but it was the first system that enabled people to turn a light on or off in their own homes at the flick of a switch.

Edison's electric lighting system had four key elements:
- a central generator
- wires to distribute the electrical energy
- something for people to use it for in their homes (at that time though it was only light bulbs!)
- low-cost electricity.

People loved it and called Edison 'The Wizard of Menlo Park' (referring to his research labs). However, even before the first light bulb glowed in Pearl Street, the design was out of date and Edison knew it.
- Pearl Street ran on 100 V d.c. Direct current cannot be 'transformed' into a different voltage (unlike a.c.), so everything on the system had to run at 100 V. This is low for distribution lines, meaning energy was lost along the wires, so houses further from the power station had dimmer lights.
- These early power stations often only supplied electricity for one purpose, such as domestic lighting.

CHALLENGE

STEP 1

Imagine you lived in the Pearl Street area of Manhattan in 1882. In pairs, practise a conversation to describe what you saw when the system first started up.

STEP 2

Why might it have been necessary to warn some of Edison's first customers not to use a match to turn on their light bulbs?

STEP 3

Why is it a problem running a d.c. power station from which you can't transmit electricity more than a few hundred metres?

STEP 4

Imagine that you are the manager of Pearl Street Power Station and you are trying to keep your generators running at a steady rate. Why is this going to be difficult if all the electricity you supply is being used for lighting in people's homes?

Maximise your grade

These sentences show what you need to include in your work to achieve each grade. Use them to improve your work and be more successful.

Grade	Answer includes...
F	Say one way in which electricity generation could affect people.
	Say two ways in which electricity generation could affect people.
	Describe how developments such as electricity generation could have a large impact on people's lives.
	Start to explain how developments such as electricity generation could have a large impact on people's lives.
C	Explain how developments such as electricity generation could have a large impact on people's lives.
	Start to explain how in times of rapid technological change early developments sometimes have flaws in their design.
A	Explain how in times of rapid technological change early developments sometimes have flaws in their design.
	As above, but with particular clarity and detail.

What's the source?

You will find out:
- About different sources of energy that can be used for generating electricity
- The advantages and disadvantages of the different sources
- How decisions about energy use are made

Wave machine

This is Seaflow. It is a turbine which uses tidal power to generate electricity. It is near Lynmouth in Devon. Seaflow is a prototype and will be replaced over the next few years with improved versions which will generate more electricity.

FIGURE 1: The Seaflow uses tidal power to generate electricity.

Generating electricity

Here is a reminder of the key parts of the process of generating **electricity** in **power stations**:

- each generator has a rotating magnet
- it needs energy to turn; the energy has to come from somewhere
- high pressure steam can be used to turn a turbine
- the turbine is connected to the generator and makes it turn
- the steam is made by heating water
- a fuel is used to heat the water.

There are some alternatives to generating electricity in this way:

- in some parts of the world, the energy coming from the Sun in solar radiation can be used to heat the water
- some sources of energy can be made to turn a turbine directly without the need for steam
- solar radiation can be used to generate electricity without turbines and generators through the use of solar cells.

Energy sources which can be used to turn turbines directly are wind power, wave power, tidal power and hydroelectric power.

Energy resources which can be used to boil water to make steam for generating electricity include the **fossil fuels**; coal, oil, natural gas and peat.

Other fuels which can be used to produce steam are nuclear fuel and biofuels.

The energy has to come from somewhere

FIGURE 2: This power station (near Ely in Cambridgeshire) burns a biofuel (straw!).

QUESTIONS

1. Name **one** fossil fuel.
2. How are fossil fuels used to produce electricity?
3. Name another type of fuel which is used in the same way as the fossil fuels.
4. If wind is used as the energy resource, no steam is needed. Why not?

...electricity   ...energy resource   ...fossil fuel   ...non-renewable

What alternative sources are there?

If you have ever had a power cut you know what a pain it is. Governments are likely to be unpopular if there is not enough electricity to go round. They have to decide which energy resources they are going to use to supply this electricity. Some key questions are:

- Is the **energy resource** cheap or expensive?
- Are the power stations that use it cheap or expensive to build and maintain?
- Will these power stations produce **pollution**?
- Is the energy resource **renewable** or **non-renewable**?

These factors affect the public's opinion of the energy resource and affect what the Government will want to do.

This table provides a rough guide to some of these factors for resources we use, or are planning to use, in Britain.

Resource name	Relative cost of resource	Relative cost of power stations	Atmospheric pollution from power stations	Renewable
biofuels	low	low build cost, low maintenance costs	yes, but does not contribute to the greenhouse effect or acid rain	yes
fossil fuels	low	low build cost, low maintenance costs	yes, contributes to the greenhouse effect and acid rain	no
hydro-electric	zero	high build cost, low maintenance costs	no	yes
nuclear	low	high build cost, high maintenance costs	not in normal operation but disposal of radioactive waste is a problem	no
tidal	zero	high build and maintenance (still at prototype stage)	no	yes
wave	zero	high build and maintenance (still at prototype stage)	no	yes
wind	zero	high build and maintenance, but reducing	no	yes

TABLE 1: Factors considered in deciding on energy resources used.

Gwynt y Môr (H)

FIGURE 3: The North Hoyle wind farm.

The picture shows the North Hoyle **wind farm** near Rhyl in North Wales. A new wind farm (Gwynt y Môr) is proposed in the same area. It will be 13 km out to sea and consist of about 200 turbines. It will generate the same amount of electricity as a conventional power station.

Wind farms remain controversial, and illustrate the problems of implementing a new technology. Planners have to take into account:

- cost of electricity produced
- reliability of supply
- amount of emissions from conventional power stations that can be saved
- use of land
- local public opinion
- impact on the wildlife.

QUESTIONS

5 Which energy resources cause the most pollution?
6 Name an energy resource which produces no air pollution.
7 Most renewable energy resources have zero fuel costs. How can some people claim they are too expensive?

QUESTIONS

8 Are you in favour of building more wind farms? Use the above information as a starting point to research the advantages and disadvantages of wind power.

Making electricity

You will find out:
- How you can generate electricity
- How a generator works
- How to produce alternating and direct current

FIGURE 1: Investigating lightning can be dramatic.

Current work

Doing science research can be great fun; the photograph on the left is from the Lightning Research Group at the University of Florida. Lightning is a huge electric **current** flowing through the air. A lightning stroke can have a current of 50 000 A or more. Of course, we need to be able to produce an electric current in a less spectacular way.

Generating electricity

When you move the **magnet** past the wire, the magnetic field of the magnet cuts through the wire. This can make an electric current flow in the wire. Remember though that you must have a complete **circuit** before a current can flow. The wire needs to be connected to something, and the best thing is an ammeter to show the current produced.

Learn what you need to make your own electricity.

- You must have a magnet and some wire.
- The wire must be in a complete circuit.
- The wire and the magnet must be close together, so the wire is in the magnetic field of the magnet.
- The magnet, or the wire, or both, must move. We say there must be relative motion.

If you change the direction of movement of the magnet, the current will change direction and flow the other way. If you do the experiment with the magnet the other way round, that will also cause the current to change direction.

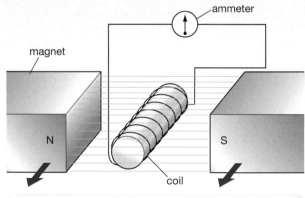

FIGURE 2: The dynamo effect experiment.

▌▌ QUESTIONS ▌▌

1 Copy and complete the table below:

Fact about	Magnet or wire?
It must be part of a complete circuit	
It can have an electric current in it	
It has a magnetic field	
It must be moved	

2 Draw a diagram to show how an electric current can be produced. The things you need to put in are shown below.

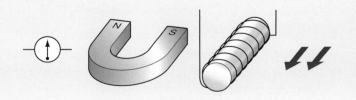

...circuit ...coil ...commutator ...current

What's in a generator?

You know from page 203 that electric current can be made by a wire cutting through a magnetic field when it (or the magnet) moves. In fact any changing magnetic field around a conductor will cause a current to flow. We say that a current has been **induced** in the conductor. This is called the **dynamo effect** and devices which make use of this are called dynamos, or alternators, or **generators**. Which name you use depends on whether it is the magnet or coil that is moving and what sort of current is produced. The picture shows how a simple generator is made.

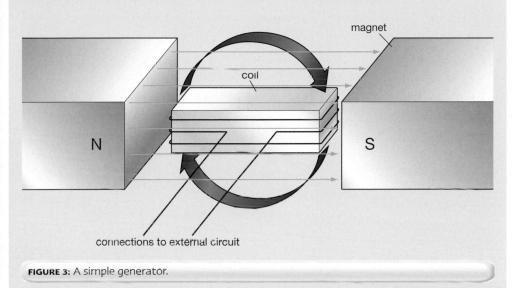

FIGURE 3: A simple generator.

This generator still works on the principle of relative movement of a conductor and magnets, but you will get a larger current produced in this arrangement.

- The generator has a **coil** of wire so that there are many pieces of wire to cut through the magnetic field; this increases the current produced.
- The coil is rotating rather than moving backwards and forwards. This allows for faster movement and the faster the movement the more current is generated.
- The coil is inside a strong magnetic field as the stronger the field, the more current is generated.

WOW FACTOR!

The rotating magnet in a power station generator rotates 50 times a second and weighs several tonnes.

You must have a complete circuit before a current can flow

QUESTIONS

3 What must you have for a current to be induced?

4 How are each of these things provided in the generator shown?

5 Why doesn't it matter whether it is the magnet or coil that is moving?

6 What changes can be made to a generator to increase the induced current?

Alternating and direct current

How the generator coil is connected determines the type of current that is produced.

- As one side of the coil is moving up, the other is moving down.
- This means that the current travels different ways in the different sides.
- If you keep connected to the same side of the coil you get a current which changes direction, an alternating current.

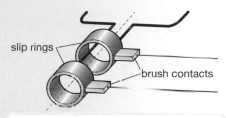

FIGURE 4: Slip rings.

- This can be done using **slip rings**.
- If you swap the contacts each half turn, you get a current which always travels in the same direction – a direct current.
- This can be done using a split ring, sometimes called a **commutator**.

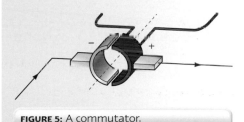

FIGURE 5: A commutator.

QUESTIONS

7 Why does the current travel in a different direction in the two sides of the coil?

8 What would happen if there was a fixed connection instead of a moving contact?

Efficiency

You will find out:
- The unit for energy is the joule (J)
- What is meant by efficiency
- How electrical power is defined and how it is calculated from current and voltage
- The efficiency of solar cells and electric motors

We do need a lot of power

Our homes are likely to contain many electrical appliances. Each appliance uses energy every second it is in use. A large coal-fired power station can produce enough energy every second to run one million cookers. Of course there might be a lot more than a million people cooking at one time, so we need a lot of power stations.

FIGURE 1: Are there enough power stations?

Efficiency

Efficiency is a measure of how much energy is transferred from one form into another. The purpose of a filament lamp is to produce light energy. However, a significant amount of the input electrical energy is transferred as heat and only a small percentage (about 5%) is converted into light. A filament lamp is therefore not a very efficient device at transforming electrical energy into light. The efficiency of any device is defined as

$$efficiency = \frac{useful\ output\ energy}{total\ input\ energy} \times 100\%$$

We can show how energy is transferred into various forms using a **Sankey diagram**. Energy is measured in joules (J). The Sankey diagram for an **electric motor** is shown in figure 2.

- 50 joule of electrical energy is supplied to the motor every second.
- 15 joules of this energy every second is transformed into kinetic energy (which is the main purpose of the motor).
- 35 joules of energy every second is converted into heat.

What is the efficiency of this electric motor?

$$efficiency = \frac{useful\ output\ energy}{total\ input\ energy} \times 100\%$$

$$efficiency = \frac{15}{50} \times 100\% = 30\%$$

A significant amount of the input energy to the electric motor is transferred to heat.

▌▌ QUESTIONS ▌▌

1. Write the equation for working out efficiency.
2. Copy this Sankey diagram for a lamp and label the 'total input energy' and 'useful output energy' components.
3. Your useful output energy is 20 J for every 100 J of input energy used. What is your efficiency?
4. Suggest **one** way some of the other 80 J gets transferred in question 3.

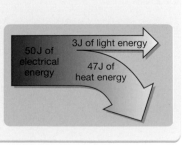

FIGURE 2: The Sankey diagram for an electric motor

Power equation

Electrical power is defined as the rate at which energy is transferred. Power may be calculated using the following equation:

$$\text{power} = \frac{\text{energy transferred}}{\text{time taken}}$$

or

$$\text{energy transfer} = \text{power} \times \text{time}$$

Power is measured in watts (W) or in joules per second (J/s). Sometimes it is convenient to measure power in kilowatts (kW), where 1 kW = 1000 W.

A filament lamp is marked as 75 W. What does this mean? The lamp transfers 75 J of electrical energy into heat and light every second.

The electrical power P of any electrical device is related to the voltage V across it and the current I it carries by the equation:

$$\text{power} = \text{voltage} \times \text{current}$$

or

$$P = VI$$

Example: An electric kettle is connected to a 230 V supply. The current through the kettle is 8.0 A. What is its electrical power and how much electrical energy does it transfer in a time of one minute (60 s)?

$$\text{power} = \text{voltage} \times \text{current}$$
$$P = VI = 230 \times 8.0 = 1840 \text{ W}$$

Since 1840 J of electrical energy is transferred in one second, the energy transferred in 60 s will be a factor of 60 times greater. Hence

$$\text{energy transfer} = 1840 \times 60 \approx 1.1 \times 10^6 \text{ J}$$

You can also calculate the electrical power P if you know the resistance R of the device and the current I through it. Since

$$\text{power} = \text{voltage} \times \text{current}$$

and

$$\text{voltage} = \text{current} \times \text{resistance}$$

We have

$$\text{power} = (\text{current} \times \text{resistance}) \times \text{current} = \text{current}^2 \times \text{resistance}$$

Therefore another equation for power is

$$P = I^2R$$

FIGURE 3: Each appliance has a power rating.

WANT TO KNOW MORE?

See more about solar towers at http://www.enviromission.com.au/project/video/video.htm.

QUESTIONS

5 What is the unit of electrical power?

6 A microwave oven is rated as 90 W. How much electrical energy does it transfer every second?

7 Calculate the electrical power of a calculator using a 1.5 V cell and drawing a current of 0.00008 A.

8 Calculate the electrical power transferred by a 10 Ω resistor carrying a current of 5.0 A.

Sun direct   (H)

Most of the energy resources used to generate electricity rely indirectly on the Sun, but solar energy can be used directly as well.

- Solar energy can be used to boil water to create steam to turn turbines.
- In solar towers the Sun's heat causes convection and the rising air turns turbines.
- Solar energy can be turned directly into electricity in **solar cells** like these on a roof in California.

FIGURE 4: Solar panels on a roof in California.

Solar cells are about 12% efficient.

At the moment they are mostly used for very low power applications, in very sunny areas or remote areas where there is no other electricity supply.

Increasing the efficiency of solar cells would make them more usable in other parts of the world.

QUESTIONS

9 Why are solar cells not used extensively in Britain?

10 Solar cells are used to recharge batteries for electric fences and farm buildings. Why are they suitable for this?

11 If solar power in Britain averages 130 W/m², what area of solar cells would you need to supply a typical household requirement of 500 W?

Electric motors

You will find out:

- How a simple motor works
- The energy changes taking place in an electric motor
- About Fleming's left-hand rule

Massive and microscopic, motors are everywhere

The photograph shows the world's smallest electric motor. The piece in the middle rotates when a varying voltage is applied. The motor is about 0.0003 mm across. One of the largest electric motors is located in the Hiwassee Dam in the US and is about 9 m across.

FIGURE 1: The smallest electric motor seen next to a match.

Motors and generators

The Hiwassee Dam **electric motor** also works as a **generator**. The system is a pump storage system:

- water usually runs down from the reservoir to generate electricity
- the water running down turns a turbine which is connected to the generator
- when demand is low the system is reversed
- the generator works as a motor and the turbine works as a pump
- water is pumped back to the reservoir to be used again when demand is high.

FIGURE 2: The Hiwassee Dam is a motor and a generator.

How can this be?

The diagram shows a simple electric motor. It has all the same parts as a generator:

- in a generator, electrical **energy** is supplied *by* the generator to the circuit
- in a motor, electrical energy is supplied *to* the motor from the circuit
- for a generator, kinetic energy is transferred into electrical energy; whereas for an electric motor the transfer is from electrical energy to kinetic energy.

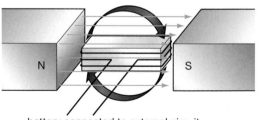

battery connected to external circuit

FIGURE 3: The electric motor.

▪▪ QUESTIONS ▪▪

1 What type of energy is supplied into a motor?
2 What type of energy is produced by a motor?
3 What is the energy change in a generator?
4 Name **two** parts that you would find in a motor and a generator.

Motors and generators are really the same machine

...commutator ...current ...electric motor

The motor effect

The motor effect was first demonstrated by Michael Faraday in 1821. His original experiment is quite difficult to set up and the effect is usually shown in an experiment similar to this. It shows:

- there is a **current** in the wire
- there is a magnetic field between the magnets acting across the wire
- the wire moves
- if the experiment is tried again with the magnets the other way round, the wire moves in the opposite direction
- the **force** on the wire is at right angles to the directions of the field and the current.

Working out which way the wire will move is done using Fleming's left-hand rule.

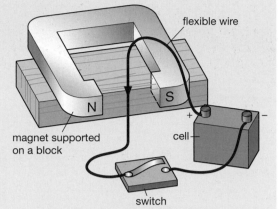

FIGURE 4: The motor effect discovered by Faraday.

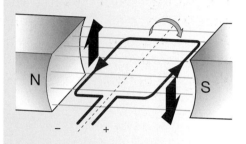

The **thumb** represents the direction the wire moves, the **motion**.

The **first finger** points from the North to the South poles of the magnets and represents the direction of the magnetic **field**.

The **second finger** points in the direction of the conventional **current** (from positive to negative).

FIGURE 5: Fleming's left-hand rule.

EXAM HINTS AND TIPS

Remember the order: Motion, Field, Current as Manchester Football Club.

QUESTIONS

5   Use the left-hand rule to choose which answer, 'up' or 'down', is correct for the direction of the force
   a   Magnetic field is pointing away from you, current flows from left to right
   b   Magnetic field is pointing towards you, current flows from left to right
   c   Magnetic field is pointing towards you, current flows from right to left

An effective motor

In the motor, current flows round the coil.

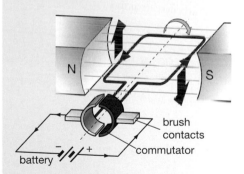

- It goes in opposite directions on the two sides of the coil.
- The force on one side is up, and the force on the other side is down.
- This makes the motor rotate.

But if the current keeps going round the coil in the same direction, after half a turn the forces would be in the opposite direction and the coil would turn back.

A split ring **commutator** is used to reverse the direction of the current every half turn to keep the motor rotating in the same direction.

This sort of motor is a d.c. motor; a.c. motors also exist.

QUESTIONS

6   What would happen if you switched the magnets round and then ran the motor?

Paying up

You will find out:
- How to calculate the cost of electricity
- About the kilo-watt hour (kWh)
- About how insulation can reduce electricity bills
- About the idea of payback time

No contest

Pay your electricity bills or go on the holiday of a lifetime? But imagine coming back to no cooking, heating, lighting or television. **Electricity** companies must pay for fuel, for maintaining their power stations and the people who work for them. The head of the US Atomic Energy Commission said in 1954 'Our children will enjoy in their homes electrical energy too cheap to meter'; this has proved to be a bit optimistic.

What are you actually paying for?

You are paying for the **energy** you have used.

- The **power** of an appliance tells you how much energy it transfers every second.

$$\text{energy (J)} = \text{power (W)} \times \text{time (s)}$$

FIGURE 1: A holiday or electricity – you choose!

Example 1:

A 40 W lamp is operated for 300 s (5 minutes). How much energy does it transfer?

energy (J) = power (W) × time (s) = 40 W × 300 s = 12 000 J

The trouble with joules

The Example 1 above already shows a problem, you get big numbers of joules even for short times and low powers.

Example 2:

A 2 kW (2000 W) electric heater is used for three hours (10 800 s) on a cold evening. How much energy is transferred?

energy (J) = power (W) × time (s)
= 2000 W × 10 800 s = 21 600 000 J

The numbers are even bigger now. Electricity suppliers certainly cannot charge us for every joule we use, nobody could afford it!

The solution

Electricity companies charge by the **kilowatt-hour**, kWh.

- Kilowatt-hours are a measure of energy (not power).
- An appliance of power 1 kW operating for a time of 1 hour uses 1 kilowatt-hour of energy.
- **Energy (kWh) = power (kW) × time (h)**
- 1 kWh = 3 600 000 J
- Electricity companies set a cost per kWh.
- The total cost of your electricity = number of kilowatt-hours × cost per kilowatt-hour.
- This can be written as:
  cost (p) = power (kW) × time (h) × cost of 1 kWh (p).
- Kilowatt-hours are sometimes called '**units**' of electricity.

▮▮ QUESTIONS ▮▮

1 Write the equation for calculating energy used in kilowatt-hours.
2 What is a 'unit' of electricity?
3 A 3 kW motor runs for 2 hours. How many kilowatt-hours are used?
4 If the cost per unit (kWh) is 6p, how much does it cost to run the motor?

...electricity ...energy ...insulation ...kilowatt-hour

Guess who needs double glazing?

FIGURE 2: Heat loss from Buckingham Palace.

In 2005, Buckingham Palace came bottom of a survey of major London buildings for energy saving. This thermal image shows areas of greatest heat loss as white or red.

Double glazing is just one way of saving energy and reducing energy costs. As there are many methods, including different types of **insulation**, it is important to be able to compare them.

One way of deciding if an energy-saving measure is cost effective is to calculate the **payback** time.

- Any energy saving measure will cost something to install.
- It will save some money every year on heating bills.
- **payback time = installation cost / annual saving**
- Payback time is measured in years.
- The table lists some popular energy saving measures and typical payback times.

Information like this is useful in deciding between the different methods.

Energy saving method	Payback time
hot water cylinder insulation	6 months
energy saving bulbs	7 months
draught proofing	2 years
loft insulation	2 years
wall insulation	4 to 6 years
double glazing	>20 years

TABLE 1: Payback times for energy saving methods.

 Kilowatts are a unit of power; kilowatt-hours are a unit of energy.

QUESTIONS

5 Explain what is meant by payback time?

6 Alice wants to insulate her loft. She finds that the insulation will cost £120 and should save £50 per year. What is the payback time?

7 Peter wants to save some money on his fuel bills. He expects to move house in three years' time. Which energy saving measures should he consider?

Using solar cells reduces electricity bills

Solar payback time

The graph shown is to do with payback time for **solar cells**. Using solar cells reduces the amount of electricity you need to get from the suppliers and so reduces electricity bills.

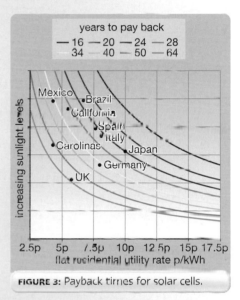

FIGURE 3: Payback times for solar cells.

The graph shows that for a particular payback time there are different possibilities in terms of amount of sunlight and electricity costs.

QUESTIONS

8 Japan and Spain are close to the same payback time of 24 years, but have different electricity costs and amounts of sunlight. Explain how their payback time can be nearly the same.

9 Why is the payback time for the UK so long?

...payback ...power ...solar cell ...unit

Be safe

You will find out:
- Some of the dangers of mains electricity
- The safety features of the mains plug
- About some medical uses of electricity

Let's be serious

Electricity is dangerous, as this photograph of shock damage to a hand shows. Used as they are supposed to be used, all the electrical appliances for sale in this country should be safe. Appliances which are misused, damaged or worn out can become dangerous. The supply system in your home has several features designed to protect you if things go wrong.

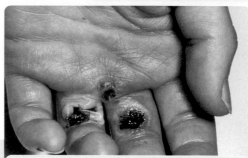

FIGURE 1: Damage done by an electric shock.

Safety begins at home

Figure 2 shows a scene with several electrical **appliances**. There are five things which are dangerous in the picture. See if you can spot them, then read the points at the bottom of the page.

FIGURE 2: Can you spot the dangers?

The wiring inside electrical appliances and the **cables** which connect them to sockets often consist of copper surrounded by plastic. Many electrical appliances are plugged in and unplugged again and moved quite frequently. This can damage the cables and make them dangerous. It is important that cables are checked regularly and replaced if they are damaged.

You should have spotted:
- a kettle being switched on with wet hands
- a frayed cable on the iron
- a broken plug
- a lot of appliances plugged into one socket
- a cable with a table leg on it.

QUESTIONS

1 Why is copper used inside electrical cables?
2 Why is plastic used on the outside of electrical cables?
3 Why should cables be checked regularly?
4 Why is it dangerous to handle electrical appliances with wet hands?

...appliance ...cable ...earth wire ...electrotherapy

A plug for electrical safety

The diagram shows what a mains **plug** is like inside.

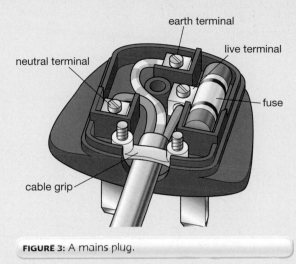

FIGURE 3: A mains plug.

- There are three wires in a UK mains plug called live, neutral and earth.
- The **live** wire is the dangerous one (it is the one that carries the alternating voltage).
- The **neutral** stays at 0 V.
- The **earth wire** is there for safety reasons and is at 0 V.
- The **fuse** is also there as a **safety** device.

Modern plugs have many safety features, including:

- The earth pin is longer than the rest so that this safety feature is in place before the current-carrying connections and, on many sockets, it opens shutters over the live and neutral holes.
- The live and neutral pins have black plastic 'shrouds' to prevent you touching them as you put the plug into the socket.
- The screw that holds the lid on is on the underside of the plug.
- There is a cable grip.

When wiring a plug you need to be careful of:

- getting each wire in the right place
- making sure there are no stray strands of wire.

JUST IN CASE

You might have to tell your local council if you are doing any electrical work at home.

WANT TO KNOW MORE?

About electricity and medicine? Look up www.paintechnology.com/051.htm

QUESTIONS

5 What colour is the neutral wire?

6 Which wire is the most dangerous?

7 Name **one** part of the mains plug which is a safety device.

8 Which wire is at 0 V?

A shocking error?   (H)

John Wesley founded the Methodist Christian denomination. He also advocated the use of electricity to treat a range of illnesses.

FIGURE 4: John Wesley thought electrotherapy was a good idea.

In fact, historically:

- Electric fish have been used since before Roman times to treat headaches and gout.
- During the 18th and 19th centuries, electrical therapy was used to treat a wide range of illnesses.
- As medicine became more scientific, the lack of reliable evidence or an explanation of how it worked, meant that **electrotherapy** became regarded with suspicion.

Some uses continue today:

- Electroconvulsive therapy (ECT) is still used to treat depression, though it remains a controversial treatment.
- TENS (Transcutaneous Electrical Nerve Stimulation) pain relief systems use electrical impulses to block pain signals in the nerves.

QUESTIONS

9 Imagine you are a medical researcher. Devise a trial to test whether electrical therapy is effective for treating headaches. You might need to find out how a new drug is tested to give you some ideas.

10 Find out why ECT continues to be controversial.

Breaking the connection

You will find out:
- The purpose of the fuse and earth wire
- How to choose the correct fuse
- About circuit breakers

No smoke without fire

Electric shock is not the only danger from electricity. Many fires start in the home and in work places as a result of electrical faults. This picture shows fire damage to a kitchen caused by an electrical fault. It is important that the safety features in electrical supply systems protect against fire as well as the danger of electric shocks.

FIGURE 1: Fire damage caused by an electrical fault

Fuses

You know that electric mains plugs each contain a **fuse**. The fuse is a **safety** device designed to isolate the appliance from the electricity supply if a fault occurs.

- The fuse is connected to the **live** wire.
- The fuse is a single thin wire inside a case.
- If a large current flows through it, the fuse gets very hot.
- If the current is high enough the fuse will get hot enough to melt.
- If the fuse melts (or 'blows') it breaks the circuit.
- A break in the circuit stops the current.

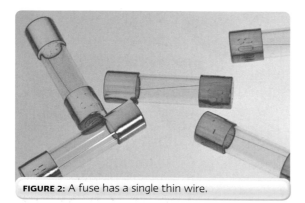

FIGURE 2: A fuse has a single thin wire.

A fault, such as a short circuit, inside an appliance can cause a high current. The wiring for the appliance will then get very hot and this could result in a fire like the one pictured above.

The earth wire and fuse form a safety system

QUESTIONS

1. Why must the fuse be in the live wire?
2. Why do wires get hot if large currents flow through them?
3. Some fuses are designed to carry larger currents than others. How would the wires be different in fuses which carry large currents, compared to those which carry small currents?
4. What is a 'short circuit'?

EXPENSIVE FUSE

There is a fuse in the supply to your home (probably about 50 A rating). It is very expensive if this blows as only the electricity supplier is allowed to work on it.

...earth wire   ...fuse   ...live   ...neutral   ...plug

Safety features

There is a danger of electric shock in many places where there aren't any warning signs. The **earth wire** and fuse form a safety system which protects you from this danger.

- The earth wire is connected to the outside casing of the appliance.
- If a fault occurs and the casing becomes live then the current travels along the earth wire.
- This is a much higher current than the usual current the appliance uses.
- This higher current causes the fuse to melt and break the circuit.

It is very important that the wires are correctly connected in a **plug**. If the live and **neutral** were swapped then the fuse would not blow and the casing would remain live.

**Danger
electric
shock risk**

FIGURE 3: Not all dangers have warning signs.

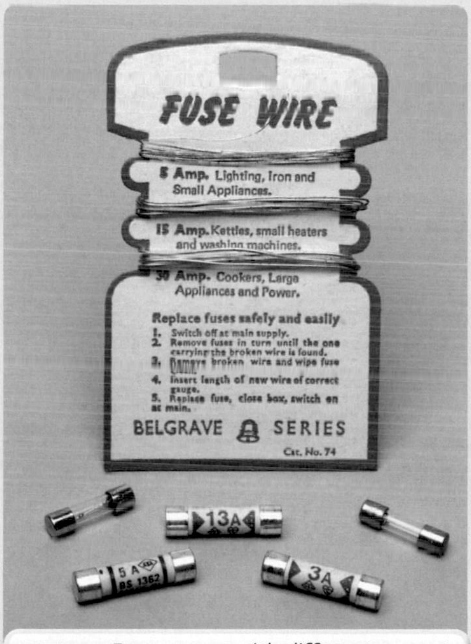

FIGURE 5: A residual current circuit breaker.

Figure 5 shows a **residual current circuit breaker** (**RCCB**). This is how it works:

- It contains a device (a sense coil) which has current induced in it if there is any difference in the currents in the live and neutral wires.
- If the appliance is operating safely there should be no difference.
- If there is a difference it means that some current is flowing to somewhere it should not.
- The RCCB responds to the current in the sense coil and breaks the connections between supply and appliance.
- RCCBs respond to very small differences in current, typically a few milliamps.
- They respond quickly enough to prevent any electric current in the body getting large enough to do damage.

Choose the fuse

Fuses come in different current values. If you have to choose a fuse for an appliance there are a few things to remember

- The fuse needs to be able to carry the normal current the appliance needs.
- This can be found from:

$$\frac{\text{power (W)}}{230 \text{ V}}.$$

There will be information on the appliance to tell you its power.

- The fuse needs to have a value **higher** than this, but as close to it as possible.

FIGURE 4: Fuses come with different current values.

QUESTIONS

5   What happens to the earth wire if there is a fault in an appliance?
6   What happens to the fuse if this fault occurs?
7   How does this make the appliance safe?
8   Courtney's 5 A fuse keeps blowing and she decides to replace it with a 13 A fuse. Why could this be a bad idea?

QUESTIONS

9   What fuse would be required for a 500 W security light operated on the mains?
10 Some appliances do not need to be earthed. What does this tell you about the outside casing of the appliance?

Unit summary

Concept map

Voltage = Resistance x Current (V = IR)

You measure current using an ammeter and voltage using a voltmeter.

Current from the mains is alternating current.

Batteries and solar cells supply direct current. Most 'batteries' are really cells. There are different types of battery and cell. There are disposal problems with batteries and cells.

Changing the voltage (potential difference) or resistance in a circuit changes the current.

Producing and measuring electricity

Applications of electricity have changed the world since the beginning of the 20th Century.

Increasing the current through a filament lamp, increases the resistance. Increasing the brightness of light falling on an LDR, decreases its resistance. In the most common thermistors (NTC thermistors), their resistance decreases as their temperature increases.

Changing the resistance in a circuit has applications in control systems.

Computers have improved since they were first invented due to the reduction in size of their circuits.

Electricity has been used and misused as a medical treatment.

Currently, most of our electricity is generated at coal-fired power stations. It is transported to our homes through the National Grid.

Electricity can be generated using a range of renewable and non-renewable energy resources.

You're in charge

The earth wire and the fuse in our electrical appliances protect us from the dangers of electricity.

A dynamo can be used to produce a current. It works because any changing magnetic field around a conductor will cause a current to flow.

Motors are constructed in the same way as generators and that they can be built to work on a.c. or d.c.

Efficiency = $\dfrac{\text{Useful output}}{\text{Total input}} \times 100\%$

Power (W) = Voltage (V) x Current (A)

Payback time (years) = $\dfrac{\text{Cost of installation}}{\text{Annual saving}}$

Cost of electricity (p) = Power (kW) x Time (h) x Cost (p)

Unit quiz

1 A circuit contains a battery and a lamp. What two factors determine how much current will flow?

2 If the resistance in a circuit is increased, what happens to the current?

3 Write down the equation which relates voltage, current and resistance.

4 What units is resistance measured in?

5 Name **three** devices whose resistance changes.

6 What term is given to a device designed to have a constant resistance?

7 Draw a circuit diagram to show how you would measure the resistance of a lamp.

8 Name **two** household appliances that you would not have had 100 years ago. Why can you have them now?

9 Name something you can have in your home now that was not available 30 years ago. Why can you have it now?

10 How does the current produced by batteries differ from that produced by the mains?

11 List what you must have to be able to induce (make) an electric current?

12 Name the parts in a simple electric motor.

13 What processes occur in a coal-burning power station?

14 Wind farms are becoming more common. What are their advantages?

15 Why can't we generate all our electricity from the wind?

16 A motor connected to a power supply draws a current of 2 A from a 12 V power supply.

   a) What is its resistance?

   b) What electrical power does it use?

   c) If the motor produces an output power of 12 W, what is its efficiency?

17 What is a 'unit' of electricity?

18 If electricity costs 8p per unit how much does it cost to run:

   a) A 2 kW heater for three hours?

   b) A 150 W light bulb for 30 minutes?

Numeracy activity

The following table shows the results of an experiment to measure a lamp's voltage and current.

Voltage (V)	0	2	4	6	8	10	12
Current (A)	0	0.25	0.49	0.64	0.73	0.8	0.84

QUESTIONS

1 Draw a line graph to show the results of the experiment.

2 The voltage is controlled by the student. Describe how the voltage increases.

3 The current increases because the voltage increases. Does it increase in the same way? Explain your answer.

4 Resistance = Voltage/Current. What is happening to the resistance of the lamp as the current increases? (HINT: if you are not sure, you can work out the resistance for each pair of results.)

5 Power = Voltage x Current. What is the power in watts when the voltage is 2 V?

6 Look at the results in the table. Without calculating, decide whether the power at 4 V will be:

twice as much as at 2 V   **less than twice as much as at 2 V**
more than twice as much as at 2 V

Exam practice

Exam practice questions

1 Choose the word that best completes each sentence.

a One end of the .... is connected to the outer metal case of some equipment.
    A earth wire   **B** live wire
    C neutral wire   **D** fuse   [1]

b The purpose of a fuse is to prevent ....
    A power cuts   **B** surges
    C electrocution   **D** overheating   [1]

c The purpose of the earth-wire is to prevent
....
    A power cuts   **B** surges
    C electrocution   **D** overheating   [1]

d Double insulation means
    A the wires are covered in two layers of plastic
    B the appliance has no exposed parts that can become live
    C the appliance has an extra metal case
    D there are two sets of wires   [1]

2 Match the words A,B,C and D to the missing information on the diagram, 1-4.

a The part labelled 1 in the diagram is the ....
    A ammeter   **B** lamp
    C motor   **D** voltmeter   [1]

b The part labelled 2 in the diagram is the ....
    A ammeter,   **B** lamp
    C buzzer   **D** voltmeter   [1]

c The part labelled 3 in the diagram is the ....
    A transformer   **B** cell
    C motor   **D** generator   [1]

d The part labelled 4 in the diagram is the ....
    A thermistor   **B** variable resistor
    C resistor   **D** motor

    [1]

3 Choose the correct answer.

a A battery labelled as 12 Amp-hours will last .... hours if it is supplying a current of 3 Amps.
    A 3   **B** 36   **C** 4   **D** 9   [1]

b The electrical power of a circuit using a 4 volt supply to provide a 3 Amp current is ....watts.
    A 0.75   **B** 7   **C** 4   **D** 12   [1]

c 6 volts is needed to make a current of 2 amps flow through a ....-ohm resistor.
    A 3   **B** 8   **C** 4   **D** 12   [1]

d If a current of 0.5 Amps flows through a 12-ohm resistor, a ....volt supply is needed.
    A 2   **B** 6   **C** 1   **D** 12   [1]

4 Choose the most appropriate answer.

a Current is ...
    A a flow of negatively charged protons
    B able to alter the resistance of a circuit
    C a flow of negatively charged electrons
    D a flow of positively charged protons   [1]

b A rechargeable cell ...
    A stores electrical energy
    B is only available in one size
    C costs less than dry cells to buy
    D can be recharged using mains electricity   [1]

c A solar cell ...
    A converts light energy into electrical energy
    B can be used in the dark
    C provides alternating current
    D can store energy to be used later   [1]

5 Choose the answer that is **false**.

a Electrical energy...
    A is measured in kilowatts-hours
    B is measured in kilowatts
    C is distributed through the national grid
    D can be supplied using renewable energies   [1]

b Batteries...
    A are best used to power vehicles for long journeys
    B contain electrolyte and electrodes.
    C are called wet batteries if they include a liquid electrolyte
    D can contain mercury compounds which are damaging to the environment   [1]

6 Choose the best answer.

  a A 60W filament bulb provides 3 J of light and 57 J of thermal energy. Its efficiency is...

    A 57% **B** 3% **C** 5% **D** 95%   [1]

  b When the bulb is used for 3 hours, the electrical energy used is ...

    A 0.18 kWh   **B** 180 kWh

    C 0.9 kWh   **D** 180 J   [1]

  c A more efficient bulb can be used to provide the same amount of light energy.

    A The more efficient bulb produces more thermal energy than the filament bulb

    B The more efficient bulb uses less electrical energy than the filament bulb

    C The more efficient bulb costs the same to run as the filament bulb

    D The more efficient bulb produces more useful energy than the filament bulb   [1]

(Total 20 marks)

Worked example

Choose the best answer.

a An alternating current can be produced by using a dynamo in a circuit.

  A Alternating current is also produced using cells

  B Alternating current changes direction at regular intervals

  C A dynamo needs electricity to run

  D A dynamo can store electrical energy

b The size of the induced voltage in the circuit is increased most by...

  A Spinning the dynamo fast and increasing the number of turns on the coil

  B Spinning the dynamo fast and using a bigger magnet

  C Increasing the number of turns on the coil

  D Increasing the number of turns on the coil and using a bigger magnet

c The resistance of a thermistor ...

  A is constant

  B depends on pressure

  C depends on light

  D depends on temperature

d An electric motor ...

  A changes kinetic energy into electrical energy

  B can be 100% efficient

  C changes electrical energy into kinetic energy

  D uses a generator

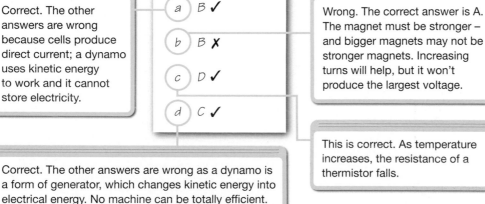

Correct. The other answers are wrong because cells produce direct current; a dynamo uses kinetic energy to work and it cannot store electricity.

a B ✓

b B ✗

c D ✓

d C ✓

Wrong. The correct answer is A. The magnet must be stronger – and bigger magnets may not be stronger magnets. Increasing turns will help, but it won't produce the largest voltage.

This is correct. As temperature increases, the resistance of a thermistor falls.

Correct. The other answers are wrong as a dynamo is a form of generator, which changes kinetic energy into electrical energy. No machine can be totally efficient.

How to get an A

Always fill in an answer. A sensible guess might get a mark but a blank will not. There may be very similar answers, which are used to test your knowledge. Make sure that you look carefully at the units for example.

DISCOVER · STARS!

Some of these distant stars may have solar systems similar to ours. If the conditions are right, there may even be life on some of the planets or moons. However, making contact with other life forms might be difficult, as it takes light over 10 000 years to travel there.

The radiation emitted by the stars created in this stellar nursery has been travelling for over 10 000 years. We know from studying this light that this infant galaxy is moving away from us at a very high speed. Discoveries like this help us to understand the Universe we live in and predict its future.

Gravitational forces pull dust and gas particles together so strongly that nuclear reactions begin. These reactions release energy, some of it in the form of radiation.

Travelling to distant galaxies is not possible at the moment. We do not have the technology to do so. Travelling to other planets in our solar system may soon be possible but there are many obstacles to overcome before any attempt could be made.

CONTENTS

Energy from waves

You will find out:

- That waves carry energy
- The difference between longitudinal and transverse waves

Energy from the Sun

Over 99% of the energy needed by plants and animals comes from the Sun. It takes just 8 minutes for this energy to travel the 150 million km to Earth and it is travelling at 300 000 km per second! This energy is carried by waves.

Energy is carried by waves

FIGURE 1: Energy from the Sun comes in waves.

Different types of waves

Waves carry **energy** from place to place.

- There are two main types of wave. They are called **transverse waves** and **longitudinal waves**.

Examples of transverse waves	Examples of longitudinal waves
ripples in a pond	sound waves
light waves	some types of shock waves created during an earthquake
gamma radiation – emitted by some radioactive materials	

TABLE 1: Different types of waves.

LIGHT WAVE

Did you know that there is nothing in our universe which can travel faster than a light wave in a vacuum? Do you know who was the first scientist to suggest this?

▮▮ QUESTIONS ▮▮

1. What do waves carry?
2. From where do plants get most of the energy they need to survive?
3. Give **two** examples of transverse waves.
4. Give **two** examples of longitudinal waves.

...electromagnetic wave ...energy ...longitudinal wave

Differences between longitudinal and transverse waves

Imagine that you have a long piece of rope, one end of which is tied to a fixed point. You can send pulses along the rope by moving the free end up and down. The pulses are carrying energy from your hand to the end of the rope which is tied. If you move the free end up and down regularly these pulses will form a wave.

If you look at just one part of the rope you will see that it is moving up and down, whilst the pulse or energy is travelling along the rope. This is typical of a transverse wave.

FIGURE 2: Creating a transverse wave.

A transverse wave has **vibrations** across or at right angles to the direction in which the wave is moving.

Imagine now that you have a long spring or slinky, one end of which is tied to a fixed point. You can send pulses along the spring by pushing and pulling the free end sharply. The compression pulses carry energy from your hand to the fixed end of the spring.

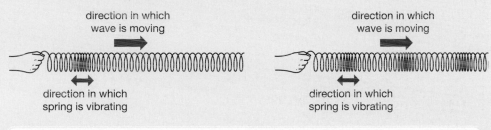

FIGURE 3: What type of wave is travelling along the slinky?

If you look at just one part of the spring you will see that it is vibrating backwards and forwards along the length of the spring, whilst the pulse or energy is travelling along the spring. This is typical of a longitudinal wave.

A longitudinal wave has vibrations along the direction in which the wave is moving.

QUESTIONS

5 What is a transverse wave? Include a labelled diagram with your answer.
6 What is a longitudinal wave? Include a labelled diagram with your answer.
7 What do all longitudinal and transverse waves have in common?
8 When an earthquake takes place, several different kinds of seismic waves are created. Find out the names of these waves and whether they are longitudinal or transverse waves.

Transverse electromagnetic waves

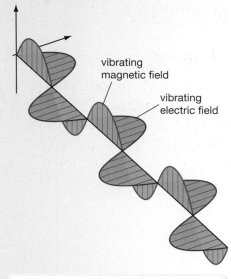

FIGURE 4: An electromagnetic wave is really two waves.

Figure 4 shows a typical **electromagnetic wave**. It consists of two waves vibrating at right angles to each other. One part of the wave is a vibrating magnetic field; the other is a vibrating electric field. Both fields are vibrating at right angles to the direction in which the wave is moving and it is, therefore, a transverse wave. As we shall see later, there are many different kinds of electromagnetic wave, including light waves, X-rays and radio waves.

QUESTIONS

9   Give **three** examples of electromagnetic waves.
10 What is strange about the vibrations of an electromagnetic wave compared with the other types of waves you have already studied?
11 Using books or the internet find out the names of some other kinds of electromagnetic waves and describe how we might use them in our everyday lives.

Basic wave properties

You will find out:
- The meaning of the terms amplitude, frequency, wavelength and speed of waves
- How to use the relationship velocity = frequency x wavelength

Penetrating power!

Unless you are Superman or Superwoman, the only way you are going to be able to see what is in this briefcase without opening it up is to use an X-ray machine.

The X-rays created by the machine are able to penetrate the briefcase. They have a large penetrating power. The penetrating power of waves depends on their frequency. The greater their frequency, the greater their penetrating power. Frequency is one of the basic properties of a wave.

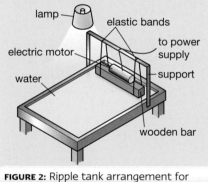

FIGURE 1: X-rays scanning a briefcase.

Ripple tank waves

A ripple tank lets us see the main properties of waves (figure 2). When the small motor is turned on, it makes the wooden bar vibrate. This creates ripple patterns. The lamp above helps us to see the wave patterns on the floor.

When the motor vibrates slowly it makes just a few waves each second and the distance between each of the tops of the waves is quite large.

The water waves being produced have a low **frequency** and a long **wavelength** (figure 3).

When the motor vibrates more quickly, lots of waves are produced each second and the distance between the tops is much smaller (figure 4).

FIGURE 2: Ripple tank arrangement for studying waves.

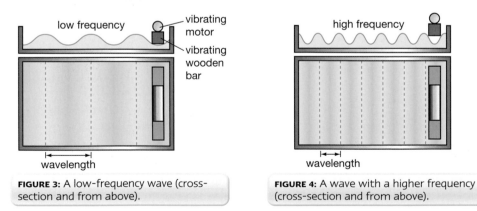

FIGURE 3: A low-frequency wave (cross-section and from above).

FIGURE 4: A wave with a higher frequency (cross-section and from above).

EXAM HINTS AND TIPS

Be very careful if you are asked to draw a wave and label its amplitude and wavelength. Many students lose marks because they label the distance between crest and trough as the amplitude when this is twice the amplitude. Others lose marks because they do not mark the crest of a wave accurately when labelling the wavelength.

QUESTIONS

1. Describe the frequency and wavelength of waves which are produced in a ripple tank when the motor is vibrating quickly.
2. What happens to the wavelength of these waves if the motor vibrates more slowly?

...amplitude ...frequency

Describing waves

Frequency

The frequency of a wave (f) is the number of waves produced each second and is measured in hertz (Hz).

Example: A motor in a ripple tank produces 5 waves every second. The frequency of the waves is therefore 5 Hz.

A second and equally useful way to describe the frequency of a wave is to count the number of waves which go past a point every second.

Example: 30 waves produced by a vibrating motor travel past a point in a ripple tank each second. The frequency of these waves is therefore 30 Hz.

Wavelength

The wavelength of a wave (λ, pronounced 'lambda') is the distance between one point on a wave and the same point on the next wave. Example: The distance between the peak of one wave and the peak of the next wave is 4 cm. The wavelength of this wave is 4 cm.

Amplitude

The **amplitude** of a wave (a) is the distance between its maximum height and its resting or no vibration position.

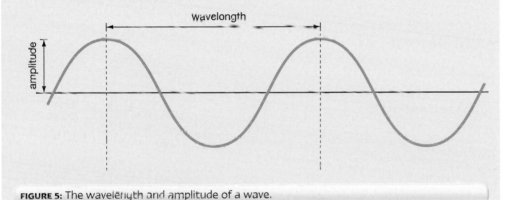

FIGURE 5: The wavelength and amplitude of a wave.

Wave speed or wave velocity

The wave speed or **velocity** (v) is the distance a wave travels each second.

QUESTIONS

3   A guitar string vibrates 100 times each second. What is the frequency of the sound waves it produces?

4   Draw **two** labelled diagrams to show the difference between waves which have a long wavelength and waves which have a much shorter wavelength.

5   Draw **two** labelled diagrams to show the difference between waves which have a large amplitude and waves which have a much smaller amplitude.

6   A sound wave travels 1700 m in 5 seconds. Calculate the speed of the sound wave.

Wave equation

The speed of a wave, its frequency and its wavelength are all linked by the equation:

speed = frequency x wavelength

or   **v = f x λ**

Example 1: A flute produces sound waves with a frequency of 200 Hz and a wavelength of 1.7 m. Calculate the speed of the sound waves.

$$v = f \times \lambda$$
$$v = 200 \text{ Hz} \times 1.7 \text{ m}$$
$$v = 340 \text{ m/s}$$

Example 2: A motor in a ripple tank produces waves with a wavelength of 0.1 m travelling at a speed of 2 m/s. What is the frequency of the waves?

$$v = f \times \lambda$$
$$f = v / \lambda$$
$$f = 2 \text{ m/s} / 0.1 \text{ m}$$
$$f = 20 \text{ Hz}$$

The penetrating power of waves depends on their frequency

QUESTIONS

7   The distance between the peaks of two successive waves travelling along a spring is 0.5 m. If the frequency of the waves is 8 Hz, calculate their velocity.

8   Calculate the frequency of sound waves which have a wavelength of 0.35 m and a velocity of 340 m/s.

9   Calculate the wavelength of seismic waves which have a frequency of 25 Hz and are travelling at a speed of 200 m/s.

Reflection and refraction

You will find out:
- That waves can be reflected
- How reflected waves can be used to measure distance
- That waves can be refracted
- How changes in density can cause a wave to be refracted

Seeing without eyes!

If we are travelling in a car or walking along a pavement, we can see everything around us and so make judgements about their distance and speed. We do this so that, even without consciously thinking about it, we can avoid bumping into other people and any objects in our way. But how would you do this if you could not see?

There are no windows in this submarine. It 'sees' by sending out waves and then waiting for any reflections. If there are no reflections, there are no objects in the way. Seeing using echoes is a very useful technique.

FIGURE 1: The submarine 'sees' using echoes.

Reflection

When **waves** strike a flat surface they may be reflected, for example, when a ray of light strikes a mirror.

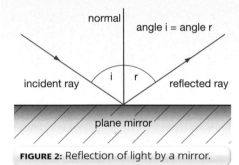

FIGURE 2: Reflection of light by a mirror.

The ray of light is reflected at the same angle as it strikes the mirror. More scientifically we say:

the **angle of incidence** is equal to the **angle of reflection**.

Some optical instruments like the simple periscope use plane mirrors to change the direction of rays of light.

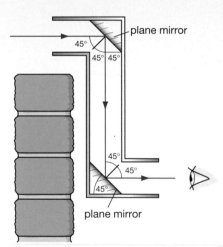

FIGURE 3: This periscope is being used to look over a wall.

Refraction

As this ray of **light** travels through the glass block, it changes direction twice. Once as it enters the block and once as it leaves. This change in direction is caused by the speed of the ray changing and is called **refraction**.

FIGURE 4: Light bends as it enters and leaves a glass block.

⊞ QUESTIONS ⊞

1. Draw a diagram showing how a ray of light is reflected from a plane mirror. Mark on the diagram the angle of incidence and the angle of reflection.
2. Name an optical instrument which uses mirrors to change the direction of rays of light.
3. What is refraction?
4. Why does refraction take place?

ECHO SOUNDING

Over the last thirty years or more, numerous groups of scientists have used echo sounding to search for the elusive Loch Ness Monster, but as yet it has remained undetected!

...*angle of incidence* ...*angle of reflection* ...*dispersion* ...*echo* ...*light*

Echo sounding and radar

Ships use the reflection of **sound** waves, that is, **echoes**, to discover how deep the water is below them.

The waves are sent down to the seabed and a receiver picks up the echo. If the speed of the waves through the water is known and the time delay between sending the waves and hearing the echo is measured the depth of the water can be calculated.

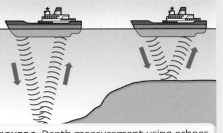

FIGURE 5: Depth measurement using echoes.

> **distance travelled = speed x time delay**

depth of water x 2 = speed x time delay

depth of water = speed x time delay / 2

Example: The time delay between emitting a sound wave and hearing its reflection is 4 seconds. If the **speed** of sound in water is 1500 m/s, calculate the depth of the water below the ship.

depth = speed x time delay / 2 = 1500 x 4 /2 = 3000 m

Air traffic controllers use reflected radio waves to discover the position of aircraft.

Effects of refraction

- When a ray of light travels from a less dense medium into a more dense medium it is slowed down and bends towards the normal.

- When a ray of light travels from a more dense medium into a less dense medium, it speeds up and bends away from the normal.

ray bends towards normal as it enters the glass

ray bends away from the normal as it leaves the glass

If you look at the bottom of a swimming pool through the water, it always looks shallower than it really is. This is because of refraction.

If you look at a pencil which is partially immersed in water it looks broken. This too is caused by refraction.

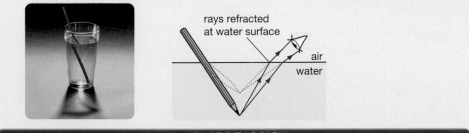

rays refracted at water surface

air
water

Prisms and rainbows

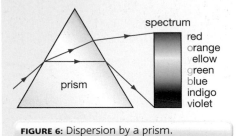

spectrum
red
orange
yellow
green
blue
indigo
violet

prism

FIGURE 6: Dispersion by a prism.

When a beam of white light travels through a prism it splits into all the colours of the rainbow. This band of colours is called a **spectrum**. This effect is called **dispersion**, and happens because white light is a mixture of colours and each of these colours is refracted different amounts by the prism.

A rainbow is produced when tiny droplets of water behave like prisms causing the dispersion of sunlight.

FIGURE 7: A rainbow - a result of dispersion.

White light is a mixture of colours

QUESTIONS

5   The time delay between emitting a sound wave and hearing its reflection is 2 seconds. If the speed of sound in water is 1500 m/s, calculate the depth of the water below the ship.

6   Find out the meaning of the words: SONAR and RADAR. Give **one** example of where each is used.

7   Draw a labelled diagram to show what happens to a ray of light as it enters a glass block at an angle of approximately 45°.

QUESTIONS

8   What is dispersion and why does it occur?

9   What is a spectrum?

10 Write down all the colours in the spectrum in order.

Total internal reflection

You will find out:
- That differences in density can cause a ray to be reflected rather than refracted
- What is meant by the phrase 'total internal reflection'
- Some important uses of total internal reflection

Optical fibres

We are all very familiar with the idea that we can see through a window because light is able to pass through glass. But this is not always the case. Figure 1 shows light travelling along an optical fibre. Even though it is made of glass, the light is unable to escape through the sides of the fibre.

In modern telecommunications networks, messages are no longer sent along copper wires. It is far cheaper and more efficient for signals to be carried by optical fibres. These new developments have been possible through our understanding of when light waves are refracted and when they are reflected.

FIGURE 1: Optical fibres in action.

Reflected or refracted?

Sometimes when a ray of light is about to travel out of a glass block, part of it is reflected at the surface rather than being refracted.

If the angle at which the ray strikes the boundary is increased, the whole of the ray is reflected. When the boundary is acting as if it were a mirror, **total internal reflection** is taking place.

For total internal reflection to occur, two conditions must be satisfied.

- The ray of light must be travelling from a more dense medium to a less dense medium, for example, glass to air or water to air.
- The ray must strike the boundary at an angle which is greater than the **critical angle**.

Different materials have different critical angles.

Material	Critical angle with air
glass	42.0°
water	49.0°
perspex	42.2°
alcohol	47.3°

TABLE 1: Critical angles of common materials.

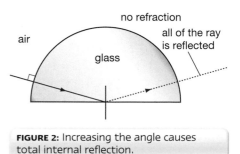

small amount of the light is reflected

air

glass

most of the ray is refracted

no refraction

all of the ray is reflected

air

glass

FIGURE 2: Increasing the angle causes total internal reflection.

▪▪ QUESTIONS ▪▪

1. Draw a diagram to show total internal reflection taking place at the boundary between water and air.

2. Draw a diagram to show what happens to the ray if it strikes the water–air boundary at an angle less than the critical angle.

Light can be made to travel around corners

...critical angle   ...endoscope   ...optical fibre

Total internal reflection in action

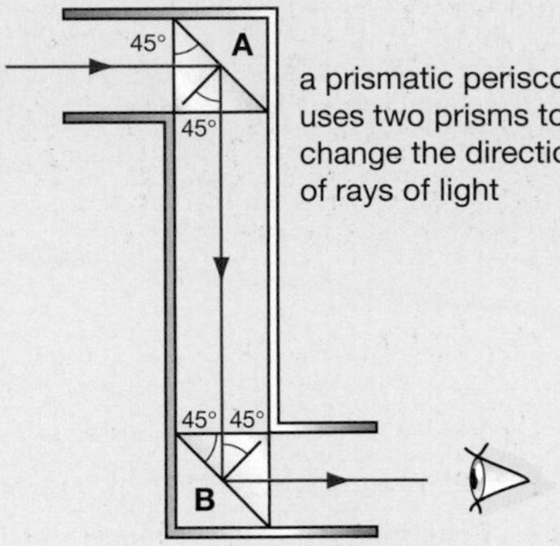

In a prismatic periscope, light from the object enters the upper **prism** and strikes the inner surface at 45°. This is greater than the critical angle so the ray undergoes total internal reflection turning it though 90°. When the ray strikes the inner surface of the lower prism, total internal reflection again takes place. The prisms have both behaved like mirrors but they produce brighter images and are less fragile.

Bicycle reflectors are designed so that total internal reflection takes place twice within tiny prisms. As a result light rays are turned through 180° and are reflected back in the direction from which they came.

Sometimes on a really hot day we see what appear to be pools of water on a road. But when we arrive at these places there is nothing there. What we are seeing are mirages. Mirages are created by total internal reflection.

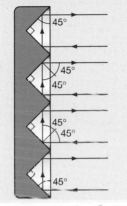

a prismatic periscope uses two prisms to change the direction of rays of light

FIGURE 3: A prismatic periscope.

FIGURE 4: A bicycle reflector.

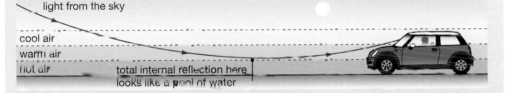

light from the sky

cool air
warm air
hot air

total internal reflection here looks like a pool of water

FIGURE 5: Mirages make us see things that are not there!

As a ray of light approaches the road surface it travels through less and less dense layers of air and so is refracted away from the normal. Eventually the angle at which it strikes a layer of hot air is greater than the critical angle so the ray is totally internally reflected.

QUESTIONS

3 Draw a ray diagram to show how light passes through a prismatic periscope.

4 How many times does total internal reflection take place in a prismatic periscope?

5 Why is it important that a bicycle reflector reflects light back in the direction from which it came?

How optical fibres work

Optical fibres are flexible rods of glass. They are made from two different types of glass, a high density glass for the core and a less dense glass for the outer coating. Light which enters the fibre is unable to escape as it always strikes the boundary between the two glasses at an angle greater than the critical angle. It undergoes a series of internal reflections until it emerges from the far end.

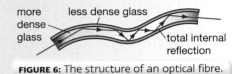

more dense glass
less dense glass
total internal reflection

FIGURE 6: The structure of an optical fibre.

The endoscope

An **endoscope** is used by surgeons to see inside the body during keyhole surgery. One bundle of fibres takes the light into the body. A second bundle brings the light back so an image can be seen.

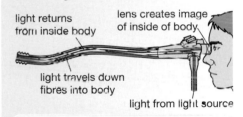

light returns from inside body
lens creates image of inside of body
light travels down fibres into body
light from light source

FIGURE 7: How an endoscope works.

Optical communications

Optical fibres are being used to replace traditional copper wires in modern **telecommunications** systems.

- The fibres are much cheaper and lighter.
- They do not corrode.
- They can carry signals more securely.
- They can carry more signals.

QUESTIONS

6 What is keyhole surgery? Why are endoscopes useful in keyhole surgery?

7 Explain what would happen if an optical fibre had the more dense glass as the outer coating and the less dense glass as the core.

8 Give **three** reasons why optical fibres are replacing copper wires in telecommunications networks.

Electromagnetic waves

You will find out:

● The names of the different electromagnetic waves

● The similarities and differences between them

● How they affect the human body

Strange sunshine

Figure 1 shows how the Sun looks if you have X-ray vision. The energy from the Sun is emitted not just as heat and light, but as a whole range of electromagnetic radiation. The visible light our eyes use is a tiny part of this range. This range is known as the **electromagnetic spectrum**. Using different electromagnetic waves lets us investigate things we can't see with our eyes or shows us new things about familiar objects.

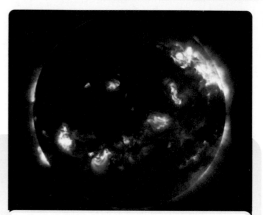

FIGURE 1: The Sun seen with X-ray eyes.

The electromagnetic spectrum

The waves in the electromagnetic spectrum are all similar because:

■ they can all travel through empty space (a vacuum) or else they would not get to us from the Sun

■ they all travel through a vacuum at the same speed, 300 000 km per second (the 'speed of light')

■ they are all **transverse waves**.

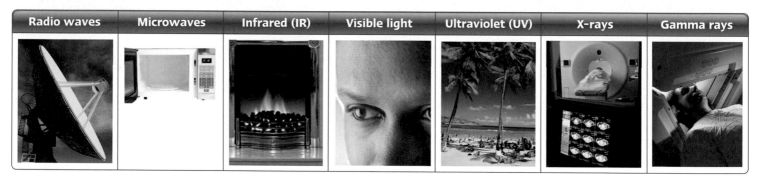

Radio waves	Microwaves	Infrared (IR)	Visible light	Ultraviolet (UV)	X-rays	Gamma rays

TABLE 1: The electromagnetic spectrum.

⊞ QUESTIONS ⊞

1 What are the missing types of radiation, A, B and C?

Radio	**A**	IR	**B**	UV	X-rays	**C**

2 Electromagnetic waves are transverse waves. What do we mean by 'transverse waves'?

3 You need to know the order of the electromagnetic waves. Make up a sentence which will help you remember the letters R, M, I, V, U, X and G. (Or learn this one: Reindeer Meat Is Very Unusual Xmas Gift)

WOW FACTOR!

The Sun releases more energy per second than people on Earth would use in 1 million years.

...electromagnetic spectrum   ...frequency   ...mutation

Spot the difference

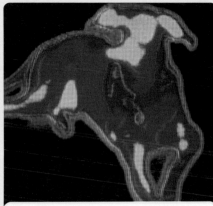

FIGURE 2: Where is the most heat escaping from this dog?

This scary hound is an ordinary dog photographed in infrared. Electromagnetic waves interact in different ways with different materials because there are some basic differences between them.

Electromagnetic waves:

■ all travel at the same speed
■ but have different frequencies and **wavelengths** – the longer the wavelength the lower the **frequency**.

Electromagnetic wave	Wavelength range (m)	Frequency range (Hz)
radio waves	> 0.6	$< 5 \times 10^8$
microwaves	0.6–0.001	$5 \times 10^8 – 3 \times 10^{11}$
infrared	$0.001 – 7.5 \times 10^{-7}$	$3 \times 10^{11} – 4 \times 10^{14}$
visible light	$7.5 \times 10^{-7} – 4.0 \times 10^{-7}$	$4 \times 10^{14} – 7.5 \times 10^{14}$
ultraviolet	$4.0 \times 10^{-7} – 1.0 \times 10^{-8}$	$7.5 \times 10^{14} – 3 \times 10^{16}$
x-rays	$1.0 \times 10^{-8} – 1.0 \times 10^{-11}$	$3 \times 10^{16} – 3 \times 10^{19}$
gamma rays	$< 1.0 \times 10^{-11}$	$> 3 \times 10^{19}$

TABLE 2: Wavelength and frequencies of electromagnetic waves.

EXAM HINTS AND TIPS

X-rays come from the electrons in atoms, gamma rays come from the nucleus and there is an overlap in their frequencies and wavelengths.

QUESTIONS

4   Which type of wave has the lowest frequency?

5   As the frequency increases, what happens to the wavelength?

6   If you multiply the frequency of a wave by its wavelength, what quantity are you working out?

Burning issue (H)

Many of the types of electromagnetic **radiation** have biological effects if the radiation is sufficiently intense, as in the case of the sunburn shown here.

The different frequencies of the different radiations determine the effect they have on the human body. The table below shows the effects of the different types of radiation on the body.

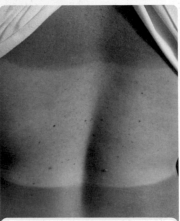

FIGURE 3: Sunburn is caused by UV radiation.

Wave	Typical frequency	Effect on body
radio	1×10^6 Hz	no proven effect on human body
microwaves	1×10^{10} Hz	can cause heating in body tissues due to absorption by water molecules
IR	1×10^{13} Hz	can cause burning of skin
visible	5×10^{14} Hz	causes chemical changes in cells in eye, making vision possible. Very high intensity, as in a laser, can cause burns
UV	1×10^{16} Hz	causes chemical changes in skin cells potentially causing sunburn and cancer
x-rays	1×10^{18} Hz	penetrating ionising radiation can cause chemical changes (**mutations**) in body cells, increasing cancer risk
gamma rays	1×10^{20} Hz	penetrating ionising radiation can cause chemical changes (mutations) in body cells, increasing cancer risk

TABLE 3: Effects of radiation.

QUESTIONS

7   Which types of radiation are able to penetrate deep inside the body?

8   How do you think the frequency of the different radiations affects their ability to do damage to the body?

9   The visible light frequency can't be stated as 1×10^{xx}. Why not? What does this tell you about the frequency range of visible light compared to the other parts of the electromagnetic spectrum?

Watch out for those waves

You will find out:
- About the dangers of radiation from mobile phones
- About the dangers of ultraviolet radiation
- Ways of limiting the damage of earthquakes and tsunamis

The worst wave

Sadly, since Boxing Day 2004, the Japanese word **'tsunami'** has become one everybody knows. The destruction caused by that wave claimed lives up to 8000 km from the epicentre of the earthquake that caused it. Many other waves bring dangers of their own.

FIGURE 1: Tsunamis can be very dangerous.

Good vibrations? (H)

Mobile phones are very popular and very useful. Most people feel that they are safer if they have a mobile phone to call for help if they get lost, miss their train or their car breaks down. Some people, though, have been worried about the mobile phones themselves being dangerous because of the **radiation** they produce.

- Mobile phones transmit and receive electromagnetic radiation.
- The radiation is low power (low **amplitude**).
- The frequencies used in Britain are 9×10^8 Hz and 1.8×10^9 Hz which are low-frequency microwaves.
- This radiation doesn't cause changes to the DNA in cells, so it can't cause cancer.
- It does cause some heating to body tissues, but only by a small amount and no more than normal changes in body temperature.
- A study published in early 2004 found no increased risk of cancer due to mobile phone use for at least 10 years.
- Some studies have suggested that mobile phone radiation may help cancers to grow.

Scientists are not yet able to decide if mobile phones do cause health problems.

- There is evidence for and against, but the evidence is not conclusive.
- There may be long-term health effects which have not yet shown up, as few people have used mobile phones for longer than 10 years.
- Many of the research studies were done on isolated cells, dead tissue or animals and the results may not apply to living human tissue.

FIGURE 2: The jury's still out on the dangers of mobile phones.

QUESTIONS

1 Give **one** piece of evidence which could suggest that mobile phones are dangerous.
2 Give **one** piece of evidence which might suggest that they are not.
3 The Government has advised that children should not use mobile phones very much. Why could children be more at risk than adults?

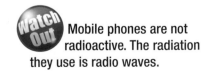

Watch Out Mobile phones are not radioactive. The radiation they use is radio waves.

...amplitude   ...earthquake   ...frequency   ...radiation

Be safe in the Sun　　　(H)

Suntanning is a trend started by the French fashion designer Coco Chanel in the 1920s.

A suntan is caused by the reaction of the skin to **ultraviolet** radiation and 'is a sign of existing tissue damage and ... is the skin's attempt to protect itself against further photo damage' (British Medical Association). There are three types of ultraviolet radiation – UVA, UVB and UVC.

- UVA radiation has the longest **wavelengths** and lowest frequencies (7.5×10^{14} to 9×10^{14} Hz). Most (about 95%) of UV radiation at the Earth's surface is UVA. It can pass through glass and penetrates most deeply into the skin.

- UVB radiation (9×10^{14} to 1×10^{15} Hz) is mostly absorbed by the ozone layer and atmosphere.

- UVC radiation (1×10^{15}–1.5×10^{15} Hz) – practically all is absorbed by the ozone layer and atmosphere.

FIGURE 3: Coco Chanel made suntans popular.

These waves affect the skin.

- UVA is thought to cause early ageing of skin, wrinkles, DNA damage and cancer at deeper levels in the skin. It causes sunburn, though to a lesser extent than UVB.

- UVB causes sunburn, tanning, wrinkles and changes to the DNA in skin cells which can lead to cancers. However, it stimulates the production of vitamin D in the body which is a useful effect.

- UVC would be even more damaging than UVB, and if the ozone layer continues to be reduced more will get through.

The higher the **frequency** of the wave the more effective it is at causing damage. So UVB is more dangerous than UVA because of its higher frequency. But it is less of a problem than it might be because due to its low amplitude more of it is absorbed by the ozone layer.

A suntan is the skin's attempt to protect itself

QUESTIONS

4　What is **one** type of damage caused by UV radiation?

5　What is **one** clearly beneficial effect of UV radiation?

6　Is a suntan a beneficial effect? Why?

Wave warnings　　　(H)

People have been trying to predict **earthquakes** for centuries. Figure 4 shows a Chinese earthquake monitor made before AD200. Tiny balls were balanced in the dragons' mouths. When vibrations occurred, the balls would be dislodged and fall into the frogs' mouths.

FIGURE 4: Chinese earthquake monitor.

- Scientists have investigated earthquake predictors ranging from animal behaviour to chemical changes in the rocks, but no reliable system has been found.

- Reliable predictions are needed to tell people when to run, but false alarms must be avoided as they have major economic consequences and make people unlikely to react to future warnings.

- Good communications are essential to make sure the message gets through.

If an undersea earthquake is recorded, it is possible to issue a warning that a tsunami is coming. Such a system is now being developed for the Indian Ocean. This should give people enough warning to reach a safe place.

QUESTIONS

7　For mobile phones or sunbeds, imagine that there is a campaign to limit their use to people over 21 years of age. Present a case against this campaign.

...tsunami ...ultraviolet ...wavelength

Scanning with waves

You will find out:

- That reflection of waves lets us check on new life
- That absorption of waves is used to spot broken bones
- That emission of waves is used to measure temperature
- That reflection and refraction of waves helps us see inside the Earth

X-ray developments

X-ray photographs have come a long way since the first pictures at the end of the 19th century. Now CT (or CAT) scans use computers to add up lots of X-ray measurements to create 3D images of other tissues in the body, not just the bones.

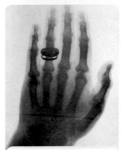

FIGURE 1: The first X-ray photograph.

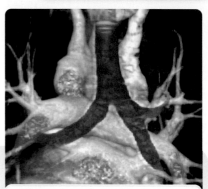

FIGURE 2: A modern CAT scan provides a 3D image.

Shed some light on it

When light hits a window most of it goes straight through.

- But you can see your **reflection** in a window if your side is brighter than the other side, so some of the light is reflected.
- If you try to look through the end of a piece of glass (or through a very thick piece), you won't see much because some light is absorbed.

Some objects (like the sun, flames, and light bulbs) give out their own light – we call this light **emission**.

What we call 'seeing' is our brain sorting out the information from our eyes about how different objects reflect, absorb or emit light.

The eyes have it

The patterns in the coloured part of your eye, the **iris**, are unique. In fact your two eyes are quite different. The iris can be photographed and the patterns of the iris recorded and stored on a computer. These can be used to check who you are all through your life. When a check is done, your eye will be scanned with a lower intensity light. The light is reflected to make an image that can be compared with the original photograph. The system is very accurate and likely to be used more and more in years to come.

FIGURE 3: See through or reflecting? Your brain will sort out the information.

⬛ QUESTIONS ⬛

1 Which of these emits light? The Sun, the Moon, a football.
2 What property of waves lets us see things which don't emit light?
3 Computers can recognise iris patterns but are not very accurate at recognising faces. Can you think of one reason why?
4 Iris scans could soon begin to be included on identity cards which everybody would eventually have to carry with them. Why do you think many people are unhappy about plans like this?

FIGURE 4: Each iris pattern in unique.

...absorption ...emission ...iris ...radiation ...reflection

Change your waves

There are lots of applications where visible light is no use. In these situations, different waves need to be used.

- **Ultrasound** (waves in the air which are at too high a frequency for us to hear) is used for prenatal scanning. Different body tissues reflect ultrasound by different amounts, creating an image of the foetus like the one seen in figure 5. Ultrasound is believed to be completely safe and is useful for spotting many problems that might affect the baby's health.

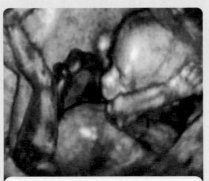

FIGURE 5: Ultrasound used for prenatal scanning.

- Measuring the infrared **radiation** emitted by an object can be used to determine its temperature. Infrared thermometers do not need to touch the object being monitored, so they can be used when, for example, moving parts need to be monitored.

- X-ray photographs rely on how the **absorption** of X-rays varies for different body tissues. Bones absorb X-rays particularly well.

- Microwaves can be used to measure the amount of water in parts of the atmosphere. Microwaves with a wavelength between about 1.6 mm and 1.3 cm are absorbed by water molecules. Satellites can monitor the amount of microwave radiation being absorbed. This is particularly useful in predicting rainfall over oceans where there is nowhere to stand a rain gauge!

- Ultraviolet radiation is used to detect forged bank notes. The UV waves are absorbed and cause parts of the note to give off visible light (fluorescence). The fluorescence shows up the difference between the paper and inks of the real and forged notes.

FIGURE 6: Is this one a forgery?

Watch Out

Ultrasound is not an electromagnetic wave; it is longitudinal, travels much more slowly and cannot travel through a vacuum.

QUESTIONS

5   What are **three** differences between a sound (or ultrasound) wave and any electromagnetic wave?

6   The upper frequency limit of human hearing is 22 000 Hz. If sound travels at 340 m/s in air, what is the wavelength of this wave?

7   Make a table like this for all the waves mentioned on this page, one has been done for you.

Wave	Electromagnetic?	Used to scan?	Wave property used
UV	yes	banknotes	absorption

8   Do you think it is a good idea to have a scan during pregnancy or not?

Beneath your feet   (H)

The deepest hole in the world is only 12 km deep, 1/500 of the way to the centre of the Earth. We know very little about the structure of the Earth. Most of what we do know comes from **seismic waves** which are generated by earthquakes and then pass through the Earth.

These waves are detected by seismographs.

- P waves travel fastest, they are longitudinal waves.

- S waves are second to arrive, they are transverse waves. They cannot travel through the liquid outer core of the Earth.

- The time delay between these waves enables us to calculate how far away the earthquake was from the detector.

- Changes in direction of the waves due to **refraction** within the layers and reflection from the boundaries enable geologists to work out the internal structure of the Earth.

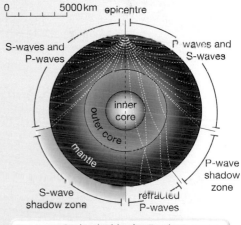

FIGURE 7: Seeing inside the Earth.

QUESTIONS

9   Which waves can you detect on the other side of the world to the earthquake?

10 A seismograph picks up the P and S waves from an earthquake 100 seconds apart. P waves travel at 5 km/s, S waves travel at 3 km/s. How far away was the earthquake?

11 One earthquake recording station can tell how far away an earthquake is, but not exactly where it is. Why not?

...refraction   ...seismic wave   ...ultrasound

Analogue and digital

You will find out:
- What is meant by the terms analogue and digital
- The advantages of transmitting digital information rather than analogue
- How digital sound has changed the music industry

It could be you ...

Could you be the next singing sensation? It's much easier these days to get yourself heard, all thanks to digital technology. You can use a home computer as the centre of a home recording studio and make a CD of your own. Of course, it might be cheaper to audition for the next 'Pop Idol' or 'Fame Academy'.

FIGURE 1: Could you be a star?

Analogue and digital

Your voice is an **analogue** signal.

- It's a **sound** wave.
- It has many different levels of loudness (**amplitude**).
- It has many different levels of pitch (**frequency**).

A graph of loudness against time might look like figure 2.

This shape can be copied as an electrical signal and added to a radio wave to transmit your voice to the ends of the Earth.

OR

A **digital** signal can be made.

- The level is sampled or measured at regular intervals (figure 3).
- These numbers are turned into a code called binary numbers.

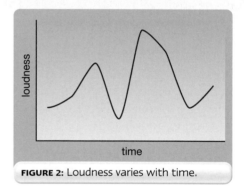

FIGURE 2: Loudness varies with time.

Sample values	3	4	7	2	10	8	3	5
binary number	0011	0100	0111	0010	1010	1000	0011	0101

- The binary numbers are sent as on/off pulses of radiation.

Binary number	0011	0100	0111	0010	1010	1000	0011	0101
pulse pattern								

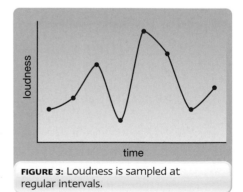

FIGURE 3: Loudness is sampled at regular intervals.

▪▪ QUESTIONS ▪▪

1. Which of these wave measurements decides the loudness of a sound wave?

   a) frequency b) wavelength c) amplitude d) speed

2. Which of these wave measurements decides the pitch of a sound wave?

   a) frequency b) wavelength c) amplitude d) speed

3. There are only **two** possible values a digital signal can have. What are they?

...amplitude ...analogue ...digital ...frequency

2, 4, 6, 8, what do we appreciate? DIGITAL!

Why?

Well digital electronics has made possible many of the objects we rely on daily, such as calculators. This first pocket calculator became available in 1971.

FIGURE 4: The first pocket calculator.

For transmitting **information**, digital makes all the difference.

First, digital signals have better quality than analogue signals.

- Any signal will have some additional unwanted noise on it.
- With an analogue signal you can't work out what is noise and what is signal, as analogue signals can have any value.
- But noise is not enough to make a 0 seem like a 1, so when a digital signal is received it is read as 0, just as in the original signal.

Second, digital signals allow more information to be passed in a given time.

- Digital signals allow multiplexing to take place.
- Multiplexing is where several signals can be sent along the same line at the same time.
- The signals are sorted out by a demultiplexer at the receiving end of the system.

MUSICAL TELEGRAPH

The first electronic musical instrument, the musical telegraph, was made in the 1870s by a man who was trying to invent the telephone.

EXAM HINTS AND TIPS

In a question about digital and analogue signals, make sure you know if they asking about *quality* of signal or *quantity* of information.

QUESTIONS

4   Why is a digital signal higher quality than an analogue signal?
5   Why can information be transmitted more quickly with a digital signal?
6   Some people think that a digital signal is 'missing something' compared to an analogue signal. Look at how a digital signal is made and explain how they could have a point.

The latest thing?

Perhaps not. Digital technology goes back further than you think.

Here are a few important dates in digital history:

- 1937 – PCM (pulse-code modulation), the first digital sampling technique, was invented
- 1971 – The first digital musical instrument, an organ, was sold to a church in the USA. In that year only one other digital product was available to consumers, the first electronic calculator
- 1979 – The Fairlight CMI, the first digital synthesiser, was produced

FIGURE 5: The Fairlight CMI.

- 1981 – The MIDI interface was developed, allowing keyboards that connect to computers to be produced
- 1982 – First CD player produced
- 1988 – CD sales surpass LP sales
- 1990 – MP3 compression system developed to allow **transmission** of audio files over telephone lines
- 1996 – DVD players go on sale
- 1998 – First digital audio players available
- 2001 – iPod launched, Napster Internet music sharing company shut down.

QUESTIONS

7   It is now possible to share music over the Internet, but people have been prosecuted for doing so. Discuss what laws you think there should be to control this.

The changing sound of music

SELF-CHECK ACTIVITY

Will loves music. As a 14-year-old he has had quite a range of influences. His mother loves opera and classical music, whereas his father likes 60s and 70s rock and pop. Will has his own tastes now and listens to groups like Reef.

However, it isn't only what he likes to listen to that's different from his parents, but how he gets the music and shares it with his friends. When his parents were teenagers they listened to music on the radio or TV and bought it on vinyl discs, or records. In either case the music was stored as an analogue signal.

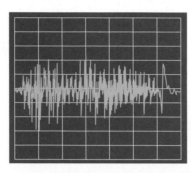

It was possible (though not necessarily legal) to make a recording of a radio programme or a record, using a tape recorder, but one of the problems with analogue signals is that the recording will lose some of the quality, and the lost quality is virtually impossible to recover.

In the late 80s, Will's parents started to buy their music on Compact Disc (CD). On a CD the music is stored as a digital signal.

Even if a digital signal deteriorates, its original shape can be regenerated quite easily, so that copies sound as good as the original. Nevertheless, people had to buy a CD to get the digital recording in the first place.

Although Will has quite a large collection of CDs, it isn't the only way he gets his music. He was given an MP3 player last Christmas and uses a computer to download music files from the internet. He stores these and copies them onto the MP3 player. He can easily copy these onto his friends' computers for them to listen to and he can pick up more music from them.

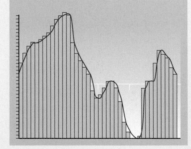

One of the advantages of MP3 files is that, as they are compressed, they can be transferred quickly and don't take up a great deal of storage space. Some of the music Will listens to is from new groups that are trying to get started. They want people to download their music, listen to it and swap it with other people. However, other music is there without the permission of the musicians or their record companies.

CHALLENGE

STEP 1

Discuss in your group how you get the music that you want to listen to. How did your parents' generation get the music they wanted to listen to when they were your age?

STEP 2

Imagine you are a musician in a group that is trying to get a contract with a record company. Why might you be interested in using the internet to get more people to listen to your music?

Maximise your grade

These sentences show what you need to include in your work to achieve each grade. Use them to improve your work and be more successful.

Grade	Answer includes...
F	Describe one change in music technologies.
	Describe several changes in music technologies.
	Describe how changes in music technologies affect storage or sharing of music.
	Start to explain how changes in music technologies affect storage and sharing of music.
C	Explain how changes in music technologies have changed the way it is listened to and shared.
	Start to explain how the changing technologies relating to the recording of music have changed the way it is listened to and shared, and the implications of this for the music industry.
A	Explain how the changing technologies relating to the recording of music have changed the way it is listened to and shared, and the implications of this for the music industry.
	As above, but with particular clarity and detail.

STEP 3

Some of the tracks that appear on the internet have been put there without the owners' consent. What is the argument for making sure that musicians and record companies make money from the music they produce?

STEP 4

Why might record companies be more concerned about illegal copying of music tracks now than they were 30 years ago?

What's out there?

You will find out:
- The layout of the solar system
- How we measure distances in space
- The sizes of the objects you'll meet in this topic

The sky at night

Since humans evolved, we have been fascinated by the night sky and have tried to explain what we see there. We may think that we now know quite a lot about it and the universe, but we're learning all the time. Maybe in a few hundred years' time people may be laughing at our thoughts and ideas about what is out there.

What we think we know!

- We live on a **planet** we call the Earth. The Earth is not stationary, it is moving. It is spinning around an axis like a top and it is orbiting the Sun.
- We have day and night because the Earth **spins** on its axis.
- We have seasons because that axis is **tilted**. This causes the Sun's rays to be concentrated over a smaller area in the summer but spread out over a larger area in the winter.

The **solar system** consists of the Sun and all the objects that **orbit** around it. These include planets, asteroids, meteors, moons and comets. The largest objects are called planets. You may already know a mnemonic to help you remember the planets, or you may prefer the one in the table.

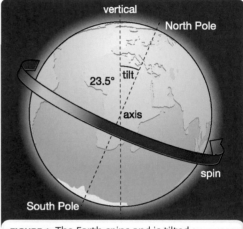

FIGURE 1: The Earth spins and is tilted.

TABLE 1: The planets of our solar system.

	Mercury (closest to the Sun)	**M**other		Jupiter	**J**am
	Venus	**V**ery		Saturn	**S**andwich
	Earth	**E**asily		Uranus	**U**sing
	Mars	**M**ade		Neptune	**N**o
	Asteroid belt (rocks that never managed to form a planet)	**A**		Pluto (Pluto's orbit is odd: sometimes it's closer to the Sun than Neptune is)	**P**eanuts

QUESTIONS

1. Copy and complete: Day and night are caused by _____, seasons are caused by _____.
2. List the planets in the correct order, starting with the one closest to the Sun.
3. Where in the solar system would you find the asteroid belt?

Another 'planet', Quaoar, was thought to have been discovered in June 2002. However, many astronomers claim that it's not really a planet but one of the many small objects orbiting way out beyond Pluto.

...astronomical unit (a.u.) ...galaxy ...light year ...moon ...orbit

A question of size

- The Sun is our nearest **star**. It is huge and contains 99% of the mass of the solar system.

- Planets orbit around stars. They're made of rock, ice or gas.

- **Moons** orbit around planets. Some planets have many moons. The Earth has one, Mercury and Venus have none.

- Asteroids are lumps of rock which orbit the Sun. Most of them are in a belt between the orbits of Mars and Jupiter. They vary in size from just a few metres across to several hundred kilometres across.

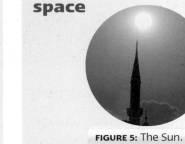

FIGURE 2: The Moon.

- Some pieces of rock fall from space towards the Earth. If they burn up in the atmosphere on the way down we call them meteors, if they reach the ground we call them meteorites.

- Comets are sometimes described as 'dirty snowballs', as they are lumps of ice in orbit around the Sun. Their orbits are very different to those of planets and asteroids as they spend some of their time way out beyond Pluto and at other times are close to the Sun.

FIGURE 3: A comet.

FIGURE 4: Galaxies.

- **Galaxies** are very large groups or clusters of stars. These groups contain billions of stars and often have a spiral shape. Galaxies are so big that it can take light 100 000 years or so to cross them. The galaxy we live in is a spiral galaxy called the 'Milky Way'. The Milky Way forms part of our local group of galaxies.

- The **universe** is the space which contains all the above and more.

WOW FACTOR!

The word planet means 'wandering star'. Planets were given this name because they look similar to stars in the night sky but they change their position each night.

Watch Out Every year people lose marks in their exams for saying that the Earth is closer to the Sun in the summer. Wrong! It's not about distance, it's about the angle.

QUESTIONS

4   Arrange these objects in order of increasing size: planet, galaxy, asteroid, star, moon, universe, solar system, local group.

5   Write a sentence describing each object in question 4.

Distance and time in space

FIGURE 5: The Sun.

The Sun is an average star. There's nothing special about it, except that it's by far the closest star to the Earth, only 150 million km away. If the Sun went out, we'd have no way of knowing until the light stopped arriving in 8.3 minutes' time.

As far as we know, nothing in this universe can travel faster than light. This means that whenever you look at a distant star or galaxy you are seeing it as it was, perhaps millions of years ago when the light left it.

Measuring distances in space

Distances in space are huge, so within the solar system we use **astronomical units** (**a.u.**), where 1 a.u. is the distance from the Earth to the Sun, 150 million km.

Beyond the solar system we use **light years**: the distance that light travels in one Earth year. Light travels at 300 000 km per second, so in one year it travels 9 467 280 000 000 km.

QUESTIONS

6   Here is a jumbled list of the distances from the Sun (in a.u.) of the planets in our solar system. Make a table with the names of the planets, and put the correct distance with each planet. 39.5, 9.54, 1.52, 1.0, 5.2, 30.06, 0.72, 19.2, 0.38

7   Sirius is a star near the constellation of Orion, and is 8.6 light years from Earth. What is this distance in kilometres? How long would it take a spaceship to get there travelling at 1% of the speed of light?

Why is gravity important?

You will find out:
- That gravity keeps the planets in their orbits
- That the force of gravity depends on mass and distance
- How to work out the gravitational attraction between two objects

Almost weightless?

They may not be dressed like athletes, but nevertheless astronauts on the Moon could break world records in events such as the long jump and the high jump. Why is this possible? It's possible because the pull of **gravity** on the Moon is only one-sixth that on the Earth.

FIGURE 1: What other sporting events might astronauts do well in?

What is gravity anyway?

Gravity is a force which causes things to fall.

In 1687 Sir Isaac Newton tried to explain why things fall by suggesting that every object in the universe attracts every other object.

The size of the force depends on the masses of the two objects and how far apart they are.

- The bigger the masses, the bigger the forces of attraction.
- The closer the objects, the bigger the forces of attraction.

Gravity is a really weak force unless one of the objects has a huge **mass**, such as a **planet**.

At the Earth's surface, we say 'the gravitational field strength is 10 newtons per kilogram (10 N/kg)'. In other words, the **weight** of a 1 kg mass is 10 newtons. So a 2 kg mass would weigh 20 N, and so on.

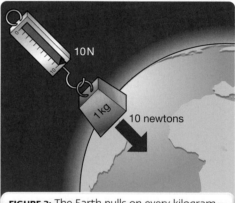

FIGURE 2: The Earth pulls on every kilogram with a force of 10 newtons.

Other planets have different gravitational field strengths. The 'surface gravity' on Earth is 10 N/kg. On the Moon it's 1.63 N/kg, so on the Moon your weight would be only one-sixth of what you're used to. On Mars the surface gravity is 4 N/kg, less than half of the gravity on Earth. Jupiter has a much greater mass than the Earth or Mars, its gravitational field strength is 26 N/kg.

Important: Your mass doesn't change if you go to another planet (you still have the same number of arms and legs, etc.), but your weight does change (because the gravitational field strength changes).

You can work out your weight on different planets using the formula:

weight = mass x gravitational field strength

$$w = mg$$

QUESTIONS

1. Explain what happens to the force of attraction between two objects when **a)** the masses of the objects are increased and **b)** the objects are moved further apart.
2. If your mass is 45 kg and the gravitational field strength on the Moon is 1.6 N/kg, calculate what your weight would be on the Moon.

WANT TO KNOW MORE?

Work out your weight on other planets at www.exploratorium.edu/ronh/weight

...black hole ...escape velocity ...gravity ...mass

Why do they move in orbits?

Any object which is moving along a curved path is experiencing a force. The force which causes planets, moons, asteroids and comets to travel along curved paths is gravity. Our Sun contains 99% of the mass of the **solar system**. It is the gravitational attraction between it and all the other bodies which holds our solar system together. Planets close to the Sun experience strong gravitational forces and so travel in the most curved paths. Those further away experience weaker forces and so travel in less curved paths.

FIGURE 3: The orbits of planets and comets (not to scale).

Although the **orbits** of the planets and asteroids look roughly circular on most diagrams of the solar system, really they're slightly elliptical (oval-shaped).

Comets have very elliptical orbits, which mean they only spend a tiny fraction of their time close to the Sun. The planets (apart from Pluto) all orbit in the same direction and in the same plane (called the ecliptic).

 Many students are confused by the difference between mass and weight. They are not the same thing but they are connected. The mass of an object is a measure of how much 'stuff' it contains and is measured in kilograms. The weight of an object is a measure of the strength of the gravitational force trying to pull it downwards and is measured in newtons.

QUESTIONS

3 How would an object move if no forces were applied to it?

4 What causes planets and comets to travel in orbits?

5 Where in a comet's orbit will it experience the greatest gravitational forces?

Black holes (H)

If you throw an object up in the air, you know that it will fall back down because of the Earth's gravitational pull. However, if you throw it fast enough, it can escape the Earth's gravity completely, and never fall back down. This is not easy, because the strength of the Earth's surface gravity means that the **escape velocity** is around 11 km per second! Escape velocity depends on the mass of the planet and its radius. A small, dense planet with a large mass would have a high escape velocity.

FIGURE 4: A black hole may form an entrance to a wormhole.

When a large star comes to the end of its life cycle, with its huge mass it may collapse inwards creating an object whose escape velocity from its surface is greater than the speed of light! We call such an object a **black hole**. Anything that comes too close will be attracted by the ferocious gravity, and will fall in. Even light can't escape from it.

QUESTIONS

6 Explain what is meant by the statement 'The escape velocity for an object on the Earth's surface is 11 km/s.'.

7 What is a black hole?

What's space like?

You will find out:
- What conditions are like in space
- How spacecraft get electrical power
- How spacecraft are controlled

No place to break down!

Maybe in the future, travellers in space will be able to call up the breakdown services if they have a problem, but they certainly can't at the moment. Spacecraft need to be designed to keep working even under the extreme conditions they meet. It's essential, therefore, that we have a good understanding of the conditions out there.

Conditions in space

Air

There is no air in space. This means that you need to take oxygen with you to breathe. On very long missions, such as a trip to Mars, perhaps plants could be used a source of oxygen. When **photosynthesis** takes place the plants release oxygen and take in carbon dioxide.

Weightlessness

Travellers in space will experience **weightlessness**. As a result many of the muscles in their bodies will be doing very little or no work. This is likely to lead to space travellers suffering from **muscle wastage**.

FIGURE 1: The international space station.

Electricity

Spacecraft need quite a lot of electrical energy to run all the systems, such as air pumps, lights, computers, instruments, flight controls, and radios. On a space station, huge **solar panels** might provide this energy.

In a spacecraft that needs to move around, such as a Space Shuttle, **fuel cells** are used to generate electricity from a **reaction** between hydrogen and oxygen. So the Shuttle needs to carry tanks of these gases.

For very long unmanned trips, such as the seven-year journey to Saturn, nuclear reactions are used to make electricity. You don't need much fuel to run them, so you're not going to run out on a long voyage.

FIGURE 2: Why do astronauts become weightless?

QUESTIONS

1. Why do we need to take oxygen with us on any space trip?
2. List **three** ways to provide electrical power for spacecraft.
3. What might happen to your body if you spent a long time in space? Can you suggest a solution to this problem?

...*acceleration* ...*fuel cell* ...*micrometeorite* ...*muscle wastage* ...*photosynthesis*

'Barbecue rolls'

In Earth orbit, sunlight is much brighter than it is down here under the atmosphere. This means that your spacecraft will get very hot on one side, and very cold on the shaded side. This can cause overheating and possible damage to some parts, whilst on the other side of your craft the fuel freezes in the pipes. Also, when you move your spacecraft and the sun reaches different parts, the expansion and contraction as the temperature changes can crack pipes and break wires.

That's why in the film *Apollo 13*, you'll hear Tom Hanks mention flying in 'barbecue mode'. This means that they gently rolled their ship as they flew, so that the Sun's heat reached all parts of the craft and they wouldn't risk overheating or freezing any equipment.

FIGURE 3: Apollo 11 on its way to the Moon.

Micrometeorites

On the Earth's surface we are protected by our atmosphere from cosmic radiation, most of the Sun's ultraviolet radiation, and the many tiny specks of rock called **micrometeorites**. These burn up as they fall through the atmosphere.

In a spacecraft, any object that hits you is likely to arrive at incredibly high speed, and punch straight through walls and equipment. As well as micrometeorites, these days any craft in Earth orbit is increasingly likely to meet fragments of other satellites, such as nuts and bolts, which could spell disaster. At these speeds even a flake of paint from an old satellite can puncture a hull! Spacecraft carry patches to slap quickly over the holes. So long as you can find the puncture it's usually easy to patch it from the inside – air pressure will hold it in place for you. Then you can organise a proper repair.

FIGURE 4: If you get a puncture in your spacecraft, you need to repair it fast!

WANT TO KNOW MORE?

Find out more about the NASA 'Vomit Comet' aircraft used for training astronauts at http://edspace.nasa.gov/astroschool/flight.

Engines in space

Aircraft engines work by pushing or blowing air backwards so that they go forwards. This is a good example of Newton's Third Law in action. Outside the atmosphere, this would not work. Rocket engines fire hot gases backwards in order that the spacecraft is pushed forwards, providing it with **acceleration**.

Small **thruster** engines dotted around the craft use the same principle to steer it. You can see some thrusters on the photo of Apollo 11 (figure 3). All spacecraft need to carry reaction mass to work their engines and thrusters. When the reaction mass runs out, they can't steer.

FIGURE 5: Newton's Third Law: 'For every action there is an equal and opposite reaction'.

QUESTIONS

7 Explain why the Space Shuttle has both a reaction control thruster system and aircraft-style control surfaces on its wing.

QUESTIONS

4 Why does the Space Shuttle use fuel cells instead of solar panels?
5 Explain why the Apollo missions flew in 'barbecue mode'.
6 Explain why micrometeorites are a danger to spacecraft.

...*reaction* ...*solar panel* ...*thruster* ...*weightlessness*

How could we live there?

You will find out:

- How our bodies are affected by living in space
- About special measures we have to take to survive in space

Adapting to space

Our bodies are adapted to life on Earth, so when we go into space there are effects on our health. This is particularly true for astronauts on long trips.

Exercise is essential (H)

As we have already seen astronauts may suffer from muscle wastage. To avoid this problem, astronauts need to use **exercise** machines.

On a typical Shuttle mission, each astronaut must spend 30 minutes each day exercising. If you're using a treadmill, you need rubber straps to pull you 'down' onto the machine as you run.

Not bog standard (H)

Weightlessness brings a whole host of problems – such as how to use a toilet. With no weight, things won't go down a bowl; they have a nasty habit of floating around the room. This is not popular with the other astronauts! The toilet on the Space Shuttle uses a vacuum pump to make sure that things go where they should. There are leg clamps to keep you on the seat; if things get serious you can strap your feet down as well.

FIGURE 1: Back on Earth and struggling with the effects of gravity.

FIGURE 2: Astronauts must exercise before a mission.

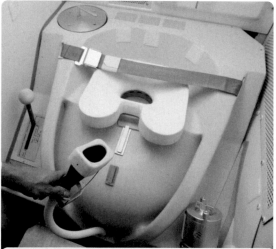

FIGURE 3: Using the toilet on the Space Shuttle is quite a performance.

The toilet on the International Space Station has quite a small hole in the seat, so believe it or not there's a camera under the seat to help you line things up correctly.

QUESTIONS

1 Why do astronauts need to use exercise machines in space?
2 List **three** features of the toilet on a Space Shuttle, and say why they are needed.

WANT TO KNOW MORE?

Watch a video about toilets in space at http://edspace.nasa.gov/livespace/gottago.html

...calcium depletion ...exercise ...microgravity ...osteoporosis

Weightlessness changes you (H)

Without the constant battle against gravity, your body changes when you spend time in weightless conditions. Fluids are redistributed, with less in the lower body and more blood pooling in your face, giving you a puffy appearance.

The skeleton

If your bones do not have enough calcium, you have problems similar to **osteoporosis**, which causes brittle bones especially in older women. On Earth, our bones are constantly being chemically broken down and rebuilt. In weightless conditions this balance is disturbed, and the calcium lost as the bones are broken down does not get replaced fast enough. This is called **calcium depletion**. Scientists believe that in

FIGURE 4: Weightlessness affects our bones.

microgravity, where the loads on the skeleton are tiny, the skeleton immediately starts to get rid of bone that it no longer needs. This happens rapidly to both men and women, even on fairly short missions, and it is believed that the effects are similar whether you fly a number of short missions or one long mission. Mission planners are considering providing artificial gravity on long spaceflights by spinning the ship, or using some other means to make the astronauts' bodies work hard.

The heart

Your heart has to work hard to pump blood around your body, fighting the pull of gravity. In space, the heart has a much easier job, and also your body won't be working as hard so your respiration will slow down. This means that when you return to Earth after a long mission, your heart will suddenly need to work hard again, increasing the risk of heart attacks. Also, re-entering the Earth's atmosphere might involve high 'g-forces', which your heart may not cope with if you've been in space a long time.

WOW FACTOR!

Astronauts need to be able to write in free-fall, on a variety of surfaces and under extremes of temperature. The Americans spent millions of dollars developing the 'Astronaut Pen'. The Russians solved the problem another way … by using pencils.

FIGURE 5: Astronauts can have bad hair days in weightless conditions!

QUESTIONS

3   What is calcium depletion? How does it affect the body?

4   What other risks are there to your health when you return to Earth? Explain as fully as you can.

Radiation (H)

The Sun emits a great deal of harmful **radiation** and charged particles. Fortunately our atmosphere and magnetic field shields us from most of it. Once you leave Earth, you need to consider some way of providing shielding.

Effective shielding is heavy, so it's difficult to build it into a spacecraft. Water provides some shielding, so if your engines use water in their reactions you could surround the craft with a thick water tank. However, launching that huge mass would be difficult, so perhaps in the future we could try to fill up on route from ice on comets or asteroids!

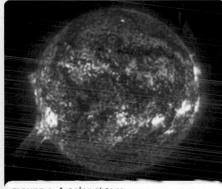

FIGURE 6: A solar storm.

Solar storms (H)

From time to time the Sun throws out sufficiently high levels of radiation and charged particles that it affects communications and electricity supplies on Earth. If you're in space when this happens, you could be in trouble. By observing the Sun we can get some warning of when these '**solar storms**' will arrive, and take appropriate action, for example, changing orbit to hide behind the Earth or taking cover in a shielded section of the craft. In the future electrostatic fields around space craft may be the solution.

QUESTIONS

5   Explain why harmful radiation from the Sun has not killed everything on Earth.

6   How can astronauts minimise their exposure to radiation?

Space tourism

You will find out:
- What it's like on other planets
- How the space tourism industry may develop

The first ever!

Since the first manned space flight by Yuri Gagarin in 1961, there have been, on average, just four manned space flights per year. However, we are now seeing the beginnings of a space tourism industry which plans to change that!

Life on other planets

Living on Earth suits us just fine. The **temperatures** aren't too extreme, the air has just the right amount of oxygen for us, and the **gravity** is exactly what we're used to.

TABLE 1: Conditions on other planets.

Planet	Surface gravity (N/kg)	Atmosphere	Temperature (°C)	Notes
Mercury	4	almost none	−170 to +350	the widest range of temperatures in the solar system
Venus	9	very high pressure, carbon dioxide	+480	hotter than Mercury due to 'greenhouse effect'. Clouds of sulphuric acid
Earth	10	nitrogen, oxygen	−20 to +40	mostly oceans, which keep the temperature steady
Mars	4	thin, carbon dioxide	−133 to +27	closest to Earth-like conditions
Jupiter	26 at cloud tops	hydrogen & helium	−153 at cloud tops	gas planet, no surface. Incredibly high pressures and temperatures deep inside
Saturn	11	hydrogen & helium	−185 at cloud tops	gas planet, no surface. Incredibly high pressures and temperatures deep inside
Uranus	11	hydrogen & helium	−214	gas planet with rocky core
Neptune	12	hydrogen & helium	−225	gas planet with rocky core
Pluto	4	very little	−236	small, rocky, very cold. Little is known for sure

Elsewhere in the **solar system** conditions are very different. We could not survive on any other **planet** without protection. If you went to Pluto, your biggest problem would be the cold. On Venus the high temperatures would burn you, the high pressure from its thick **atmosphere** would crush you and the sulphuric acid in the atmosphere would eat right through your ship. Jupiter and Saturn are great balls of gas and so don't have surfaces that you can stand on. So landing on them is probably out of the question.

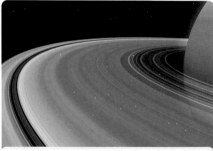

FIGURE 1: Saturn is just a ball of gas – plus those rings!

QUESTIONS

1 If you wanted to live on another planet, which ones would give you problems with extreme cold?
2 Which planets have higher temperatures than Earth?
3 Which planets couldn't you land on at all?
4 Which planet has the hottest and most hostile conditions? Describe what it is like there.

...atmosphere ...gravity ...moon ...orbital habitat

Why bother leaving Earth? (H)

So far we've looked at conditions on other planets. Mars has spectacular scenery, and Saturn has magnificent rings. But there are many other places that are worth a visit.

FIGURE 2: Would you like to holiday on Titan?

The outer planets have many **moons**, which have low gravity and provide opportunities to live there using the local materials. Titan, one of Saturn's moons, was visited by the Huygens probe on 14 January 2005, launched from the Cassini orbiter. We found a world slightly larger than Mercury, made mainly of ice and rock, which had a significant atmosphere.

Europa, one of Jupiter's moons, is covered with ice. We think that there is liquid water underneath, and a rocky core. If we're looking for life out there in the solar system, Europa looks like a good bet.

FIGURE 3: An artist's impression of Jupiter from Europa.

Or perhaps we would prefer not to land at all, and live in an **orbital habitat**. This would make it much easier to get a space tourism industry going, as the operators wouldn't have the huge expense of fuel to escape from the gravitational pull at each destination. Perhaps the tour companies will offer a combination of orbital and surface visits, depending on what's on offer at each destination.

FIGURE 4: Try a new sport at your orbiting hotel.

WANT TO KNOW MORE?

Find out about what it's like on the planets and their moons at www.bbc.co.uk/science/space/solarsystem. For each planet, notice the 'Reasons to visit', 'What to see' and 'When you arrive'.

When can I go into space? (H)

Until very recently, the only way into space was to join a government space programme such as NASA. That is now changing. A British company called Starchaser has already made unmanned test launches of their Nova rocket, and is planning manned flights soon.

FIGURE 5: SpaceShipOne landing.

Burt Rutan, famous for experimental aircraft, made history when SpaceShipOne won the 'X Prize' as the first privately-funded craft to successfully reach space twice.

Want to book a ticket? Virgin Galactic already exists and is taking bookings. But it won't be cheap!

QUESTIONS

5   Why would Europa be a good place to look for extraterrestrial life?

6   Why might space tourist operators concentrate on hotels in orbit?

7   Find out about conditions on another planet or moon. If you were a tourist, why would you go to that place? What would it be like there? How would you get there, and where would you stay?

QUESTIONS

8   Using news articles or the Internet, write a report on the space tourism industry – which companies exist, their technology and their plans.

...planet ...solar system ...temperature

Searching for answers

You will find out:
- How we find out about the universe
- Why we need to send probes to find out about the planets

Finding out

Apart from the Earth and the Moon, humans haven't actually been anywhere else in the solar system. Robot **probes** have only landed on Venus, the Moon, Mars and Titan (a moon of Saturn). So how do we know so much about the universe? A lot of our information has come from **telescopes** (some in Earth orbit) and fly-bys and **landers**, a few of which are mentioned on this page.

What can we see up there?

We can learn much about the Moon, our neighbouring planets and many of the **stars** in our galaxy using the naked eye. But when Galileo invented the first optical telescope in 1609, our abilities to observe these and many more bodies improved greatly. The optical telescope has for many years been one of the greatest aids to improving our knowledge of the universe.

With his telescope Galileo was the first to see the four largest moons of Jupiter. He named them Europa, Callisto, Ganymede and Io.

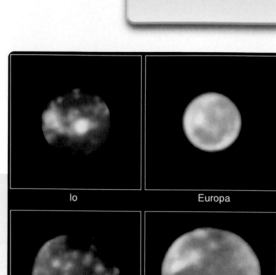

| Io | Europa |
| Callisto | Ganymede |

FIGURE 1: The four largest moons of Jupiter.

FIGURE 2: A mountain-top observatory.

Large optical telescopes are placed on mountain-top observatories such as the one in Figure 2, where they suffer less interference from the Earth's atmosphere.

The Hubble Space Telescope was placed in orbit around the Earth in 1990. It can see farther into space and is totally unaffected by the Earth's atmosphere.

QUESTIONS

1. Who invented the first telescope and what did he discover when he used it to look at the planet Jupiter?
2. Why are large astronomical telescopes built on mountain tops?
3. Where is the Hubble telescope?

...interplanetary ...lander ...probe

Probing the solar system

Fly-bys

Instead of manned **interplanetary** flights, probes are sent to fly close to a planet or moon, or put into orbit around it. They send back data and images to Earth. The first was Luna 1 launched in 1959, passing within 6000 km of the Moon. In 1962, Mariner 2 passed within 35 000 km of the surface of Venus.

Landers

Some probes release a second craft, which lands on the surface. These can collect samples, carry out experiments and then send the results back to Earth.

NASA's Viking Project became the first mission to land safely on another planet when it landed on Mars. Two spacecraft were built, both launched in 1975. They discovered some odd chemical activity in the soil, but nothing conclusive. The landers were designed to operate for 90 days, but being powered by nuclear reactions they kept working for several years.

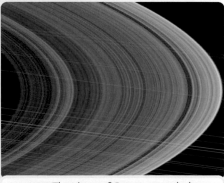

FIGURE 3: The Mars rover.

In early 2004, two Mars rovers, 'Spirit' and 'Opportunity', arrived with much more advanced equipment. These concentrated on the geology of Mars, especially signs of water activity. Solar powered, they carried cameras to direct the vehicles and a variety of instruments on an arm to investigate rocks.

In 1997, Cassini–Huygens was launched, passing Jupiter and arriving at Saturn in July 2004. Cassini is teaching us a great deal about the Saturn system.

The Huygens probe, launched from Cassini, landed on Titan on 14 January 2005. The battery-powered instruments sent data to Cassini, which relayed it to Earth.

Under Titan's thick cloudy atmosphere, we had never seen the surface before. It is darker than we expected, and made of an icy mixture of water and hydrocarbons. The rock-like objects are thought to be ice.

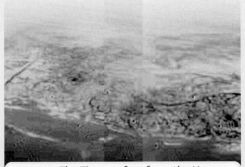

FIGURE 4: The Titan surface from the Huygens probe.

QUESTIONS

4   What is a fly-by? Give **one** example of a fly-by.

5   What is a lander? Give **one** example of a lander.

6   Why are fly-bys and landers much cheaper than manned interplanetary flights?

Using other wavelengths of light to see

Most modern probes are able to observe objects using a range of wavelengths, including infrared and ultraviolet. Pictures taken using these wavelengths reveal extra information.

FIGURE 5: The rings of Saturn revealed.

Using ultraviolet wavelengths instead of visible light, we can tell a great deal about what Saturn's rings are made of, as it shows the way the **ring particles** cool down as they orbit into Saturn's shadow and heat up as they come out into the sunlight. We can't study this from Earth, as from here Saturn is always lit 'edge on', whereas Cassini, in orbit around Saturn, can get pictures from different angles.

By comparing pictures taken using ultraviolet and infrared we can tell that Titan's atmosphere contains methane, by the way that the gas scatters ultraviolet and absorbs infrared.

QUESTIONS

7   Why can Cassini get pictures of Saturn that we can't get from Earth?

8   Why is infrared useful for studying Saturn's rings?

9   Search the Internet for pictures of planets, stars and galaxies taken using infrared or ultraviolet light.

Is there anybody there?

Are we alone?

The universe is incredibly large. It contains billions of **galaxies**, each made of billions of stars. So we think that it is likely that there are other civilisations out there somewhere. If they exist, what are our chances of meeting them? In these pages we are going to explore some of our ideas about **extraterrestrial** life.

Any signs of civilisation?

We're pretty sure that there are no other civilisations in our solar system. If there were they would be emitting large amounts of heat, light and radio energy – just as we are. We would therefore have detected them long ago.

But what if an extraterrestrial civilisation was far older and more advanced than us? Could they be using technology that we simply aren't clever enough to detect? From what we know about our solar system, we don't think that it's old enough for that to be happening.

So we think that if there are any alien civilisations, they must be beyond our solar system, which means a long way away. Detecting their existence and communicating with them is therefore not going to be easy.

There is of course another possibility. Perhaps there is life elsewhere in our solar system but it may be very simple life, for example, microbes. We will have to wait until we have sent **probes** and landers to investigate all planets and moons before we can answer that question.

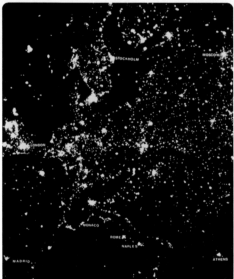

FIGURE 1: City lights across Europe are visible from space.

EXAM HINTS AND TIPS

extraterrestrial = outside the Earth and its atmosphere; **extrasolar** = beyond the solar system

▪▪ QUESTIONS ▪▪

Copy and complete

1   We think that the universe is likely to contain other civilisations because…

2   We don't think there are any extraterrestrial civilisations in our solar system because…

3   We think that any alien civilisations must be a long way away because…

WANT TO KNOW MORE?

What are we actually doing about finding aliens? Visit www.seti.org. In particular, try their online game 'Who's out there?' in the education section.

…biosphere   …extrasolar   …extraterrestrial

Vital statistics! (H)

In our galaxy alone, there are many billions of stars.

- Only a fraction of them have planets, though we're discovering more extrasolar planets all the time.
- Of these, only a fraction may be suitable for life to appear.
- Only a fraction may have evolved any life.
- Only a fraction may have evolved any life more complex than microbes.
- Only a fraction may be home to a technological civilisation right now. Considering the age of the universe, it's more likely that aliens are either far more advanced than us or way behind.

Think about the assumptions we've made here. We've assumed that life needs a planet to evolve on; that it needs the same sort of temperatures that we do, and that life tends to evolve into complex forms and build civilisations. And just because we want to communicate doesn't mean that aliens do.

Yet we think it's likely that there are plenty of civilisations out there. However they're probably so thinly scattered that our chances of meeting them are tiny.

FIGURE 2: Is there life in our galaxy?

How do we find aliens? (H)

We could send spaceships to other stars, but the journey would take many thousands of years. So we would have to build enormous **biosphere** ships where many generations of crew would live. They would be incredibly expensive to build; yet we would need a huge number of them to investigate enough star systems.

FIGURE 3: A biosphere space ship.

We could send unmanned probes, but again the journey times would be huge. Imagine that a dinosaur 65 million years ago sent a probe to another star – the information might be coming back around now!

A better idea is to communicate instead of travel. Aliens are likely to be sending radio waves rather than light, as light is blocked by gas and dust between stars. So we use **radio telescopes** to scan the sky and listen for messages.

FIGURE 4: A radio telescope.

Would we know an intelligent signal if we saw it? (H)

Radio telescopes receive a huge amount of data all the time, from stars, other galaxies, quasars and many other objects. The signals from pulsars are very regular. They were thought to be from aliens when we first detected the signals in 1967.

If we detected a series of long and short pulses like this, we'd be sure it had an intelligent origin and was not from a natural source:

-, - -, - - -, - - - - -, - - - - - - -, - - - - - - - - - -

Bear in mind that aliens won't use the same alphabet as us, if they use one at all. It might make more sense for them to send numbers. We sent such a message from the radio telescope at Arecibo, Puerto Rico, in 1975. It will reach its intended target the M13 globular cluster in about 25 000 years.

QUESTIONS

4   Why do we think that civilisations must be thinly scattered across the universe?

5   Why do we use radio telescopes to look for aliens, instead of sending ships?

6   By sending a biosphere ship to another star, we need unborn generations to continue the mission for the whole of their lives, knowing that they will die before reaching the destination. Do we have the right to do that? Discuss your ideas.

QUESTIONS

7   What might the series of long and short pulses (above) mean? Can you see a pattern?

8   Search the Internet for information about SETI (Search for ExtraTerrestrial Intelligence).

Why bother with space?

You will find out:

- Some examples of how we have benefited from space research
- How our survival could be threatened from space

Is it worth it?

Exploring space is incredibly expensive. How can we justify the huge sums spent when there are so many urgent problems right here on Earth which need financial support? The answer to this question in the eyes of many scientists is that space exploration has led to the discovery of many things which have been beneficial to man. In this spread we are going to look at some of these spin-offs.

Useful inventions   (H)

All of these inventions came about as a result of the space programme: smoke detectors, flat-panel TVs, hang gliders, freeze-dried foods, air traffic control collision avoidance systems, weather forecasts using satellites, high-power batteries for cordless tools, virtual reality computer systems, and ... sports bras.

In fact, over 1400 inventions that are used in our daily lives and in industry are a direct result of **space research**.

FIGURE 1: These survival blankets were originally invented for NASA. Athletes and mountaineers benefit from them.

FIGURE 2: Some space research spin-offs.

Medical spin-offs   (H)

The development of charge coupled devices (CCD camera chips) for the Hubble Space Telescope has not only produced affordable mobile phone cameras and web cams, but also allowed doctors to use advanced imaging techniques in many areas. One example is Digital Imaging Breast Biopsy, where CCD sensors can spot dangerous tumours without the need for surgery. This reduces pain, scarring, cost and recovery time for patients.

Programmable heart pacemakers and **ultrasound** scanners have also helped countless patients. Ultrasound scans are used to monitor the development of unborn babies. They are also used in diagnosing some cancers and kidney infections.

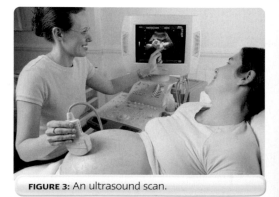

FIGURE 3: An ultrasound scan.

QUESTIONS

1 CCD chips are used in digital cameras. What does 'CCD' stand for?
2 Describe how ultrasound is used in medicine.
3 Use the Internet to find out more about 'NASA spin-offs' – inventions that owe their existence to space research.

...asteroid   ...communication   ...geostationary   ...low polar orbit

Satellite technology (H)

One obvious application of space technology is the use of **satellites**.

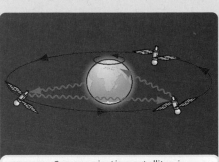

FIGURE 4: Communication satellites in geostatic orbit.

- **Communication** satellites are placed in a **geostationary** orbit (also called 'geosynchronous') 35 786 km above the equator. In this orbit it takes them exactly 24 hours to orbit the Earth. This means that they stay above the same part of the Earth the whole time. These satellites enable instant news coverage live from almost anywhere in the world, as well as international telephone calls, the Internet and e-mail.

FIGURE 5: Geostationary satellites are also used to monitor the weather.

- Working out what the British **weather** is about to do is never easy! Pictures from Meteosat, a geostationary satellite, give forecasters a continuous view of weather fronts and how they are moving. Pictures such as these (figure 5) enable us to predict the weather several days in advance. This can be vital for seafarers, pilots, mountaineers, and farmers planning harvests.

- Handheld and car satellite **navigation** receivers use signals from satellites to work out where they are. The orbits of the 24 satellites are arranged so that a receiver can always 'see' at least three. Positions are then found by comparing the timings of signals from each.

- Military 'spy' satellites are placed in **low polar orbits**. As the satellite is low, it can take very detailed pictures. Satellites placed in these orbits circle the Earth approximately once every 90 minutes.

FIGURE 6: The Navstar GPS satellite network.

- Environmental satellites, such as Landsat, are used to track changes to the landscape, such as erosion, deforestation, changes in ocean temperature and even what type of crops farmers are growing. These satellites are also often placed in polar orbits. As they follow their orbit the Earth rotates beneath them. This means that after each orbit, they pass over a different part of the Earth. A single satellite can photograph the whole of the Earth's surface in one day.

QUESTIONS

4 Give **two** uses for a geostationary satellite.

5 Give two uses for a satellite put into a low polar orbit.

Asteroid problems

The whole future of life on Earth could depend upon our ability to track the motions of **asteroids** and respond to any that are large and on a collision course with our planet. Many small asteroids collide with the Earth each year but most burn up in the atmosphere and so cause no damage to the Earth's surface.

Within the next million years it is likely that the Earth will be struck by an asteroid 1–10 km in diameter. At the lower end of the range, millions of people will be killed and an area the size of Europe will be affected.

At the upper end, so much dust and smoke will be ejected into the atmosphere that light will be unable to reach the Earth's surface. As a result photosynthesis will cease and most plant life will die. Land surface temperatures will plummet killing most animal life.

Many small asteroids collide with the Earth each year

QUESTIONS

6 Why are small asteroids no threat to the Earth?

7 Why is it important to monitor the motion of large asteroids?

The life of a star

You will find out:

- How stars are created
- How stars change with time
- About the role played by gravity and nuclear reactions in the life of a star
- What a black hole is

Supernova

The top photograph on the right is of a nearby galaxy. The lower photograph is of the same galaxy taken some years later. The bright light on the right of the lower photograph is being emitted by a star as it explodes and dies. The energy released during the explosion was so great that for a few months this single star outshone an entire galaxy.

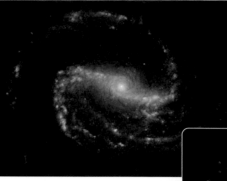

FIGURE 1: The death of a star.

Birth of a star

It was once believed that the stars and the universe had existed forever and would never end. We now know that this is not true. The universe is continually changing. Over long periods of time, stars are created, exist and then die. We say that stars have a **life cycle**. These cycles can last millions or even billions of years depending upon the size of the star.

FIGURE 2: In the Orion Nebula, stars are being created from these huge gas and dust clouds.

- Stars are formed from clouds of gases and dust in space.
- **Gravitational forces** pull the gases and dust particles together.
- As this happens the temperature of this material increases and **nuclear reactions** start to take place.
- These reactions release enormous amounts of heat and light. A star is born.

▌▌ QUESTIONS ▌▌

1. What materials are needed to create a star?
2. What forces pull these materials closer together?
3. What kinds of reactions start to occur when these materials are squashed together?
4. What is released when these reactions begin?

...black hole   ...gravitational force   ...life cycle   ...neutron star

Changing with age

Stars gradually change with time. As the fuel for one kind of nuclear reaction runs out, a different kind of nuclear reaction will begin. This results in changes in the colour and size of the star.

When a star forms, it experiences two forces: gravitational forces trying to make it smaller; and expansive forces created by nuclear reactions which are trying to make it bigger.

At some point these two forces will balance. When they do, we say that the star is in its main stable period. This may last for several billion years. Our Sun is in its main stable period.

The nuclear reactions in the main stable period mainly involve hydrogen nuclei but gradually this supply will be used up and reactions involving helium nuclei now take over. As a result the star is a little cooler and expands to become much bigger than it was in the main stable period. The star is now a **red giant**.

What happens next depends upon how much mass the star contains. If the star has an average mass similar to our Sun, when it begins to run out of nuclear fuel the forces of gravity cause it to contract. The star now changes into a **white dwarf**. Its density is so high that a handful of it would have a mass greater than 1000 tonnes!

As the nuclear reactions cease altogether the star cools and becomes a black dwarf.

If, however, the mass of the star is much greater than that of our Sun, it has a very different, much more exciting future. After the main stable period, the forces created by the new nuclear reactions and the forces of gravity create a red giant star which is hundreds of times bigger than our Sun. It is called a red supergiant.

When the nuclear reactions within a super red giant cease, it collapses, becomes very unstable and then explodes, throwing dust and gas into space. This exploding star is called a **supernova**.

The star left behind after a supernova is called a **neutron star** and is likely to be just a few kilometres across. It will emit no light and just a handful of it will have a mass of 10 000 million tonnes!

If the star is extremely large, when it collapses it may leave behind a **black hole**, a place in space where gravitational forces are so strong that not even light can escape from it.

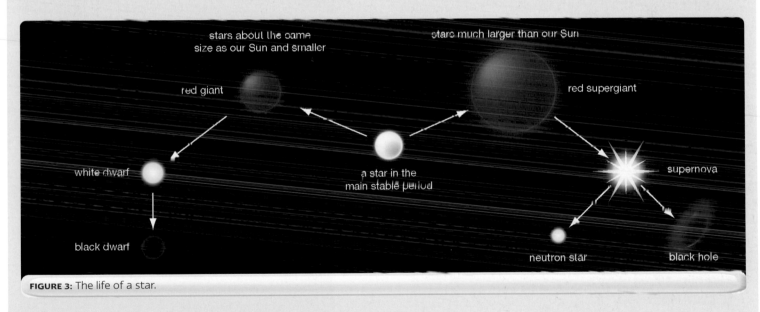

FIGURE 3: The life of a star.

QUESTIONS

5   What is the main stable period?

6   What kinds of nuclei are reacting during the main stable period?

7   What kinds of nuclear reactions are taking place in a red giant?

8   Explain what happens to a red giant when its nuclear fuel begins to run out.

9   What is a red supergiant?

10   What is a supernova?

11   Name **two** things that might be left behind after a supernova.

The Universe is continually changing

How did it all start? How will it all end?

You will find out:
- How we believe the universe came into existence
- How the universe is changing
- How we think it may end

The driving force of science ... curiosity

Human beings, like cats, are naturally curious. They are constantly asking questions about our place in the universe and about the universe itself. How did the universe begin? How old is the universe? Will the universe go on forever or will it end? We have certainly come a long way since man first asked these questions but, as is often the way in science, some of our discoveries have raised more questions than they have actually answered.

How it all started

Many people used to believe that the **universe** had no beginning and it would have no end. This was known as the **steady state theory** of the universe. Most people now think that this is not the case.

- It is now thought the universe came into existence about 15 billion years ago.
- It started with a tremendous explosion known as the **Big Bang**.
- Since the Big Bang the universe has been expanding.
- The question scientists are now asking is 'Will the universe continue to expand forever?'

Will the universe go on forever or will it end?

FIGURE 1: Hubble helps us to see deep into space.

QUESTIONS

1. What is the steady state theory of the universe?
2. How old do scientists think our universe is?
3. How do we think the universe began?
4. What is happening to our universe now?

...Big Bang   ...cosmic microwaves   ...dark matter   ...expansion   ...galaxy

Putting the picture together (H)

There are several key bits of information which support the Big Bang and expanding universe theory.

- Studies of the light emitted by distant galaxies prove that the galaxies are moving away from us. They also show that the more distant a **galaxy** is, the greater its velocity away from us. This is precisely what you would expect if all matter started from the same point and then exploded outwards.

- If the universe was very hot when it first came into existence and is cooling as it expands, we should still be able to detect some of this heat. In 1965, two radio astronomers, Arno Penzias and Robert Wilson, discovered this left-over energy in the form of **cosmic microwaves**. These waves would not be present if the steady state theory was correct.

- Large amounts of light elements such as hydrogen and helium have been detected throughout the universe, giving further support to this theory.

FIGURE 2: Arno Penzias and Robert Wilson who discovered cosmic microwaves.

Red shift (H)

Figure 3 shows spectra from three different sources. The first is a spectrum produced using light from the Sun. Across this band of colours are several dark lines caused by elements in the outer layers of the Sun absorbing some of the light.

The second spectrum is from light from a distant galaxy. Clearly the dark lines are now moved slightly towards the red end of the spectrum. This is called **red shift** and indicates that the source of the light, that is the galaxy, is moving away from the Earth.

The third is from a very distant galaxy. The red shift here is even greater, showing that the further away a galaxy is the faster it is moving away from the Earth.

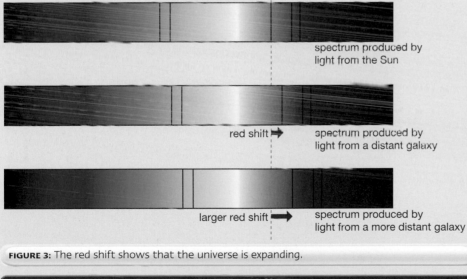

spectrum produced by light from the Sun

red shift ➡ spectrum produced by light from a distant galaxy

larger red shift ➡ spectrum produced by light from a more distant galaxy

FIGURE 3: The red shift shows that the universe is expanding.

The future of our universe (H)

Scientists now believe that there are three possible futures for our universe:

- If there is enough matter in the universe, gravitational forces may slow down the rate of **expansion** and eventually may start to pull matter back together resulting in an event they call the Big Crunch. Some scientists suggest that another big bang will then take place and the universe expand again. This theory of an expanding and collapsing universe is known as the **oscillating theory**.

- If there is not enough matter in the universe it may continue to expand forever.

- If there is just the right amount of matter in the universe it may reach a certain fixed size.

Many scientists at present are trying to measure the total mass of the matter in the universe in order to determine its final fate, but in doing so they are making new discoveries, for example, the existence of **dark matter** forcing them to re-evaluate the model they have of our universe.

QUESTIONS

5 Explain how distant galaxies are moving relative to the Earth?

6 Why can scientists detect microwaves throughout the universe?

7 How are the black lines seen in the spectrum of the Sun created?

8 What happens to these lines if the light we are investigating comes from a distant galaxy? What does this prove? What is this phenomenon called?

QUESTIONS

9 What is the Big Crunch?

10 Find out about dark matter. Why do we think it exists?

Unit summary

Concept map

Exploring space

A number of useful inventions are the result of our studies of space. These include space blankets, smoke alarms and flat panel TVs.

New data from orbiting telescopes and unmanned flights are continuously improving our understanding of the history and future of our universe.

Life as we know it can only exist in specific conditions. It requires a certain temperature, gravitational field strength, atmosphere and the presence of water.

Gravity is a crucial force in our Universe. It keeps planets in orbit around the Sun, moons in orbit around a planet and plays an important role in the life and death of stars.

Using manned flights to explore our Universe is far more complicated than using unmanned flights as it is necessary to maintain stable conditions for life. A manned spacecraft requires a constant air supply, food, artificial gravity and sufficient fuel for the return journey.

Waves

Waves transfer energy. There are two main families of waves: transverse and longitudinal.

Electromagnetic waves are a large group of transverse waves that include radio waves, microwaves, infrared waves, visible light, ultra violet waves, X-rays and gamma rays. They all travel at the same speed and can travel through a vacuum. Differences in their properties, such as penetrating power and biological effects, are due to their different wavelengths and frequencies.

The features of a wave are:
- Amplitude
- Frequency (f)
- Wavelength (γ)
- Speed (v)

The wave equation states: $v = f \times \gamma$

Wave phenomenon include:
- Reflection
- Refraction
- Total internal reflection
- Diffraction
- Absorption
- Penetrating power.

We use waves in the following ways:
- Eye – seeing
- Ultrasound – observing developing foetus
- Microwaves – measuring water content
- Ultra violet – detecting forged bank notes
- Seismic – tells us about the structure of the Earth.

We communicate using waves in the following ways:
- Visual signals, for instance semaphore using light waves
- Speaking using sound waves
- Mobile phones using microwaves
- Analogue and digital signals.

Unit quiz

1 Calculate the speed of a wave with a wavelength of 1.7 m and a frequency of 200 Hz.

2 Give **one** example of a transverse wave which can travel through a vacuum and **one** example of a longitudinal wave which cannot travel through a vacuum.

3 What are the two conditions necessary for a ray of light to undergo total internal reflection?

4 Old telecommunication networks send messages along copper wires. What do modern communication networks use? Suggest **two** advantages of these new networks.

5 The time delay between emitting a sound wave and hearing its reflection from the seabed is 10 seconds. If the speed of sound in salt water is 1500 m/s, calculate the depth of the water below the ship.

6 What kind of wave is used by mobile phones to carry messages? What medical concerns do people have with these waves?

7 Why is UVB more harmful to humans than UVA?

8 Which part of the electromagnetic spectrum has: **a)** the lowest frequency, **b)** the shortest wavelength and **c)** the greatest penetrating power?

9 What is the main advantage of a digital signal compared with an analogue signal?

10 What is multiplexing?

11 X-rays could be used to observe the development of a foetus in a womb but we use ultrasound instead. Explain why this is the case.

12 List the following astronomical object in order of their size, biggest first.
Planet   Moon   Sun   Asteroid
Galaxy   Constellation   Solar System

13 Calculate the weight of an object which has a mass of 2 kg **a)** on Earth, **b)** on Mars and **c)** on Jupiter. (The gravitation field strength is 10 N/kg on Earth, 4 N/kg on Mars and 26 N/kg on Jupiter.)

14 Why is light unable to escape from a black hole?

15 Why might astronauts suffer from muscle wastage whilst in space? How can they avoid this?

16 Explain the difference between an orbiter and a lander.

17 What is SETI?

18 What is a geostationary satellite and what might it be used for?

19 Write a flow diagram to show the life of a star which is much larger than our sun.

20 What quantity will determine the future of our Universe?

Literacy activity

Sonar equipment

Modern sonar equipment uses ultrasounds rather than 'normal' sound waves. This is because normal sound waves are absorbed as they travel through water and spread out as they move away from their source. The echoes these waves produce are therefore quite weak and more difficult to detect. Ultrasonic waves, however, can be emitted as a narrower beam which does not spread out as much as it travels away from the source. A much stronger echo is therefore produced.

QUESTIONS

1 What is sonar?

2 What are ultrasounds?

3 What are 'normal' sound waves?

4 What is the advantage of using ultrasounds for sonar?

5 Calculate the wavelength of an ultrasound which travels at 1500 m/s and has a frequency of 30 kHz.

Exam practice

1 Choose the word that best completes each sentence.

  a At the centre of any solar system is a ....
    A planet   **B** moon
    C galaxy   **D** star   [1]

  b In our Solar System, ...orbit around the Sun.
    A man-made satellites   **B** moons
    C planets   **D** galaxies [1]

  c It is occasionally possible to see a ....as its orbit takes it close to the Sun.
    A comet   **B** asteroid
    C man-made satellite   **D** space probe [1]

  d The Milky Way is an example of a ....
    A universe   **B** galaxy
    C moon   **D** planet   [1]

2 Match the words A,B,C and D to the missing information on the diagram, 1-4.

1	Microwaves	**2**	Visible	**3**	X-rays	**4**

  a The type of electromagnetic radiation that is found at position 1 in the spectrum is...
    A seismic waves   **B** infra-red radiation
    C radio waves   **D** sound waves [1]

  b One use for the radiation that is found at position 2 in the spectrum is...
    A monitoring temperature
    B cooking food
    C scanning inside the body
    D detecting fraud   [1]

  c One use for the radiation that is found at position 4 in the spectrum is...
    A mobile phones   **B** broadcasts
    C monitoring rain   **D** sterilising surgical instruments [1]

  d The type of electromagnetic radiation that is found at position 3 in the spectrum is...
    A ultra-violet   **B** seismic waves
    C ultrasound   **D** gamma rays [1]

3 Choose the word that best completes each sentence.

  a An example of a longitudinal wave is ...
    A a seismic s-wave **B** an ultrasound wave
    C a radio wave   **D** a gamma ray [1]

  b The maximum disturbance of a wave is its ...
    A amplitude   **B** frequency
    C pitch   **D** wavelength [1]

  c If a wave travels at 30 m/s, and its frequency is 6 Hz, its wavelength is ...
    A 5 cm **B** 36 m **C** 180 m **D** 5 m [1]

  d The name given to waves that are too high-pitched to hear is ...
    A seismic waves
    B electromagnetic waves
    C ultrasound waves
    D underground waves   [1]

4 Choose the best answer.

  a An analogue signal ...
    A has discrete values
    B can vary continuously
    C can be used to send signals down optic fibres
    D is the most efficient way to transmit data long distances [1]

  b The most practical ways of discovering about the Solar System are ...
    A Using a combination of telescopes, radio receivers and space probes
    B Using telescopes and sending radio messages
    C Visiting the different planets to take samples
    D Analysing debris that lands on Earth from outer space [1]

  c Seismic waves ...
    A can only be detected near the site of an earthquake
    B can travel through all parts of the Earth's internal structure
    C can be predicted with certainty
    D can be transverse and longitudinal. [1]

5 Choose the answer that is **false**.

  a It is thought that extraterrestrial life could...
    A exist on Earth
    B exist in many parts of the Universe
    C exist on certain planets depending on their position in the Solar System
    D be more advanced or more primitive than life on Earth [1]

  b Scanning by reflection can be used ...
    A to scan unborn babies during pregnancy
    B with optical and ultrasound waves
    C to see bone fractures
    D as a security measure to identify individuals [1]

c Mobile phones...
  A are believed to pose possible long-term health threats
  B are not considered to pose any health threats
  C use a network of masts to boost the signal
  D use microwave radiation [1]

6 Choose the best answer.

a A star like the Sun has formed from nebula. What is the order of the next two stages that it will evolve through after it has exhausted its hydrogen supply?
  A red giant, neutron star
  B red giant, white dwarf
  C white dwarf, red giant
  D white dwarf, black dwarf [1]

b At the red giant stage ...
  A the Sun's surface is the same temperature
  B the Sun's surface is hotter, and the star has expanded
  C the Sun's surface is cooler, and the star has expanded
  D the Sun has expanded [1]

c Scanning by absorption ...
  A can be used to scan a foetus during pregnancy
  B can be used to monitor temperature
  C is used in iris recognition systems
  D can be used to see bone fractures [1]

(Total 23 marks)

Worked example

Choose the best answer.

a Why does a rocket in outer space accelerate forwards?
  A because it pushes against the atmosphere
  B as a reaction to gases being forced backwards
  C because of friction
  D because of gravity

b Calculate the acceleration of a rocket if its mass is 2million kg and the rockets provide a force of 30 million N.
  A 15 million m/s^2
  B 15 million m/s
  C 60 million m/s^2
  D 60 million m/s

c State one problem of long space flights
  A Astronauts feel weightless in space so they cannot drink
  B Water runs out, as it cannot be reused
  C Astronauts feel weightless in space so their muscles do not stay healthy
  D The rocket uses lots of fuel after it leaves the atmosphere

d The universe is thought to have ....
  A always existed
  B started as a big explosion thousands of years ago
  C started as a big explosion billions of years ago and have reached its biggest size.
  D started as a big explosion billions of years ago and still is expanding

B is correct. There is no atmosphere outer space so there is no friction, and gravity will not cause the forward acceleration.

a D ✗

b A ✓

c C ✓

d B ✗

Correct. Force = mass x acceleration. The unit of acceleration is m/s^2.

Correct. Water can be reused, and the rocket uses very little fuel after launch. Astronauts can drink but it is a different experience as the liquid can float!

The correct answer is D. It has existed for billions of years, and there is evidence that it is still expanding.

How to get an A
Look at any very similar answers and try to eliminate the ones that you think are definitely wrong first. Examiners may try to test your understanding by changing only a small part of the question to see if you know the details.

How to maximise your marks!

Practical skills

While studying GCSE Science, you will develop new skills by carrying out practical tasks. These tasks require you to follow instructions, to make observations and to take readings using a range of apparatus and measuring instruments. You are also asked to present your data appropriately.

Your teacher will assess your practical skills using various criteria. This assessment is worth 10% of your overall marks. The criteria your teacher uses will be:

● ability to follow instructions
● collecting data
● presenting results.

The table below shows how you can aim to score top marks in each of these areas.

	A student scoring between 1 and 2 marks	A student scoring between 3 and 4 marks	A student scoring between 5 and 6 marks
Follow instructions	Can follow written instructions with some explanation, but usually requires help to set up simple equipment, including any ICT equipment. 1–2	Can follow written instructions to set up standard equipment, including any ICT equipment without help, although changes may be required when the set-up is checked. 3–4	Can follow written instructions to set up equipment, including any ICT equipment, correctly and without any help to carry out practical work involving a number of stages and several pieces of apparatus. 5–6
Collecting data	Can make simple readings, observations and measurements, including the use of ICT techniques, to collect data safely, but accuracy is limited. 1–2	Can decide how to make standard readings, observations and measurements, including the use of ICT techniques and can collect data safely and accurately, normally. 3–4	Can carry out tasks involving a number of stages and several pieces of equipment including the use of ICT techniques to collect data safely and accurately and considers the reliability of the data. 5–6
Presenting results	Can complete simple results tables (which include column headings) to record the data. 1–2	Can construct results tables, including column headings with units, without assistance. 3–4	Can construct meaningful results tables from complex data complete with correct column headings and units. 5–6
			Total /18

© Edexcel Limited

How science works

An important part of studying GCSE Science is understanding how science works. This is all about learning to engage with and challenge the science you meet in everyday life. You need to adopt a critical, questioning frame of mind, going 'behind the scenes' to understand the workings of science and how it impacts on society and people's lives. Understanding how science works can help you to:

- identify questions that science can, and cannot, address
- see how scientists look for the answers
- evaluate scientific claims by judging the reliability of the evidence
- question the scientific reports you see in the media, and communicate your own findings
- consider scientific findings in a wider context
- make informed judgements about science and technology, including any ethical issues that arise.

Assessment activities

Throughout the year, your teacher will set you activities for each of Biology, Chemistry and Physics. These activities will allow you to explore **how science works** in the context of the units you are studying. Your best mark for one activity from each of Biology, Chemistry and Physics will be submitted towards your overall grade. This assessment is worth 30% of your overall marks in GCSE Science.

The activities will be broken down into a short series of tasks. Some activities will be based on practicals that you carried out or have experience of. You will be asked to interpret and present results and to consider the wider scientific implications. The quality of your written communication will also be considered.

Sample assessment activity

Below is a sample assessment activity for you to practise on.

Unit C1b Topic 7 – There's one Earth

1. Oil – A treasured resource or a major source of pollution?

Anita and Faisal carried out a fractional distillation of synthetic crude oil. ('Synthetic' means that it was not a real sample of crude oil, but was made from a mixture of chemicals, which the school had in their storeroom.)

They were given 20 cm³ of the synthetic crude oil mixture, which had been prepared by the Science Technician a few days earlier. Their teacher showed them the apparatus below, and explained how they should set it up in order to carry out a fractional distillation task.

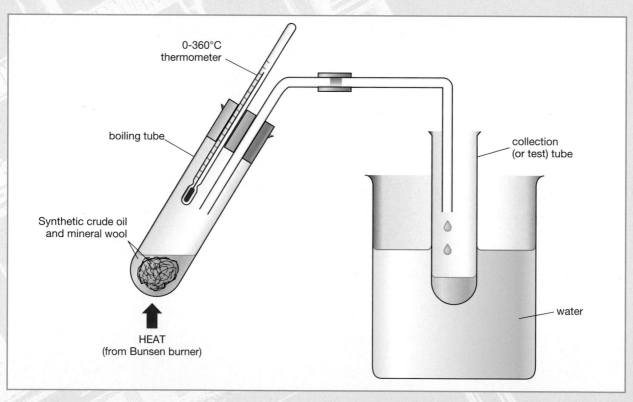

During the experiment, different fractions of crude oil, A to E, were produced at different temperatures. The fractions are alkanes and each fraction is made up of different numbers of carbon atoms. The teacher gave the number of carbon atoms in the molecules making up each of the fractions to Anita and Faisal.

They put this information in a table. In the same table, Anita and Faisal recorded the temperature range used to collect fractions A to E. They also recorded the colour of each fraction.

The table below shows Anita and Faisal's results.

Fraction letter	Number of carbon atoms in the molecules of each fraction	Temperature at which fraction was collected (°C)	Colour of fraction
A	5	35	Colourless
B	7	70	Very Pale yellow
C	7	95	
D	9	150	Yellow
E	11	195	Yellow/Orange
F	12	This fraction was not distilled – remained in the test tube	

a) Anita and Faisal noted a pattern in the colours of the different fractions. Fill in the missing colours in the table [2 marks].

b) Draw a graph to show how the number of carbon atoms in the molecules of each fraction affects the temperature at which the fraction is collected [4 marks].

c) Describe the pattern in the graph [2 marks] and explain the reason for the shape of the graph [3 marks].

d) Following the experiment, Anita and Faisal also noticed a difference in viscosity of the different fractions. Describe the difference in viscosity they would have noticed from fractions A to E [2 marks]. Explain the difference in viscosity with regards to the number of carbon atoms in the molecules of the different fractions [2 marks].

[Total 15 marks]

© Edexcel Limited

2. Solar panel saver?

Bob has had solar panels fitted on the roof of his house to provide hot water for heating and other household uses. The solar panels mean that Bob uses less gas and therefore saves money. The solar panels cost £2,000.

This is Bob's gas bill for the three months before he had solar panels fitted.

GAS BILL

Name:	Bob Green
Address:	190 Sunray Avenue, London
Billing:	01 April 2005 to 30 June 2005

Edexcel
Energy Corp.

Meter point: *190S.AXXXX*   Acount reference number: *012345XXXXX*

Total bill: £198   (see summary below for breakdown of bill)

....

Summary: Bill issued on 30 June 2005

Billing period from
01 April 2005 – 30 June 2005

Thank you for using Edexcel Energy

This is Bob's gas bill for the first three months after he had solar panels fitted.

GAS BILL

Name:	Bob Green
Address:	190 Sunray Avenue, London
Billing:	01 July 2005 to 30 September 2005

Edexcel
Energy Corp.

Meter point: *190S.AXXXX*   Acount reference number: *012345XXXXX*

Total bill: £105   (see summary below for breakdown of bill)

....

Summary: Bill issued on 30 September 2005

Billing period from
01 July 2005 – 30 Sept 2005

Thank you for using Edexcel Energy

Bob tells his friend Jay all about his new solar panels.

a) Work out how many years it will take Bob to save enough money on his gas bill to cover the cost of the solar panels using the steps below.

How much does Bob save in three months? [1 mark]

How much will Bob save in one year? [1 mark]

How many years will it take to save enough money on the gas bill to pay for the solar panels? [1 mark]

My solar panels will save on my gas bills.

They are too expensive to have fitted. They are not worth it.

I didn't just want to save money. I wanted to help the environment too.

You didn't save money through July and September because of the solar panels

b) Suggest two other reasons why Bob's bill was less for the period July to September than from April to June [2 marks].

c) The second bill was for July to September. Explain how the bills Bob receives might change over the coming year.

(How the bill may change [1 mark]; explanation [2 marks].)

d) Bob believes he is helping to reduce problems within the environment in terms of:

- global warming
- acid rain
- respiratory (breathing) diseases.

Do you agree with Bob? Explain your answer fully [7 marks].

[Total 15 marks]

© Edexcel Limited

The Periodic Table

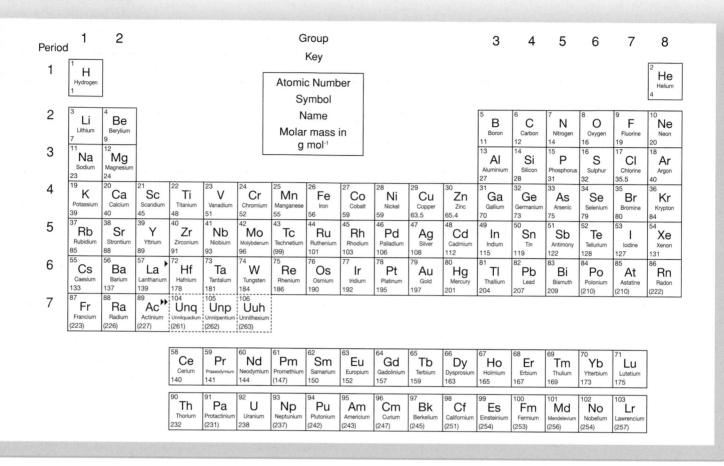

Physical quantities and units

Fundamental physical quantities	
Physical quantity	**Unit(s)**
length	metre (m); kilometre (km); centimetre (cm); millimetre (mm).
mass	kilogram (kg); gram (g); milligram (mg).
time	second (s); millisecond (ms); hour (h).
temperature	degree Celsius (°C); kelvin (K).
current	ampere (A); milliampere (mA).
voltage	volt (V); millivolt (mV).

Physical quantities and units

Derived physical quantities	
Physical quantity	**Unit(s)**
area	m^2; cm^2; mm^2.
volume	m^3; cm^3; mm^3; litre (l); millilitre (ml).
density	kg/m^3; g/cm^3.
force	newton (N).
speed	m/s; cm/s; km/h.
acceleration	m/s^2; cm/s^2.
energy	joule (J); kilojoule (kJ); megajoule (MJ); kilowatt-hour (kWh).
power	watt (W); kilowatt (kW); megawatt (MW).
frequency	hertz (Hz); kilohertz (kHz); megahertz (MHz).
gravitational field strength	N/kg.
radioactivity	becquerel (Bq).
specific heat capacity	J/kg°C; J/kgK.
specific latent heat	J/kg.

voltage = current x resistance
$$V = I \times R$$

power = current x voltage

$$\text{efficiency} = \frac{\text{useful energy output}}{\text{total energy input}} \times 100\%$$

cost of electricity = power x time x cost of 1 kWh

weight = mass x acceleration of free-fall
$$W = mg$$

force = mass x acceleration

Glossary

abiotic	to do with non-living factors. e.g. rainfall, sunshine	20-21
acid	a chemical that turns litmus paper red – it can often dissolve things that water cannot.	138-141
adrenaline	a hormone produced by the adrenal gland which prepares the body for vigorous activity.	70-72
alkali	a substance which makes a solution that turns red litmus paper blue.	138-141
allele	inherited features are carried as pairs of alleles on a pair of chromosomes. A feature may be the result of a single gene acting or may involve several genes working together. Different forms of a gene are different alleles.	44
alternating current	a current that rapidly reverses in direction.	204-205
amino acid	the sub-units making up protein molecules. There are over 20 different amino acids used by living things.	38
ampere	the unit used to measure electrical current. Often abbreviated to amp.	200-201, 206-207
amplitude	the difference between the highest and lowest points on a wave, the larger the amplitude of a sound wave the louder the sound.	242-243, 250, 254
analgesic	a painkiller	98
analogue	a signal that shows a complete range of frequencies. Sound is analogue.	254-255
antibiotic	a substance produced by a microbe which kills other microbes. Some antibiotics can be purified and used to treat infections.	30-31, 94-97
antibodies	chemicals produced by cells called B lymphocytes which attack invading microorganisms.	90-93
antigens	chemicals found in cell membranes and cell walls which trigger a reaction by the immune system.	90-93, 96-97
atoms	the building blocks of an element. Atoms consist of negatively-charged electrons flying around a positively-charged nucleus.	110-111, 116-117, 131, 137, 185, 208-209
axon	a long projection from a nerve fibre that conducts impulses away from the body of the nerve cell.	64-65
bacteria	microscopic single-celled living organisms that have no nucleus.	84-85, 88-89, 94-97
barbiturate	a drug that calms people down. They include sleeping pills and pills to treat anxiety.	98-99
beta-carotene	a chemical found in plants like carrots that can be easily converted into Vitamin A in the body.	32-33
Big Bang	the event believed by many scientists to have been the start of the universe.	278
biodegradable	a substance which can be broken down by biological action in the environment.	161, 174
biofuel	a fuel that is produced by a living organism, for example wood or oil from a plant like rapeseed.	161, 183
biosphere	the thin layer covering the surface of the Earth where living organisms can be found. It consists of the lower atmosphere, the seas, the surface of the land and a few metres below ground.	270
biotechnology	technology that uses biological materials in an industrial context, e.g. enzymes. Also used to describe a range of genetic engineering techniques in use today.	54
biotic	biotic factors are the activities of living systems which affect another organism, e.g. competition for food or water, hunting.	20-21
carbohydrates	chemicals found in all living things. They contain the elements carbon, hydrogen and oxygen. Sugars are carbohydrates which dissolve in water and taste sweet. Starches are carbohydrates which cannot dissolve in water and do not taste sweet.	18
carbon fibres	microscopic fibres made of carbon atoms joined together in long chains.	161, 170
carbon monoxide	a poisonous gas containing only carbon and oxygen.	100, 168-169
cardiovascular disease	a disease affecting the heart and blood vessels.	100-101
catalyst	a chemical that speeds up a reaction but is not changed by it or used up by the reaction.	148-149
central nervous system (CNS)	the brain and spinal cord.	62-63
chemical transmitter	a chemical that carries a signal across the small gap between nerve cells.	66-67
chlorofluorocarbons (CFCs)	chemicals containing carbon, hydrogen, chlorine and fluorine. They used to be used in refrigerators and aerosols but have been phased out because they seem to damage the ozone layer.	161, 178
cholesterol	a chemical found in animal fats and foods made from them, such as butter or lard. The body uses cholesterol to make nerve tissue and some hormones. High levels of cholesterol may make heart attacks more likely.	50
chromosome	a thread-like body made of DNA and protein found in the nucleus. It only becomes visible during cell division.	40-41
circuit	the complete path around an electrical circuit that electricity can flow along.	198-199, 206-207, 210-211, 222
circulatory system	a system of tubes and a pump to move fluids around a body. The heart and blood vessels form the human circulatory system.	90
cirrhosis	a disease of the liver often caused by excessive alcohol intake.	102-103

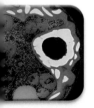

Glossary

genetic modification	GM: a process whereby genes from another species are added to an organism using DNA technology.	33, 80-81
genotype	the combination of genes carried by an organism.	44, 55
global footprint	a measure of the environmental impact of a person or country on the Earth.	26-27
global warming	the gradual rise in average global temperature, caused mainly by the burning of fossil fuels.	24-25
glucose	a type of sugar, sometimes called dextrose.	80-81
gravitational force	the force of attraction between two bodies caused by their mass: the larger the mass, the larger the force.	274

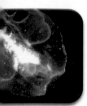

haemoglobin	a complex chemical found in red blood cells that can combine with oxygen to help transport it around the body.	101
hallucinogen	a drug like LSD that causes hallucinations.	98-99
halogen	a group of reactive non-metals with only one electron missing from their outer electron shell, e.g. chlorine and iodine.	124-125, 130
hormone	a chemical produced by an endocrine gland which changes the way other parts of the body work.	71-72, 74-76, 78
human genome	the complete map of the genes in human beings.	52-53
hydrocarbon	hydrocarbon molecules are molecules that contain only carbon and hydrogen atoms. Many fuels are hydrocarbons, e.g. natural gas (methane) and petrol (a complex mixture).	149, 167
hydrogen	a colourless, odourless gas that burns easily in oxygen to form water.	161, 167
immiscible	two liquids are immiscible if they do not form a stable mixture, for example oil and water.	189
immune system	the parts of the body that produce antibodies to protect against infection.	96-97
impulse	a nerve signal.	62-65
insoluble	a substance that will not dissolve. Something that is insoluble in water may be soluble in other liquids.	142-143
insulation	material which slows down the movement of energy, typically used with respect to heat and electricity.	226-227

interdependence	two things show interdependence if they depend on each other and a change in either one affects the other.	24-25
interspecific	competition for resources between organisms from different species.	22-23
liposome	an artificial microscopic bag consisting of a watery core covered in one or more phospholipid layers. Liposomes are used to carry vaccines, drugs, enzymes, or other substances to target cells or organs.	49
longitudinal wave	in longitudinal waves, the vibration is along the direction in which the wave travels.	240-241
magnetic levitation	lifting something up by magnetic forces.	216
mercury	a liquid, silver-coloured metal	213
microbe	another word for microorganism.	84, 88-95

micrometeorite	a tiny particle of meteoric dust, particularly one that falls to the surface of the earth or moon.	262
mitosis	the process of cell division which ensures that new cells have a complete copy of inherited information.	41
molecule	a group of atoms joined together by chemical links.	115, 131, 137, 167
mutation	a random change in the genotype of an organism. Mutations are almost always disadvantageous.	30, 43, 46-47, 248
nanotechnology	technology that works with objects at the atomic or molecular level.	161, 172
natural selection	factors in the environment affect animals and plants so that some survive to reproduce successfully and pass on their good combinations of genes. Others survive less well and do not pass on their poor combinations of genes as often.	30, 31

neurone	a nerve cell.	64-67, 69
neurotransmitter	a chemical which carries information across the small gap between nerve cells at a synapse.	66-67
neutralisation	a reaction between an acid and an alkali to produce a neutral solution.	138-142, 151
neutron	a particle found in the nucleus of an atom with no charge and a mass of one atomic mass unit.	110-111
nitrogen	a non-reactive gas that makes up most of the atmosphere.	160-161
non-renewable	non-renewable fuels are not being made fast enough at the moment and so will run out at some point in the future.	161, 176, 220-221

nucleus	the control centre of the cell, surrounded by a membrane.	110-111
oestrogen	a hormone produced by the ovaries.	75-77
optical fibre	a flexible optically transparent fibre, usually made of glass or plastic, through which light passes by successive internal reflections.	246-247
orbit	the path a satellite takes around a larger object. Planets orbit around the Sun.	258, 261
oxidation	a reaction which adds oxygen to a compound or element, for example combustion and respiration are both oxidation reactions.	144-147

Acknowledgements

The authors and publishers are grateful to the following for permission to reproduce photographs. Whilst every effort has been made to trace the copyright holders, in cases where this has been unsuccessful or if any have been inadvertently overlooked, the Publishers will be pleased to make the necessary arrangements at the first opportunity.

The authors and publishers are grateful to the following for permission to reproduce photographs:

p.3 ©Nils Jorgensen/Rex Features, ©Adam Kuert/istockphoto.com, ©Ace Stock Ltd/Alamy, ©Philippe Plailly/Eurelios/SPL©Victor Habbick Visions/SPL; p.6 figs1-4 ©Gareth Price; p.7 fig1 ©Monika Wisiewska/istock.com, fig2 ©Allen Johnson/istock.com, fig3 ©Monika Wisiewska/istock.com, fig4 ©istock.com; p.8 fig1 ©Tiago Fernandes/istock.com, fig2 Alfred Pasieka/SPL; p.8 fig4 ©2005 Jupiterimages Corporation; p.9 fig1 ©2005 Jupiterimages Corporation, fig2 ©Jasmin Awad/istock.com, fig4 ©2005 Jupiterimages Corporation; p.10 fig1 ©2005 Jupiterimages Corporation, fig2 ©Andrew Lambert Photography/SPL, fig3 ©2005 Jupiterimages Corporation, fig4 ©Cordelia Molloy/SPL; p.11 fig1 ©2005 Jupiterimages Corporation, fig2 ©Clayton J. Price/Corbis, figs 3&4 ©2005 Jupiterimages Corporation; p.12/13 ©Eye of Science/SPL; p.14 fig1 ©Graham Usher , fig2 t ©Jupiterimages Corporation, b ©Jupiterimages Corporation; p.15 fig4 ©Jupiterimages Corporation, fig5 ©Nils Jorgensen/Rex Features; p.16 fig1 ©Graham Usher; p.17 figs4&6 ©Graham Usher; p.18 fig1 Burger/Phanie/Rex Features, fig2 ©Suvi Suni/istockphoto; p.19 fig4&5 ©Gareth Price; p.20 fig1 ©Historic NWS Collection/National Oceanic and Atmospheric Administration/Department of Commerce; p.21 fig2 ©Hal Horton/istockphoto; p.22 fig1 ©Matthew Sherf/istockphoto, fig2 ©John Lund/Corbis; p.23 fig3 ©L. R. Kyllo/istockphoto, fig4 ©Robert Deal/istockphoto, fig5 ©Jonathan Clark/istockphoto; p.24 fig1 ©Daniel Cox/Oxford Scientific/Photo Library/OSF; p.26 fig4 ©Bettmann/Corbis; p.27 fig3 ©Gareth Price; p.28 fig1 ©Everett Collection/Rex Features, fig2 ©Ashok Rodrigues/istockphoto; p.29 fig3 ©David Gilder/istockphoto; p.30 fig2 ©Robert Kyllo/istockphoto; p.31 fig3 Phototake Inc./Oxford Scientific/OSF; p.32 fig1&2 ©Gareth Price; p.36 fig1 © Victor Fisher/Genetic Savings & Clone used with kind permission, fig2 ©Gareth Price; p.39 fig2 ©Barrington Brown/SPL; p.40 fig1 ©L. Willatt, East Anglian Regional Genetics Service/SPL; p.41 fig3 ©Adam Kuert/istockphoto, fig4 ©John T. Fowler/Alamy; p.42 fig2 ©Gareth Price; p.43 fig4 ©Gareth Price; p.46 fig2 ©US Department of Energy; p.48 fig1 ©Mauro Fermariello/SPL, fig2 ©SPL; p.50 fig1 ©www.glofish.com; p.51 fig3 ©Kim Cheung/Reuters/Corbis; p.52 fig2 Victor de Schwanberg/SPL; p.53 fig4 ©Betrand Collet/ istockphoto.com; p.55 fig2 ©Helen McArdle/SPL; p.56 fig1 ©Mark Evans/istock.com; p.57 fig2 ©Deb Gleason/istock.com; p.60/61 ©Manfred Kage/SPL; p.62 fig1 ©Christoph Ermel/istock.com; p.63 fig4 ©James MacAllister/istock; p.64 fig1 ©Jupiterimages Corporation; p.65 fig3 ©Manfred Kage/SPL, fig4 ©Steve Gschmeissner/SPL; p.66 fig1 ©Luis C. Torres/istock.com, fig2 ©Nick Gordon/Oxford Scientific/Photo Library; p.67 fig4 ©Jupiterimages Corporation; p.68 fig2 ©Joey Nelson/istock.com; p.69 fig4 (both) ©BSIP, Chassenet/SPL; p.70 fig1 ©Jupiterimages Corporation, fig2 ©Paul Rapson/SPL; p.71 fig4 ©Eye of Science/SPL; p.72 fig1 ©Peter Chen/istock.com, fig2 ©Jupiterimages Corporation; p.73 fig4 ©Paul Rapson/SPL, fig5 ©Joe Gough/istock.com; p.74 fig1 ©Dr M. A. Ansary/SPL; p.75 fig5 ©Jupiterimages Corporation, fig6 ©Jupiterimages Corporation; p.76 fig1 ©Rebecca Ellis/istock.com; p.77 fig3 ©Biophoto Associates/SPL; p.78 fig1 ©Penny Tweedie/SPL, fig2 ©Amander Rohde/istock.com; p.79 fig3 ©Mark Evans/istock.com, fig4 ©Pascal Goetgheluck/SPL; p.80 fig1 ©Dana Blankenship/istock.com, fig2tl ©Jose Antonio Santiso/istock, tr ©Jupiterimages Corporation, br ©Edyta Pawlowska/istock.com, bl ©Stephen Walls/istock.com; p.81 fig4 ©SPL; p.84 fig1 ©Getty Images, fig2 l-r ©Diane Diedrich/istock.com, ©Paul Cowan/istock.com, ©Rodolfo Arpia/istock, ©Radu Razvan/istock.com, ©Amanda Rohde/istock.com; p.85 fig7 ©Sinclair Stammers/SPL; p.86 fig1 ©Dr John Brackenbury/SPL; p.87 tr ©Graham Barclay/BWP Media/Newsmaker/Getty Images; tl ©BWP Media/Getty Images, bl ©Reuters/Corbis, fig2 ©Sinclair Stammers/SPL; p.88 fig1 ©Dr Tony Brain & David Parker/SPL; p.89 fig3 ©Peter Chen/istock.com; p.90 fig1 ©Pro. S.H.E. Kaufmann & Dr J.R. Golecki/SPL; p.92 fig1 ©Tomasz Resiak/istock.com; p.93 fig2 ©SPL, fig3 ©Jaime Gonzalez/istock.com; p.94 fig1 l ©SPL, r ©Jupiterimages Corporation; p.95 fig3©St Mary's Hospital Medical School/SPL; p.96 fig1 ©Alexander Joe/Getty Images; p.97 fig2 ©istock.com, fig3 ©ISM/SPL, fig4 ©Stanley B. Burns, MD & The Burns Archive N.Y./SPL; p.98 fig1clockwise ©Andrea Gingerich/istock.com, ©Anthony Ladd/istock.com, ©Ula Kapala/istock.com, ©Sascha Burkard/istock.com, ©James E Hernandez/istock.com; p.99 fig2 ©BSIP, Ragueth/SPL, fig3 ©Tom McNemar/istock.com; p.100 fig1 ©Roberta Osborne/istock.com; p.102 fig1 l ©Tomaz Levstek/istock.com, r ©Kenneth C Zirkel/istock.com; p.103 fig3 ©Peter Dench/Corbis, fig4 ©CNRI/SPL, fig5 ©CNRI/SPL; p.104 ©Christian Jasiuk/istock.com; p.108/109 ©Paul A. Souders/Corbis; p.110 fig1 ©Jupiterimages Corporation, fig2 ©IBM/SPL; p.112 fig1 ©Jupiterimages Corporation; p.113 fig2 ©Steffen Foerster/istock.com, fig3 ©Jupiterimages Corporation, fig4 ©Jupiterimages Corporation; p.114 fig1 ©Squib/Alamy, fig2 ©Jupiterimages Corporation; fig3 ©Jupiterimages Corporation; p.115 fig4 ©Jupiterimages Corporation, fig5 ©Andrew Lambert Photography/SPL, fig7 ©Adam Hart-Davis/SPL; p.116 fig1 ©Jupiterimages Corporation, fig2 ©Sciencephotos/Alamy, fig4 ©Owen Franken/Corbis; p.118 fig1 ©Jupiterimages Corporation, fig2 ©Fiona Hanson/PA/Empics; p.119 fig3 ©Andrew Lambert Photography/SPL; p.120 fig1 ©Victor de Schanberg/SPL, fig2 ©Valerie Loiseleux/istock.com, fig3 ©Nicolas Hansen/istock,cin, p.121 fig4 ©Johnny Green/PA/Empics, fig4 ©Thermit Welding (GB) Limited, used with kind permission, fig5 ©Le Segretain Pascal/Corbis Sygma; p.122 fig1 ©Jupiterimages Corporation, fig2 ©Andrew Lambert Photography/SPL; p.123 fig3 ©Andrew Lambert Photography/SPL, fig4 ©Andrew Lambert Photography/SPL, fig5 ©Crown Copyright/Health & Safety Laboratory/SPL; p.124 fig1 ©James McQuillan/istock.com, fig2 ©Andrew Lambert Photography/SPL; p.125 fig3 ©Andrew Lambert Photography/SPL, fig4 ©Crown Copyright/Health & Safety Laboratory/SPL; p.126 fig1 ©Robert Harding World Imagery/Robert Harding Picture Library Ltd/Alamy; fig2 ©Martyn F. Chillmaid/SPL; p.127 fig3 ©SPL, fig4 ©Day Williams/SPL; p.128 fig1 ©Lesley Garland Picture Library/Alamy; p.129 fig3 ©Astrid & Hanns-Frieder Michler/SPL; p.130 fig1 ©Bettmann/Corbis, fig2 ©Jupiterimages Corporation; p.131 fig3 ©Jupiterimages Corporation, fig4 ©Tomislav Stajduhar/istock.com, fig5 ©Paige Foster/SPL; p.132 figs1-4 ©Jupiterimages Corporation; p.134 fig1 ©istock.com, fig2 ©Jupiterimages Corporation; p.135 fig3 l ©James King-Holmes/SPL, r ©Victor de Schwanberg/SPL, fig4 ©Nicola Stratford/istock.com; p.136 fig1 ©SPL; p.137 fig4 ©Charles D. Winters/SPL, fig5 ©Steve Raymer/Corbis; p. 138 fig1 ©Jupiterimages Corporation, fig2 ©Miroslaw Modzelewski/istock.com; p.139 fig3 ©J. P. Getty Trust/Corbis, fig4 ©Charles D. Winters/SPL; p.140 fig1 ©Ted Spiegel/Corbis, fig2 ©Andrew Lambert Photography/SPL; p.141 fig3 ©Cordelia Molloy/SPL, fig4 ©Andrew Lambert Photography/SPL; p.142 fig1 ©Simon Lewis/SPL, fig2 l ©Christie's Images/Corbis, r ©Geoff Delderfield/istock.com, fig3 ©Geoff Kidd/SPL; p.144 fig1 ©John Giles/PA/Empics, fig2 ©Kevin Tate/istock.com; p.145 fig2 ©Ace Stock Ltd/Alamy, fig4 l ©Ulrike Hammerich/istock.com, r ©Andrew Lambert Photography/SPL, fig5 ©Renee Lee/istock.com; p.146 fig1 ©Bossu Regis/Corbis Sygma, fig2 ©Stephanie Maze/Corbis; p.147 fig4 ©Newscast/Corus Education, used with kind permission; p.148 fig1 ©Ben Walker/istock.com, fig2 ©Alex Bartel/SPL; p.149 fig3 ©Stone/Getty Images, fig4 ©Kaj R. Svensson/SPL; p.150 fig1 ©Edyta Pawlowska/istock.com, fig2 ©Jupiterimages Corporation, fig3 ©Joao Freitas/istock.com, fig4 ©Diane Diederich/istock.com; p.152 fig1 ©Mary Evans Picture Library, fig3 ©Sheila Terry/SPL; p.153 fig4 ©Andrew Lambert Photography/SPL, fig5 ©Jupiterimages Corporation; p.154 ©2005 Jupiterimages Corporation; p.155 ©CCI Archives/SPL; p.158 ©Jason Childs/Getty Images; p.160 fig1 ©Elizabeth Shoemaker/istock.com, fig2 ©Gregg Cerenzio/istock.com; p.161 fig4 ©Yogi, Inc./Corbis; p.162 fig1 ©Michael Lok/istock.com, fig2 ©Kelly Cline/istock.com; p.163 fig3 l-r ©Carlos Dominguez/SPL, ©Richard R. Hansen/SPL, ©Martyn F. Chillmaid/SPL, fig4 ©Charles D. Winters/SPL; p.164 fig1 ©Robert Brook/SPL, fig2 ©Maximilian Stock Ltd/SPL; p.165 fig3 ©Martin Bond/SPL, fig4 ©James King-Holmes/SPL; p.166 fig1 ©Jupiterimages Corporation, fig2 ©Jupiterimages Corporation; p.167 fig2 ©Jupiterimages Corporation; p.168 fig1 ©Justin Allfree/istock.com, fig2 ©Emma Holmwood/istock.com; p.169 fig3 ©Gusto/SPL, fig4 ©Cordelia Molloy/SPL; p.170 fig1 ©TBA; p.171 fig2 ©Simon Fraser/SPL; p.172 fig1 ©Jupiterimages Corporation; p.173 fig3 ©Chris Bjornberg/SPL; p.174 ©Vera Boaerts/istock.com, fig2 ©Thomas Blaser/istock.com; p.175 fig3 ©Michael Marten/SPL; p.176 fig1 ©Joy Fera/istock.com, fig2 ©Jupiterimages Corporation; p.177 fig3 ©Maximilian Stock Ltd/SPL, fig4 ©Detlev van Ravenswaay/SPL; p.180 fig1 ©Paul Cowan/istock.com, fig2 ©Philippe Plailly/Eurelios/SPL; p.181 fig3 ©Jerry Mason/SPL, fig4 ©Stockbyte Gold/Alamy, fig5 ©Peter Grumann/Alamy; p.182 fig1 ©Christian Darkin/SPL, fig2 TBA; p.183 fig3 ©Laguna Design/SPL, fig4 ©Dr Kostas Kostarelos & David McCarthy/SPL, fig5 ©Jupiterimages Corporation, fig6 ©Jupiterimages Corporation; p.184 fig1 ©Robert Fried/Alamy, fig2 ©Tek Image/SPL, fig3 ©Paul Topp/istock.com; p.185 fig4 ©Bill Grove/istock.com, fig6 ©Ton Kinsbergen/SPL; p.186 fig1 ©Jupiterimages Corporation, fig2 ©Andrew Lambert Photography/SPL; p.187 fig3 ©Donald Gruener/istock.com, fig4 ©Kenneth Murray/SPL, fig5 ©NREL/US Department of Energy/SPL; p.188 fig1 ©Mark Evans/istock.com, fig2 ©ImageState/Alamy; p.189 fig4 ©Jaimie D. Travis/istock.com, fig6 ©Food and Drug Administration/SPL; p.190 fig1 ©Rachel Blaser/istock.com, fig2 ©John Shepherd/istock.com, fig3 ©SPL; p.191 fig4 ©Greg Nicholas/istock.com; p.192 fig2 ©2005 Jupiterimages Corporation, fig3 ©2005 Jupiterimages Corporation; p.199 fig6 ©Mark Evans/istock.com; p.200 fig1 ©Jupiterimages Corporation, fig2 ©Andrew Lambert Photography/SPL; p.201 fig6 ©The Photolibrary Wales/Alamy; p.202 fig1 ©Sheila Terry/SPL, fig2 Artur M./istock.com; p.204 fig1 ©Jim Reed/SPL; p.205 fig4 ©Richard Levine/Alamy, fig5 ©Sheila Terry, Lecroy/SPL; p.206 fig2 Sean McBride; p.208 fig1 ©Jupiterimages Corporation; p.209 fig4 ©Linda Edel/istock.com, fig6 ©Sheila Terry/SPL, fig7 ©Chaleerat Ngamchalee/istock.com; p.210 fig1 ©Sciencephotos/Alamy, fig2 ©Fred Dimmick/istock.com, fig3 ©Sciencephotos/Alamy, fig4 ©Sampsa Kaijaluoto/istock.com; p.211 fig3 ©Jann Lipka/Nordicphotos/Alamy, fig6 ©Nicola Stratford/istock.com, fig7 ©Craig Aurness/Corbis; p.212 fig1 ©Science Museum/Science & Society Picture Library; p.213 fig4 ©Joern Sackermann/Alamy; p.214 fig1 ©Corbis, fig2 ©Popperfoto/Alamy; p.215 fig3 Sheila Terry/SPL, fig4 ©Jupiterimages Corporation, fig5 ©Sipa Press/Rex Features; p.216 fig1 ©Keren Su/China Span/Alamy, fig2 ©Science Museum/Science and Society; p.217 fig3 ©Bettmann/Corbis; p.218 fig1 ©Photo Researchers/SPL; p.220 fig1 ©Marine Current Turbines™ Ltd, used with kind permission, fig2 © Mark Fairhurst, used with kind permission; p.221 fig2 ©Paul Glendell/Alamy; p.222 fig1 ©University of Florida, used with kind permission; p.224 fig1 ©BL Images Ltd/Alamy; p.225 fig3 ©Sheila Terry/SPL, fig4 ©Spence Inga/Photolibrary.com; p.226 fig1 ©Klocke Nanotechnik Germany, used with kind permission of Dr Volker Klocke, fig2 TBA; p.228 fig1©PCL/Alamy; p.229 fig2 ©British Gas/IRT Surveying, used with kind permission; p.230 fig1 ©St Stephen's Hospital; p.231 fig2 ©Bettmann/Corbis; p.232 fig1 ©Michael Donne/SPL, fig2 ©Bildagentur Franz Waldhaeusl/Alamy; p.233 fig4 ©Sciencephotos/Alamy, fig5 ©Sheila Terry/SPL; p.240 ©NASA/Goddard Space Flight Centre(NASA-GSFC); p.242 fig1 ©Royalty Free/Corbis; p.244 fig1 ©R. Maisonneuve, Publiphoto Diffusion/SPL; p.246 fig1 ©Steve Kaufman/Corbis, fig4 ©Leslie Garland Picture Library/Alamy; p.247 bl ©Erich Schrempp/SPL, fig7 ©Jupiterimages Corporation; p.248 fig1 ©Alfred Pasiek/SPL, fig2 ©Jeremy Woodhouse/Photodisc Green/Getty; p.250 fig1 ©Dr Leon Golub/SPL; table 1 l-r ©David Gilder/istock.com, ©Johanna Goodyear/istock.com, ©istock.com, ©Jupiterimages Corporation, ©Jupiterimages Corporation, ©Mauro Fermariello/SPL, ©James King-Holmes/SPL; p.251 fig2 ©Alfred Pasieka/SPL, fig3 ©Christine Gonsalves/istock.com; p.252 fig1 ©David Hardy/SPL, fig2 ©Bettmann/Corbis; fig4 ©Science Museum/Science and Society Picture Library; p.254 fig1 ©Bettman/Corbis, fig2 ©BSIP, Gondelon/SPL; fig4 ©Jupiterimages Corporation; p.255 fig5 ©GE Medical Sysems/SPL, fig6 ©Philippe Psaila/SPL; p.257 fig4 Used with kind permission of The Vintage Calculators Web Museum at www.vintagecalculators.com, fig5 TBA; p.260 fig2a-d, f-j ©George Touþalis/istock.com, fig2e ©Michael Knight/istock; p.261 fig2 ©Daniel Hyams/istock.com, fig3 ©Michael Puerzer/istock.com, fig4 ©David A. Hardy, Futures: 50 years in space/SPL, fig5 ©Jupiterimages Corporation; p.262 fig1 ©NASA/SPL; p.263 fig2 ©Steve Gray/istock.com; p.264 fig1&2 ©Jupiterimages Corporation; p.265 fig3 ©NASA/SPL, fig4 ©Bruce Frisch/SPL; p.266 fig2 ©NASA/SPL, fig3 ©Roger Ressmeyer/Corbis; p.267 fig4 ©Jupiterimages Corporation, fig5&6 ©NASA/SPL; p.268 fig1 ©Lars Lentz/istock.com; p.269 fig2 ©Chris Butler/SPL, fig3 ©David A. Hardy, futures: 50 years in space/SPL, fig4 ©Victor Habbick Visions/SPL, fig5 ©John Sanford/SPL; p.270 fig1 ©NASA/ESA/STScI/SPL. fig2 ©Jupiterimages Corporation; p.271 fig3 ©NASA/SPL, fig4 ©European Space Agency/SPL, fig5 ©NASA/JPL/University of Colorado/SPL; p.272 fig1 ©US Air Force/SPL; p.273 fig2 ©Jason Ware/SPL, fig 3 ©Victor Habbick Visions/SPL, fig4 ©David Gilder/istock.com; p.274 fig1 ©Ali Kabas/Alamy, fig2 t ©Matthew Scherf/istock.com, bl ©Alex Hinds/istock.com, br ©Martin Workman/istock.com, fig3 ©Samuel Ashfield/SPL; p.275 fig5 ©PLI/SPL, fig6 ©ESA/CE/Eurocontrol/SPL; p.276 fig1 both ©Chris Butler/SPL, fig2 ©J-C Cuillandre/Canada-France-Hawaii Telescope; p.278 fig1 ©Digital Image ©1996 Corbis; Original image courtesy of NASA/Corbis; p.279 fig2 ©Roger Ressmeyer/Corbis; p.280 ©2005 Jupiterimages Corporation; C1A US ©CCI Archives/SPL; B1aEQ ©Michael W. Tweedie/SPL; p.309 ©George Ranalli/SPL; p.310 fig1 ©Dr Jeremy Burgess/SPL, fig2 ©Dr Karl Lounatmaa/SPL; p.311 fig3 ©Dr Jeremy Burgess/SPL